# MARKET STRUCTURE OF THE AGRICULTURAL INDUSTRIES

# Market Structure of the Agricultural Industries

SOME CASE STUDIES—EDITED BY

## John R. Moore

AND

## Richard G. Walsh

THE IOWA STATE UNIVERSITY PRESS
AMES, IOWA, U.S.A.

# PREFACE

THIS BOOK is a joint venture. Each of its 14 industry chapters is the contribution of one or two economists specializing in the area. The advantage of this approach lies in the fact that each industry study is the result of more careful and expert scholarship than could be expected of a single author preparing all 14 industry studies. The disadvantage lies in the virtual inability of 14 separate studies to be entirely consistent and integrated in outlook. Our chief task as editors has been to encourage all contributors to ask and to seek answers to essentially the same questions. We have not, however, sought to reduce differences of interpretation and inference among the contributors which reflect the controversial nature of the problems discussed. All statements of the contributors are their personal views and do not necessarily reflect those of their fellow contributors.

The introduction presents the conceptual framework used throughout the book and points out some variations in its application. The final chapter draws upon the 14 studies, and is a cross-sectional analysis of market conditions in these agricultural industries. Although tentative, and often based on less than completely adequate data, we feel enough new insight is developed to justify its presentation and discussion. If these studies aid a few young scholars in the practice of agricultural marketing, or induce others to explore the relationships with greater success than was ours, we shall be more than content that the book served its purpose.

This book is a result of the direct and indirect contribution of many people, not all of whom can be acknowledged in this limited space. The importance of the contributors goes without saying. The book's content is the result of their careful research and writing. We are indebted to Robert L. Clodius, University of

Wisconsin; Willard F. Mueller, Federal Trade Commission, Washington, D.C.; and Stephen H. Sosnick, University of California, who read parts of the manuscript. We are also indebted to John M. Curtis, University of Maryland; and Howard W. Ottoson, University of Nebraska, for their encouragement and assistance. Finally, we recognize the contribution of our wives in helping us maintain our equilibrium throughout the project.

JOHN R. MOORE

RICHARD G. WALSH

# CONTRIBUTORS

**HUGH L. COOK,** Professor of Agricultural Economics, University of Wisconsin.

**BERT M. EVANS,** Agricultural Extension Economist, University of Nebraska.

**HOMER C. EVANS,** Professor and Chairman of the Department of Economics and Rural Sociology, West Virginia University.

**PAUL L. FARRIS,** Professor of Agricultural Economics, Purdue University.

**LEHMAN B. FLETCHER,** Associate Professor of Agricultural Economics, Iowa State University.

**MARK L. FOWLER,** Associate Professor of Agricultural Economics, Texas A & M University.

**LEON GAROIAN,** Professor of Agricultural Economics, Oregon State University.

**PETER G. HELMBERGER,** Associate Professor of Agricultural Economics, University of Wisconsin.

**SIDNEY HOOS,** Professor of Agricultural Economics, University of California.

**DONALD D. KRAMER,** Research Associate in Agricultural Economics, Iowa State University.

**JESSE W. MARKHAM,** Professor of Economics, Princeton University.

**JOHN R. MOORE,** Associate Professor of Agricultural Economics, University of Maryland.

**DANIEL I. PADBERG,** Associate Professor of Agricultural Economics, Cornell University.

**W. G. PHILLIPS,** Professor and Head of the Department of Economics and Sociology, University of Windsor, Canada.

**EWELL P. ROY,** Professor of Agricultural Economics, Louisiana State University.

**RICHARD G. WALSH,** Associate Professor of Agricultural Economics, University of Nebraska.

**WILLARD F. WILLIAMS,** Professor and Head of the Department of Agricultural Economics, Texas Technological College.

# CONTENTS

# INTRODUCTION

INDUSTRIES related to agriculture constitute the largest economic sector in the United States. They contribute 15 to 20 percent of the Gross National Product and employ 20 to 25 percent of the labor force. By comparison, commodities valued at the farm gate represent only 4 to 5 percent of GNP, and labor in farming amounts to about 8 percent of the labor force.

Changes in the structure of agricultural industries pose problems of an increasingly general concern. For example, there is an ever-widening spread between the prices received by farmers and those paid by consumers for food. During the 16 years between 1947 and 1963, farm prices for food commodities declined 12 percent, while retail food costs increased 29 percent. In the summer of 1964, the Congress of the United States authorized the National Commission on Food Marketing to study the market structure of food industries from the producer to the consumer. The national commission inquiry and several of the chapters in this book may be considered as independent yet complementary treatments of recent market changes in the food industries.

## WHY THIS ANALYSIS?

Presented here is a representative, comprehensive, and up-to-date view of the agricultural industries—their diverse and evolving market conditions.

Every society is vitally concerned with the performance of its agricultural economy—from the supplying of farm inputs, to the actual farm production process, to the marketing of farm products as consumer goods. The concern is heightened by the twentieth century industrial revolution. In U.S. industries that supply farm inputs and market farm commodities, industrialization is an important source of employment and economic growth. Yet the dwindling number and expanding size of firms in most agriculture-related industries present a challenge to the public interest in competitive efficient markets.

Performance of the agriculture-related industries is of particular importance to farmers who depend upon them for about two-thirds of farm production inputs. Farmers also depend upon them for processing and distribution services which contribute about two-thirds of the total value of consumer goods produced from farm commodities. Farmers who have seen their share of the consumer's food dollar drop from 44 percent to about 37 percent in the past dozen years ask, "What's going on in the dark?," that complex and little understood area between them and the consumer.

Businessmen operating in the agricultural supply and commodity marketing industries are concerned with market changes affecting them. The structure of their markets is continuously evolving and requires constant adaptation. They find themselves forced to "roll with the punches," not always sure from where they come or how best to cope with them. Their interest too is aroused by the investigations of the National Commission on Food Marketing and current discussion of concepts such as oligopoly, product differentiation, and vertical integration.

It is primarily for these people in the agricultural industries and for the farmer and consumer who depend upon them that this book is written. In addition, it should prove of interest to students who seek improved understanding of the nation's largest industrial sector. Policy makers should find new insight into problems of these industries and alternative public and private remedies.

The fourteen industries selected for study annually purchase 75 to 80 percent of all farm products in the United States and sell 35 to 40 percent of the farm supplies. In these fourteen industries is found a laboratory illustrating various kinds of market structure, conduct, performance, and public policy. Included are:

*food retailing,* whose structure, until recently, was characterized by a large number of small firms, but now the price and nonprice conduct of large buyers is of national concern;

the *broiler* industry, in which technological advance and declining concentration have been accompanied by cutthroat competition;

fresh and processed *meat packing,* illustrating the contrasting conduct and performance of markets with government grading and brand differentiation, respectively;

*farm machinery* (tractors), demonstrating the mixed price and product consequences of a highly concentrated market structure accompanied by insurmountable barriers to entry;

the *grain procurement* industry, the prime example of imperfections of quality and price determination in markets where buyers and sellers lack essential information;

the *apple processing* industry, where, in the absence of product differentiation, the market is disciplined by an effective farmer cooperative;

the *fluid milk* and *baking* industries, illustrating the increasing role of nonprice competition in oligopolistic markets;

the *ice cream* industry, where large buyers secure large price concessions on private label products;

the *fertilizer* industry, exemplifying the imperfect relation between entry and price results, under conditions in which farmers have inadequate knowledge;

the *vegetable processing* industry, the countervailing influence of grower bargaining associations continuing to have mixed results;

the *soybean processing* industry, having low product differentiation and low entry barriers, experiencing increased efficiency of resource utilization;

the *mixed feed* industry with the brand differentiation of large companies being offset by the locational and service advantages of the small firm fringe;

the *cotton industry*, where free entry and restricted economic alternatives augur for continued government price protection to the industry.

Many other agriculture-related industries might or should have been included in this volume. For example, the lumber, wool, tobacco, and beverage industries were omitted, and a chapter on apples is the only representative from the numerous fruit industries. Particularly remiss is the lack of a chapter on one of the government supply or price regulated industries related to agriculture such as those supplying farm petroleum, agricultural credit, and electric power. Moreover, in virtually all agricultural product areas, several processing industries have been excluded. For example, in the case of wheat processing, absent are the biscuit and cracker, macaroni and spaghetti, flour, prepared flour mix, and breakfast cereal industries. Combined, they represent about one-half of total domestic wheat utilization. Still, the industries considered represent a significant part of the total picture.

The information presented in this book is organized as the research itself was done, with 14 synoptic industry studies authored by specialists in each area. We believe the *industry* is a relevant and practical basis for organizing the subject matter here presented. Each of the agricultural industries has distinctive characteristics. Statistics are collected on an industry basis. Company management thinks and acts in terms of the industry and of its position in it. Trade associations and other interest groups operate on an industry basis. Public policy is largely determined in relation to specific industry problems.

In the main, the content of this book builds on previous research findings by the contributors and others in agricultural economics. Its contribution rests on the organization and relationship of the ideas presented. In 1941, Professor William H. Nicholls published a pioneering work on agricultural marketing entitled, *Imperfect Competition Within Agricultural Industries*. He recommended that we conduct fewer narrowly defined studies and broader industrial ones. His orientation included "(1) description of the *conditions in the market*; (2) description of the *policies* of individual firms; (3) determination of the *results* of these policies; and (4) consideration of the alternative means of improvement in these results." Thus, Nicholls outlined the basic questions of a meaningful study of agricultural industries, albeit based on the work of earlier economists, notably Chamberlin and Robinson. In broad outline, the application of these questions to agricultural industries, which appeared fruitful to farsighted students more than two decades ago, is well under way, enough so that this first edition of case studies is possible. Much more analysis is needed, however, of these and other agriculture-related industries before we will understand all of the persistent relationships between market structure conditions in the agricultural industries. These studies should be viewed as partial and first approximations to be verified or rejected by further study.

## THEORETICAL BASIS FOR THE ANALYSIS

The purpose of this book is to describe and analyze (1) the recent history of the industries and present problems, (2) the principal characteristics of market structure and conduct, and (3) the important performance results and remedial policy alternatives.

Market *structure*[1] includes those characteristics of market organization related to firm conduct and industrial performance. Market structural variables measured in these studies include the number and size of buyers and sellers operating within the relevant markets, the extent to which firms sell identical or differentiated products, the height of barriers to entry of firms, and the extent of vertical integration. Market *conduct* refers to patterns of behavior

---

[1] Stephen H. Sosnich, "A Critique of Concepts of Workable Competition," *Quarterly Journal of Economics* (August 1958), pp. 380–423. Joe S. Bain, *Industrial Organization* (New York: John Wiley & Sons, 1959), p. 9. More recently, Robert L. Clodius and Willard F. Mueller, "Market Structure Analysis as an Orientation for Research in Agricultural Economics," *Journal of Farm Economics* (August 1961), pp. 513–53.

that enterprises follow in relation to their markets. Market conduct variables measured in these studies include the methods employed by groups of firms in determining price and output, sales promotion policy, product variation policy, and the incidence of predatory and exclusionary tactics. Market *performance* refers to the important economic results of market structure and conduct patterns. Market performance variables measured in these studies include the relative efficiency of procurement, plant utilization, scale and distribution; the amount and type of sales promotion costs; the improvement in quality of products; and the level of profits. Market *policy* refers to the important public and private remedial programs. Market policies considered in these studies include the antitrust laws relative to mergers, collusion and discriminatory practices; government grades, standards, research, information programs, price support programs, market orders and agreements; cooperatives; grocery chain countervailence; futures and terminal markets.

The market structure framework outlined above focuses on market performance and the factors affecting it. Market performance is influenced by market conduct or the nature of competition in the market. Adequate performance is related to vigorous but fair price and product competition. Weak competition tends to lead to excessive profits, uneconomic size of plants, excess plant capacity, lack of progressiveness, and the like. Cutthroat competition involving sales below cost, unjustified price discrimination, and exclusion of competitors may result in lower short-run prices but tends to eliminate competitors necessary to preserve vigorous competition in the long run. The type of competition that prevails in a market is related to its structure. The structural hypotheses are as follows:

The more firms in the market, the less interdependence of price among them and the more difficult it is for sellers to communicate. The more even the size distribution of firms in a market, the more difficult it is for any one firm to dominate the market or to coerce rivals into following the price and product policy most satisfactory to it. The greater the difference in the design, quality, and customer acceptance among competing products, the more difficulty sellers have in finding a mutually acceptable price or price differential among their products. The easier it is for new firms to enter a market, the less likely it is that firms in the market will maximize their joint profits because this would attract new firms with whom they would have to share sales and profits. Overall, this may be the principal deterrent to joint-profit maximization in American industry.

The market structure framework permits inclusion and use of

the rich literature and theory recently developed which is related to the explanation of *changes* in market structure and behavior. Explanation of the dynamic factors underlying changes in agriculture-related markets relies, in large part, on the many questions raised by oligopoly theory.

Markets have been classified into three basic types: pure competition, monopoly, and oligopoly.[2] Under pure competition, no one firm can affect the overall market price by changes in its own output or price. A monopoly market has but one seller. Monopolists set their output and prices at a level that maximizes their own profits. Since there is no competition to force them to excel, their prices and products are likely to be less desirable than would otherwise be the case.

Oligopoly is a Greek term meaning few sellers. Where sellers are few, a price or output change by one firm affects the sales and/or prices of competitors. Their prices and outputs are thus interdependent. Oligopoly is by far the most common and important type of market structure in the agricultural supply and marketing industries.

Firms in oligopolistic markets often exemplify schizophrenic behavior. As individual firms they are motivated to take the competitive offensive and strengthen their market position at the expense of competitors. But realizing that a price cut will usually be fully met by competitors, with no appreciable increase in sales (unless demand is highly elastic) and a loss in net revenue, they tend to refrain from open price competition. They may as a group agree implicitly or explicitly to raise prices to the level that would result in the maximization of their joint profits, akin to the behavior of a single monopolist.

Though firms in an oligopoly are motivated to maximize their joint profits, often they are able to do so only to a limited extent because of a combination of market restraints. As a result, competitors in oligopolistic markets tend to operate under an uneasy truce. Fear of retaliation limits open price competition and therefore aggressive firms tend to come as close to it as possible without actually incurring direct retaliation. Price cuts tend to be secret and discriminatory, with the large customers of competitors most often favored. They may be explicit such as an additional discount off the list price, or they may be hidden in the form of absorbed freight charges, additional advertising allowances, or furnishing signs and equipment. Nonprice forms of competition are also used including product differentiation through advertising,

---

[2] These terms *designate* the structure of the selling side of the market. Their counterparts on the buying side are pure competition, monopsony, and oligopsony.

promotion, and product improvement. In addition, firms may exclude competitors from their customers by price wars, exclusive dealing, full-line forcing, and vertical integration.

## SCOPE AND METHOD

Readers will observe that the following fourteen industry studies, though using the same basic approach, vary somewhat in industry scope, level of the market system analyzed, market structure, conduct and performance variables emphasized, and the degree of theoretical treatment. These variations result from several factors, particularly the relevant variables in the industry under study, the varying interests of the researchers involved, and the somewhat inexact nature of economic research. The latter is a function of the inability of social scientists to control the environment of their subjects, the difficulty of quantifying social variables, and the variation in training and perspective of the authors.

Most of the chapters are concerned with market structure on a national scale. Three chapters, however, emphasize the structure of markets within a particular state or region. These are on ice cream, apples, and grain procurement. In each case generalizations can be made concerning the national scene.

Three chapters are concerned with industries supplying farm inputs while eleven deal with markets for farm products. The latter stress various levels in the marketing system. The farm-processor market level is stressed in the chapters on apples, processed vegetables, and grain, and is discussed to some extent in the chapters on cotton and meat. The processor-retailer market is discussed in the chapters on meat, cotton, processed vegetables, and soybeans, and is dealt with almost exclusively in the chapters on ice cream, fluid milk, and bread. In the case of soybeans, it is the processor-refiner market. The food retailing chapter does not deal with a specific commodity. It is concerned with changes in market structure, conduct, and performance in the procurement and retail sale of groceries and meat.

Emphasis in the chapters is on actual market conditions. Several theoretical tools are used, however. Evans uses Chamberlinian diagrams in his chapter on processed apples to show the theoretical impact of a cooperative and a new entrant on prices and profits. Moore discusses and uses the joint-profit maximization model in the chapter on fluid milk. Helmberger and Hoos analyze the impact of varying supply elasticities for canning crops on the market position of local canners, and Williams draws the reader's attention to the relevant theoretical variables to analyze livestock markets.

# MARKET STRUCTURE OF THE AGRICULTURAL INDUSTRIES

# 1

# GROCERY RETAILING[1]

## LEON GAROIAN[2]

GROCERY RETAILING occupies a strategic position in the American economy. Its sales—currently over $58 billion annually—are greater than any other segment of retailing and, in fact, greater than any other American industry. The significance of grocery retailing in the nation's economy is evidenced by the fact that nearly one out of every six dollars spent by American consumers is spent in food retailing stores. Food processors and manufacturers depend largely upon grocery retailers as outlets for their products, and over two-thirds of all farm products ultimately are channeled through food stores. In addition, food retailing stores have become significant outlets for an ever-increasing number of nonfood items: clothing, hardware, magazines, housewares, toys, appliances, garden supplies, drugs, cosmetics, etc.

In the past few decades, vast and significant changes have occurred in food retailing as in other parts of the economy. These changes have apparently been generated by a complicated mixture of technological and economic factors, which have also induced marked changes in industrial structure. Because the farming, processing, and distribution industries are integrally related, changes in one affect the others. Because of this strategic position of food retailing in the distribution process, consumers, processors, and farmers, as well as food retailers themselves, have a vital interest in the way it performs its functions, both in terms of operating and pricing efficiency.

---

[1] Material in this chapter is based on a Ph.D. dissertation written for the University of Wisconsin by the author, and the subsequent book *Changes in the Market Structure of Grocery Retailing* by W. F. Mueller and Leon Garoian (Madison: University of Wisconsin Press, 1961).

[2] Professor and Extension Marketing Management Specialist, Oregon State University.

## MARKET STRUCTURE IN GROCERY RETAILING

### Types of Retail Food Stores

Traditionally, firms owning three or less stores are called independent food retailers and, when they operate more than this, they are referred to as chain retailers. In recent years some sources, including the Bureau of Census, have defined independents as firms with under 11 stores and chains as firms with 11 or more stores. In this chapter, a chain is defined as *a firm operating four or more stores except when specifically stated otherwise.* This definition is adhered to because much of the basis of this market structure study relates to the time period when chains were identified in this manner, and therefore it provides comparability over time.

In addition to the distinction between *types* of food retailing firms, independent firms are further identified as to whether or not they are *affiliated* in certain respects with other independents. Affiliated independents in turn are further divided into *cooperative* and *voluntary* chains of independents.

### Horizontal Integration and Market Concentration

By *horizontal integration* is meant that a firm increases in size by selling an increased volume of its existing product lines.[3] In grocery retailing, this can be done by increasing the size of grocery store, or by increasing the number of stores owned by one firm. The replacement of a small store by a supermarket is an example of the former, and the grocery chain is an example of the latter. The extent to which a firm is horizontally integrated is one measure of its absolute size.

*Market concentration* refers to the extent to which sales in a particular market are channeled through a certain firm or number of firms. The greater the share handled by a given number of firms, the greater the concentration in the market. It is obvious that there is a relationship between market concentration and the degree of horizontal integration of firms in the market. However, the two concepts are not identical. Strictly speaking, horizontal integration is solely an indication of the absolute size of firms. Since it is possible for a firm to be large in an absolute sense and yet constitute only a small part of a specific market, the two concepts must not be interchanged indiscriminately.

Economic theory and industrial experience suggest that relative firm size and market concentration are significant variables conditioning competitive behavior. To the extent that sales are con-

---

[3] This is the definition commonly used today by students of market structure. Cf. Andreas G. Papandreou and John T. Wheeler, *Competition and Its Regulation* (New York: Prentice-Hall, Inc., 1954), p. 307.

centrated through a few firms, those firms may have an incentive to follow an interdependent pricing policy. In other words, each firm comes to recognize that its selling—or buying—policy affects the entire market because the firm is such a large part of that market. Market concentration and firm behavior or conduct seem sufficiently related that special emphasis will be given to these factors.

Traditionally, grocery retailing has been one of America's least concentrated industries, but the transformation of an industry from many to relatively few firms affects the competitive conduct of the remaining firms more than any other conceivable factor, except for institutional or external restraints on the conduct of firms. But determining the relevant market in which to measure market concentration is not a simple matter. This is particularly true when the measure is used to determine the relative importance of particular firms in both buying and selling, as in food retailing where we find firms sell in essentially local markets but buy in regional or national markets. Moreover, even in buying, the relevant market varies from one commodity to another. For example, a retailer may buy its canned fruits and vegetables in a primarily national market, but its dairy products may come from an entirely local market. Thus, no single measure of market concentration serves all purposes and, in this chapter, a variety of measures are used.

### Changes at the National Level

Grocery retailing remains an industry of large numbers in spite of a continuing decline in store numbers since 1940. The number of grocery and combination stores decreased about one-third from 1940 to 1962—from 352,637 to 244,375. Moreover, most 1962 grocery sales were concentrated in a relatively small percentage of stores—27,125 supermarkets which, while constituting 11.5 percent of all grocery stores, accounted for 68.2 percent of all grocery store sales.

The concentration of sales in large stores has proceeded at a rapid pace in recent years. Between 1953 and 1962, the concentration of grocery store sales in supermarkets increased from 48 percent to over 68 percent. This comparison is solely in terms of concentration of sales in grocery *stores* and does not show the changes in concentration of sales by firms or companies, which is also of extreme significance.

Concentration among chain firms can be measured by determining the concentration of sales among firms with varying numbers of stores. On this basis, in 1958, the 790 corporate chains operating four or more stores accounted for 43 percent of all grocery store sales. This was more than a 5 percent point increase since 1948. Between 1940 and 1947, chains' share of sales averaged between about 33 percent and 39 percent of total sales.

A decreasing number of chain firms are doing an increasing share of the total grocery business. In 1953, there were 866 chains with four or more stores and 279 chains with 10 or more stores, but by January 1, 1958, there were 790 chains with four or more stores and 247 chains with 10 or more stores (Table 1.1).

This increased concentration is best reflected in the increasing share of grocery business done by the country's largest chains. Significantly, the four largest chains' share of grocery sales declined from 23.0 percent in 1940 to 22.4 percent in 1958; their share of chain sales decreased from 61.5 percent in 1940 to 52.1 percent in 1958. This significant decline in concentration was due mainly to the failure of A & P to maintain its share of national sales during this period. Its share of chain sales fell from 35.8 percent to 26.6 percent.

The 5th to 8th largest grocery chains' share of grocery sales climbed from 3.2 percent in 1940 to 6.1 percent in 1958. Their share of chain sales climbed from 8.6 percent to 14.1 percent in this period.

The 9th to 20th largest chains experienced the most dramatic increase in market shares. They more than doubled their 1940 share of 3.0 percent of grocery sales by 1958, when they accounted for 7.2 percent. Their share of chain sales rose from 8.1 percent to 16.6 percent.

In total, the 20 largest chains of 1958 accounted for 35.6 percent of grocery store sales, compared to 29.3 percent in 1940. They increased their share of chain sales from 78.2 percent in 1940 to 82.8 percent in 1958.

It is estimated that the 21st to the 50th largest chains accounted for about 3.1 percent of total grocery store sales and 7 percent of grocery chain sales in 1958. Thus, while there were 790 grocery chains with four or more stores in 1958, the 50 largest of these accounted for about 90 percent of chain sales and the remaining 740 accounted for 10 percent. This indicates that grocery sales have become increasingly concentrated among the chain sector of grocery retailing and that in turn, chain sales are becoming more and more concentrated among the 20 largest chains.

The independent sector of grocery retailing in 1958 was composed of 266,000 stores. Independents had combined sales accounting for 57 percent of total grocery store sales. This was down from 63 percent in 1940 and from their World War II high of 67 percent in 1943.

Unaffiliated independents still accounted for the largest num-

### TABLE 1.1
### Food Chain Companies by Size, and Stores Operated, 1953–58

| Year | 2 and 3 Stores | | 4 to 9 Stores | | 10 to 15 Stores | | 16 to 25 Stores | | 26 or More Stores | | Totals* | |
|---|---|---|---|---|---|---|---|---|---|---|---|---|
| | Chains | Stores | Chains | Stores | Chains | Stores | Chains | Stores | Chains | Stores | Chains | Stores |
| 1953 | 2,013 | 4,654 | 587 | 3,040 | 95 | 1,136 | 76 | 1,484 | 108 | 17,564 | 2,879 | 27,878 |
| 1954 | 2,234 | 5,122 | 592 | 3,109 | 92 | 1,103 | 71 | 1,378 | 112 | 17,279 | 3,101 | 27,991 |
| 1955 | 2,301 | 5,235 | 587 | 3,033 | 97 | 1,155 | 70 | 1,382 | 108 | 16,795 | 3,164 | 27,600 |
| 1956 | 2,464 | 5,560 | 598 | 3,116 | 88 | 1,052 | 65 | 1,296 | 103 | 16,703 | 3,318 | 27,727 |
| 1957 | 2,508 | 5,652 | 568 | 2,942 | 87 | 1,018 | 62 | 1,215 | 106 | 16,774 | 3,331 | 27,601 |
| 1958 | 2,335 | 5,207 | 543 | 2,848 | 88 | 1,043 | 58 | 1,153 | 101 | 16,848 | 3,125 | 27,099 |

Source: Compiled by Business Guide, Inc., publisher of *Chain Store Guide Directories*, New York, and published by National Association of Food Chains, Washington (June 1958).

* Totals include Canadian stores operated by United States companies. Data are for January 1 of each year.

ber of firms in food retailing (173,600 stores), but accounted for only 27 percent of independents' sales and 15.4 percent of total grocery store sales. This represents a significant drop in their share of sales since 1940, when they accounted for about 54 percent of independent grocery store sales.

Retailers affiliated with the 20 largest voluntary chains and cooperative chains accounted for an estimated 23 percent of the total sales of affiliated independents (Table 1.2). This represented about 15 percent of total grocery store sales.

It should be emphasized that the purchases of affiliated retailers through their affiliated voluntary and cooperative wholesalers are considerably less than the above comparisons might suggest. Affiliated independents purchase only about 20 percent of their products through their affiliated voluntary and cooperative wholesalers. They make their remaining purchases from unaffiliated suppliers. Retailers affiliated with the 20 largest cooperative and voluntary chains purchase about 44 percent of their requirements from their affiliated wholesalers.

Therefore, while affiliated independents do about 42 percent of all retail grocery store sales they purchase through their affiliated wholesalers only about 8.4 percent of total purchases of all retail grocery stores. Also, while the 20 largest voluntary cooperative chains account for about 15 percent of total retail grocery store sales, their purchases through their affiliated wholesalers make up only 6.6 percent of total purchases of all retail grocery stores.

This represents a significantly different concentration of purchases and sales than the 20 largest chains, which accounted for about 36 percent of total retail grocery sales and 36 percent of total purchases of retailers. These comparisons indicate that it could be a serious error to conclude that the market structure of affiliated independents is a close kin to that of corporate chains.

TABLE 1.2

PERCENT OF TOTAL GROCERY STORE SALES AND INDEPENDENT GROCERY STORE SALES
ACCOUNTED FOR BY THE LARGEST COOPERATIVE AND VOLUNTARY CHAINS
IN 1955

| Size Group | Total Sales | Percent of Total Grocery Store Sales | Percent of Total Independent Store Sales |
|---|---|---|---|
| | | *millions* | |
| 4 Largest | 2,718 | 7.4 | 12.5 |
| 5–8 Largest | 890 | 2.4 | 4.1 |
| 9–12 Largest | 615 | 1.7 | 2.8 |
| 13–20 Largest | 715 | 3.6 | 3.3 |
| 20 Largest | 4,938 | 15.1 | 22.7 |

Source: *Voluntary and Cooperative Groups Magazine* (April 1956), pp. 39, 40.

In addition to the above affiliations of independents, affiliated independents were indirect members (through their affiliated voluntary and cooperative wholesalers) in a number of national organizations. In 1956, the three largest of these national organizations—Cooperative Food Distributors of America, Independent Grocers Alliance (IGA), and Red & White Corporation—included as indirect members those independent retailers with retail sales of about $10.25 billion, or about 45.1 percent of total affiliated independent sales and 26.2 percent of total grocery store sales.

| Corporate chains | Percent of total grocery store sales in 1958 | |
|---|---|---|
| 4 largest | 22.4 | |
| 5–8 largest | 6.0 | |
| 9–20 largest | 7.2 | |
| 21–50 largest | 3.1 | |
| 182 other chains with over 10 stores | 3.0 | |
| 558 chains with 4–10 stores | 1.3 | |
| 790 corporate chains (19,400 stores) | | 43.0 |
| **Cooperative and voluntary chains** | | |
| 4 largest | 7.4 | |
| 5–8 largest | 2.4 | |
| 9–20 largest | 5.3 | |
| 443 others | 26.5 | |
| 463 cooperative and voluntary chains (92,000 stores) | | 41.6 |
| Unaffiliated independents (173,600 stores) | | 15.4 |

## Concentration in Regional and Local Markets

Market concentration at the national level is an important structural consideration because it indicates the relative absolute size of firms and is important in considering the competitive relationships between retailers and their suppliers which sell in a national market. But in terms of competition among retailers in selling, and between retailers and their suppliers which sell in less than national markets, the market structures of local and regional markets become most relevant.

Although only two corporate chains accounted for 5 percent or more each of total retail grocery sales in 1958, 17 of the 18 largest corporate chains had retail sales of over 5 percent of the total retail sales in the regions in which they operated (Table 1.3). The average for all 18 chains was 10.1 percent. This indicates that while many of these chains are relatively insignificant in terms of national sales, all are relatively important in their operating regions. For example, A & P accounts for 11.4 percent of national grocery sales and Weingarten only .3 percent, but A & P accounts for 13.8 percent of the sales in the regions where it operates and Weingarten 14.4 percent.

Analysis of the growth in local markets of the 20 largest national chains suggests that all but one for which such estimates could be made experienced an increase in share of sales in the cities

TABLE 1.3

SALES OF 20 LARGEST CHAINS AS A PERCENT OF TOTAL SALES IN THE CITIES AND REGIONS IN WHICH THEY OPERATED, OF TOTAL GROCERY CHAIN SALES, AND OF U.S. GROCERY STORE SALES

| Chain | Average Percent of Food Sales in Operating Cities* | | Percent of Sales in Areas Operating† | Percent of U.S. Chain Grocery Sales | | Percent of U.S. Grocery Store Sales | |
|---|---|---|---|---|---|---|---|
| | *1942* | *1957* | *1956* | *1940* | *1958* | *1940* | *1958* |
| A & P | 12.0 | 15.6 | 13.8 | 35.8 | 26.6 | 13.4 | 11.4 |
| Safeway | 25.0 | 22.6 | 11.3 | 12.8 | 11.6 | 4.8 | 5.0 |
| Kroger | 11.0 | 15.7 | 10.5 | 8.3 | 9.3 | 3.1 | 4.4 |
| American | 12.7 | 19.6 | 9.6 | 4.0 | 4.6 | 1.5 | 2.0 |
| National Food | 4.3 | 9.1 | 8.6 | 2.0 | 4.1 | .7 | 1.8 |
| Food Fair | 4.6 | 18.1 | 7.8 | .9 | 3.7 | .4 | 1.6 |
| Winn-Dixie | 9.6 | 22.9 | 16.3 | .4 | 3.3 | .2 | 1.4 |
| First National | 12.2 | 18.2 | 13.6 | 4.6 | 2.9 | 1.7 | 1.2 |
| Grand Union | 6.9 | 17.4 | 6.0 | 1.1 | 2.6 | .4 | 1.1 |
| Colonial | 12.7 | 14.4 | 12.3 | 1.5 | 2.3 | .6 | 1.0 |
| Jewel Tea | 8.2‡ | 24.6‡ | 13.8‡ | .9 | 2.3 | .4 | 1.0 |
| ACF-Wrigley | n.a. | 12.9 | 12.4 | .07 | 2.0 | .02 | .9 |
| Loblaw | 7.9 | 12.7 | 9.4 | .7 | 1.5 | .3 | .6 |
| Stop and Shop | 2.8 | 13.7 | 6.1 | .7 | 1.0 | .3 | .4 |
| Penn Fruit | n.a. | n.a. | 8.3 | n.a. | .8 | n.a. | .4 |
| Thriftimart | n.a. | n.a. | n.a. | .2 | .9 | .1 | .4 |
| Red Owl§ | 6.0 | 11.3 | 11.3 | .4 | .9 | .2 | .4 |
| Bohack | n.a. | n.a. | 7.3 | .8 | .8 | .3 | .4 |
| Lucky | n.a. | 13.3 | 3.4 | .2 | .7 | .1 | .3 |
| Weingarten | n.a. | 14.4 | n.a. | .4 | .7 | .2 | .3 |
| Average (unweighted) | 9.7 | 16.3 | 10.1 | 4.0 | 4.1 | 1.5 | 1.8 |

\* These are the cities in Table 1.5 in which these chains operated in 1942 and 1957 and for which necessary data are available. The share of each chain's sales in each city was computed by assuming that each of its stores in the city had sales equal to the average sales of all its stores in that year.
† *Chains* (published by *This Week Magazine*, 1957).
‡ These comparisons exclude the sales of Jewel's home service routes.
§ These comparisons exclude Red Owl's wholesale sales.

in which they operated. It is estimated that in 1957 each of the 20 largest chains accounted for an average of about 16 percent of the sales in the cities in which they operated. The chain with the lowest market share averaged 9.1 percent and the one with the highest share averaged 24.6 percent (Table 1.3). A greater increase in market shares occurred in slow-growing cities than in rapid-growing ones.

It was estimated that the largest corporate chain in each of 133 selected cities averaged 25.4 percent of sales in each city, the two largest grocery retailers averaged 42.2 percent, and the four largest retailers averaged 58.3 percent (Table 1.4). And while reliable estimates of local sales concentration among affiliated independents are not available, it is the author's judgment that, in cities with over 25,000 population, the four largest retail firms and the four largest voluntary and/or cooperative chains typically account for over 85 percent of total retail grocery store sales. Since most of the remaining sales are channeled through independent retailers, many of whom are in essentially different economic markets, it is concluded that market concentration on the selling side of grocery retailing is very high.

Another significant aspect of the changing structure of local markets is that the 20 largest chains increasingly are located in the same markets as a result of their geographic expansion (Table 1.5). In 1942, three or more of the 20 largest chains operated in only 18 percent of 211 of the country's largest cities, but by 1957 this number of chains was operating in 60.8 percent of these cities.

TABLE 1.4

Average Share of Grocery Store Sales Accounted For by Largest Two Largest, and Four Largest Grocery Retailers in 133 Cities, 1958

| Population of Cities | Number of Cities | Average Percent of Grocery Store Sales | | |
|---|---|---|---|---|
| | | Largest retailer | Two largest retailers | Four largest retailers* |
| *(000)* | | | | |
| 35 – 74 | 17 | 30.6 | 48.7 | 61.6 |
| 75 – 99 | 22 | 22.4 | 38.7 | 55.6 |
| 100 – 199 | 43 | 25.9 | 42.6 | 60.6 |
| 200 – 499 | 26 | 26.4 | 44.8 | 60.2 |
| 500 – 999 | 20 | 24.0 | 39.8 | 55.4 |
| 1000 and over | 5 | 16.8 | 26.8 | 40.5 |
| Total | 133 | | | |
| Average | | 25.4 | 42.2 | 58.3 |

Source: Computed from *Distribution of Food Store Sales in 133 Cities,* prepared by *Supermarket News* (1958).
* Eight cities listed fewer than four retailers. These cities are not included in the averages appearing in this column.

TABLE 1.5

FREQUENCY DISTRIBUTION OF 211 CITIES IN WHICH VARIOUS NUMBERS OF THE 20
LARGEST CHAINS OF 1957 WERE OPERATING IN 1942, 1945, 1950, 1955, AND 1957*

| Number of the 20 Largest Chains Operating in City | Number and Percent of Cities | | | | | | | | | |
|---|---|---|---|---|---|---|---|---|---|---|
| | 1942 | Per-cent | 1945 | Per-cent | 1950 | Per-cent | 1955 | Per-cent | 1957 | Per-cent |
| 1 | 56 | 26.5 | 45 | 21.3 | 41 | 19.4 | 33 | 15.6 | 33 | 15.6 |
| 2 | 117 | 55.5 | 127 | 60.2 | 115 | 54.5 | 73 | 34.6 | 50 | 23.6 |
| 3 | 35 | 16.6 | 36 | 17.1 | 47 | 22.3 | 87 | 41.2 | 81 | 38.4 |
| 4 | 3 | 1.4 | 2 | 0.9 | 8 | 3.8 | 12 | 5.7 | 42 | 19.9 |
| 5 | 0 | ... | 1 | 0.5 | 0 | ... | 6 | 2.8 | 5 | 2.4 |
| Total | 211 | | 211 | | 211 | | 211 | | 211 | |

Source: Computed from *Editor and Publisher, Market Guides* (1943, 1946, 1951, 1956, and 1958 editions).

* In addition to these 211 cities, there were 47 cities among the country's 258 largest cities for which data were not available for at least one of the years. In these 47 cities, the frequency distribution in the last year for which these data were reported was as follows: one chain (11 cities); two chains (12 cities); three chains (11 cities); four chains (9 cities); five chains (3 cities); and seven chains (1 city).

While four or more of the top 20 chains were operating in only 1.4 percent of these cities in 1942, by 1957 the percentage was 8.5. These findings indicate that today more large chains are located in the same market than ever before, with important implications on competitive behavior, to be discussed later.

### Impact of Horizontal Mergers on Market Structure

Firms grow horizontally either through internal expansion or by external expansion involving acquiring, merging, or consolidating with other concerns. Most often, large firms grow externally as well as internally during some period of their growth history. Our concern is with the importance of external growth—growth by mergers, consolidation, or acquisitions—because industrial experience teaches that extensive use of this method of growth often results in drastic and rapid transformations in industrial structure. The current concern with mergers in food retailing is based on the belief that grocery mergers are resulting in a drastic transformation of the structure of grocery retailing.

During 1940–58, 342 acquisitions of grocery retailers by other grocery retailers were recorded (Table 1.6). These acquired concerns operated at least 4,061 grocery stores with estimated retail sales of $3.2 billion (expressed in 1957 dollars). This was equal to 7.4 percent of total retail sales of grocery stores in 1958. It is estimated that there may have been as many as 1,000 grocery stores acquired during 1940–58 which were not reported by the sources used in the study. Thus the total sales of all grocery retailers acquired from

TABLE 1.6

NUMBER OF RETAIL GROCERY FIRMS AND STORES ACQUIRED BY GROCERY
RETAIL FIRMS, BY YEARS, 1940–58

| Year | Number of Acquired Firms | Number of Acquired Stores | Sales of Acquired Firms | Sales of Acquired Firms (1957 dollars) |
|------|------|------|------|------|
| | | | *(000)* | *(000)* |
| 1940 | 8 | 22 | 26,083 | 61,033 |
| 1941 | 6 | 745 | 112,083 | 238,431 |
| 1942 | 1 | 6 | 2,633 | 4,777 |
| 1943 | 3 | 47 | 20,438 | 33,212 |
| 1944 | 1 | 17 | 15,429 | 25,425 |
| 1945 | 3 | 40 | 18,799 | 30,548 |
| 1946 | 3 | 135 | 37,171 | 53,362 |
| 1947 | 4 | 62 | 40,529 | 47,184 |
| 1948 | 3 | 52 | 35,792 | 38,775 |
| 1949 | 4 | 49 | 35,267 | 39,890 |
| 1950 | 2 | 10 | 7,210 | 8,150 |
| 1951 | 6 | 97 | 63,816 | 64,926 |
| 1952 | 7 | 234 | 49,649 | 49,020 |
| 1953 | 26 | 103 | 93,526 | 95,568 |
| 1954 | 25 | 89 | 99,816 | 102,443 |
| 1955 | 61 | 876 | 674,528 | 701,542 |
| 1956 | 59 | 435 | 431,925 | 447,144 |
| 1957 | 47 | 387 | 458,544 | 458,544 |
| 1958 | 73 | 655 | 672,897 | 662,313 |
| Total | 342 | 4,061 | 2,896,135 | 3,162,287 |

Source: Merger data were derived from the following: *Moody's Industrials,
Chain Store Age, Progressive Grocer, Super Market News,* and miscellaneous
sources. The first three sources were used for each year from 1940 to 1958, whereas all sources were used beginning with 1953. We estimate that these sources
understate mergers (measured by store numbers) of large chains by not over 10
percent and all retailers by not over 25 percent.

1940–58 may have been as large as $4.3 billion (1957 dollars). This
is equal to nearly 10 percent of total grocery store sales in 1958.

It is the author's judgment that these retail mergers (1) explain much, and perhaps most, of the increased share of total
grocery sales of the largest chains, (2) were responsible for much of
the increased concentration within the chain sector of food retailing, (3) contributed to increased local market concentration, and
(4) played a prominent role in the rapid growth of individual
firms.

Firms acquired by the 20 largest grocery retailers of 1958 had
sales equal to 56 percent of all acquired retailers. The adjusted
sales of these acquired retailers were 4.8 percent of total grocery
store sales and 10.3 percent of chain sales in 1958. This is a significantly large percentage since, between 1940 and 1958, the top 20

chains' share of total grocery store sales increased by 6.3 percentage points. Hence, the aggregate sales of retailers acquired by the top 20 chains were about 76 percent as great as the increase in their share of total grocery store sales.

Thus, the increase in these chains' share of national grocery store sales may be explained largely by the extensive merger activity of some chains. Had none made mergers it seems probable that the 20 largest chains' share of grocery store sales would not have increased. This conclusion is further supported by the fact that only the three chains of the top 20 *which made no mergers*—A & P, First National, and Fisher Brothers—experienced a decline in their share of grocery sales during 1940–58 (Table 1.7).

TABLE 1.7

NUMBER OF FIRMS, STORES, AND SALES OF STORES ACQUIRED DURING 1941–58 BY THE 20 LARGEST CHAINS IN 1958

| Acquiring Chain* | No. of Mergers | No. of Stores | Sales of Acquired Stores (1957 $) | Acquisitions as Percent of 1958 U.S. Grocery Store Sales | Acquisitions as Percent of 1958 U.S. Chain Sales |
|---|---|---|---|---|---|
| | | | *(millions)* | | |
| National Food† | 26 | 585 | 349.4 | .81 | 2.14 |
| Winn-Dixie | 11 | 336 | 242.2 | .56 | 1.31 |
| American | 4 | 356 | 189.5 | .44 | 1.03 |
| Grand Union | 15 | 155 | 171.4 | .40 | .93 |
| ACF-Wrigley | 9 | 142 | 166.4 | .39 | .90 |
| Kroger | 8 | 146 | 166.3 | .39 | .90 |
| Safeway | 6 | 629 | 162.5 | .38 | .88 |
| Food Fair | 11 | 124 | 148.5 | .35 | .81 |
| Colonial | 10 | 106 | 147.2 | .34 | .80 |
| Lucky | 7 | 72‡ | 94.7 | .22 | .51 |
| Jewel Tea | 2 | 43 | 52.2 | .12 | .28 |
| Stop and Shop | 5 | 23 | 26.8 | .06 | .15 |
| Thriftimart | 3 | 16 | 20.6 | .05 | .11 |
| Loblaw† | 2 | 19 | 20.1 | .05 | .11 |
| Weingarten | 1 | 6 | 14.0 | .03 | .08 |
| Red Owl | 1 | 12 | 9.1 | .02 | .05 |
| Bohack | 1 | 5 | 5.3 | .01 | .03 |
| A & P | ... | ... | ... | ... | ... |
| First National | ... | ... | ... | ... | ... |
| Fisher Brothers | ... | ... | ... | ... | ... |
| Total | 123 | 2,775 | 1,986.2 | 4.62 | 11.02 |

\* Penn Fruit was among the top 20 in 1958 but was excluded because its sales for 1940 were not available.
† National Food and Loblaw are treated as separate firms although George Weston, Inc., has an interest in each.
‡ Number of stores in one merger not reported. This merger was counted as involving one store.

The retail mergers of the 20 largest chains also contributed somewhat to the high level of local market concentration in 1958. Analysis of the acquisitions of these chains reveals that the acquiring chains operated in only 22 percent of the cities in which acquired firms operated stores. This indicates that most mergers did not have an immediate effect on local market concentration.

Perhaps the most dramatic effect of mergers by the top 20 chains is that they played a dominant role in transforming some relatively obscure chains to national prominence in a decade or less. The most spectacular example is the ACF-Wrigley Company. In 1940, Wrigley had retail grocery sales of only $2.1 million but, by 1958, it had sales of $383 million. About 46 percent of this growth was the direct result of acquisitions.

Analysis of the growth experience of the 20 largest firms reveals that there is a close relationship between their growth rates and the relative extent to which they used mergers in their growth (Table 1.8). However, this does not prove that mergers were responsible for their different growth rates. These facts support both the hypotheses (1) that fast growing firms make most extensive use of mergers and (2) that the extensive use of mergers by some firms causes their high growth rates.

In attempting to determine which of these hypotheses most correctly interprets the relationship between mergers and growth rates, the changes in the relative sizes of the top 20 firms were analyzed. This indicates that most of the changes between 1940 and 1958 in the relative sizes of the 20 largest firms were due to their differing rates of internal growth rather than differences in the extent to which they used mergers.

This conclusion should be interpreted carefully. First, this method of measuring the effects of mergers takes account only of their *direct* effect on growth. Hence it is possible that the rankings based on the 20 largest firms' estimated 1958 sales exaggerate the instability which would have occurred had they grown entirely internally.

Second, in 1940, most of the firms were quite small and many of similar size; consequently, even slight differences in their growth rates during 1940–58 would have resulted in significant changes within their ranks by 1958.

Third, it is not inferred from these findings that mergers are unimportant in firm growth or market structure. The overall analysis of the importance of horizontal mergers demonstrates that they have played a prominent part in the growth of many large retail firms and that their net effect has been to increase national market concentration significantly above that which would have occurred had none of these firms used mergers.

TABLE 1.8

SALES OF ACQUIRED RETAILERS AS A PERCENT OF THE 1940 SALES OF ACQUIRING
CHAINS AND THE PERCENT INCREASE IN SALES OF THE ACQUIRING CHAINS BETWEEN
1940 AND 1958, 20 LARGEST CHAINS IN 1958

| Name of Chain | Sales of Acquired Firms as Percent of 1940 Sales of Acquiring Firm | Percent Increase in Sales, 1940–58 |
|---|---|---|
| A & P | 0 | 87.9 |
| First National | 0 | 58.9 |
| Fisher Brothers | 0 | 81.8 |
| Average* | 0 | 76.2 |
| Bohack | 9.0 | 159.0 |
| Safeway | 17.4 | 129.3 |
| Kroger | 27.5 | 183.4 |
| Red Owl | 30.7 | 437.8 |
| Loblaw | 37.7 | 414.5 |
| Average* | 24.5 | 264.8 |
| Weingarten | 45.4 | 336.4 |
| Stop and Shop | 50.4 | 250.0 |
| American | 64.9 | 188.5 |
| Jewel Tea | 76.4 | 525.7 |
| Colonial | 136.1 | 289.2 |
| Thriftimart | 137.5 | 985.9 |
| Average* | 85.1 | 429.3 |
| Grand Union | 208.5 | 490.9 |
| Food Fair | 217.5 | 912.0 |
| National Food | 241.2 | 427.8 |
| Lucky | 861.7 | 1,142.6 |
| Winn-Dixie | 855.4 | 2,046.3 |
| ACF-Wrigley | 3,231.8 | 7,063.6 |
| Average* | 936.0 | 2,013.9 |

Source: These are the 20 largest chains which were listed in *Moody's Industrials* in 1940 and still operating in 1958. Actually, Penn Fruit and Mayfair Markets were larger in 1958 than was Fisher Brothers, but they were not listed in the 1940 *Moody's*.
   * Simple average.

## Vertical Integration of Grocery Retailers

Vertical integration by corporate grocery chains dates back over 50 years. By 1920, five of the largest chains operated a total of 37 manufacturing plants. During the 1920's, many chains entered manufacturing, and by 1930, 25 chains operated one or more grocery manufacturing plants. By 1958, 62 grocery chains operated a total of 326 food manufacturing plants. Products manufactured by these chain-owned plants had a wholesale value of $1.3 billion and 85 percent of these products were sold through the chains' own stores.

The leading products processed by chains in 1958 were meat, dairy, baking, coffee, and canning. In terms of relative importance, baking, coffee, and concentrated milk led all others. The author estimated that in 1958 chains manufactured the following percentages of their requirements of these products: baking, 39; coffee, 38; and evaporated milk, 20. On the other hand, they processed only about 5 percent of the meat products, 8.9 percent of their dairy products (other than concentrated milk), 6.8 percent of their canned products, and 1.2 percent of their poultry products.

The most significant change in vertical integration by chains in the past 30 years is that more chains have become integrated and chains have entered more fields of grocery manufacturing.

### Vertical Integration of 20 Largest Chains

In 1958, the country's 20 largest corporate chains operated over 90 percent of all chain manufacturing plants. And the top four chains operated more grocery plants than all other chains combined.

There is a clear relationship between chain size, measured by total sales, and the extent of vertical integration. By 1957, the top four chains on the average had integrated into 10.5 of 17 grocery manufacturing industries, while the fifth to eighth largest chains had integrated into 4.6 of these industries and the ninth to twentieth largest chains on the average had integrated into only 1.9 of these (Table 1.9).

Perhaps the most striking change since 1940 in the vertical integration variable of market structure is the increase of potential integrators into various fields. The most crucial factor determining whether a chain is capable of integrating into a particular industry is its size. Consequently, one effect of the increased horizontal integration of many chains since 1940 has been to place increasing numbers of chains in the position to integrate into many fields. The author's analysis of the number of *potential* integrators into

TABLE 1.9

AVERAGE NUMBER OF 17 INDUSTRIES INTO WHICH THE 20 LARGEST CHAINS OF 1957 HAD INTEGRATED IN 1940 AND 1957*

| Size Grouping | Average Number of 17 Industries Into Which Chains Integrated | |
|---|---|---|
| | *1940* | *1957* |
| Four Largest Chains | 6.5 | 10.5 |
| Fifth to Eighth Largest Chains | 4.0 | 4.6 |
| Ninth to 20th Largest Chains | .8 | 1.9 |
| Average of 20 Largest Chains | 2.6 | 4.2 |

* These are the industries listed in Table 1.10 plus fluid milk. Because the operations of some plants are not disclosed, this understates the actual extent of integration for chains of all size classifications. This table is based on *Moody's* whereas Table 1.10 includes information from other sources.

16 different grocery manufacturing industries in 1940 and 1957 indicates the magnitude of this change. For example, in 1940, only 14 out of the 40 largest corporate chains were large enough to have integrated into baking, but by 1957, all 40 were large enough to do so (Table 1.10).

The comparable numbers of potential chain integrators in 1940 and 1957 for some other important fields were poultry dressing, 14 and 40; ice cream, 10 and 32; meat packing, 8 and 31; cheese, 5 and 12; evaporated milk, 4 and 12; and biscuits and crackers, 1 and 5. These findings indicate that an ever-growing number of chains are becoming potential integrators into grocery manufacturing.

The reason chains can integrate into so many fields is due to their unique position of being able to overcome the main barrier which makes entry difficult or impossible for other firms; that is, the product differentiation barrier to entry. As chains become large they are able to develop consumer acceptance of their own

TABLE 1.10

NUMBER OF ACTUAL AND POTENTIAL INTEGRATORS AMONG THE LARGEST FOOD CHAINS IN 1940 AND 1957, 16 INDUSTRIES

| Industry | Sales of Smallest Integrator* (1957 dollars) | Number of Top 20 Chains Actually Integrating | | Number of Potential Integrators Among the Top 20 Chains of 1957† | | Number of Potential Integrators Among the 21 to 40 Largest Chains | |
|---|---|---|---|---|---|---|---|
| | (millions) | 1940 | 1957 | 1940 | 1957 | 1940 | 1957 |
| Poultry Dressing | 30.9 | 1 | 2 | 14 | 20 | 0 | 20 |
| Baking | 34.9 | 11 | 19 | 14 | 20 | 0 | 20 |
| Butter | 50.1 | 1 | 4 | 14 | 20 | 0 | 14 |
| Coffee Roasting | 53.3 | 8 | 15 | 14 | 20 | 0 | 12 |
| Ice Cream | 58.7 | 1 | 4 | 10 | 20 | 0 | 12 |
| Meat Packing | 68.9 | 3 | 7 | 8 | 20 | 0 | 11 |
| Jams and Jellies | 137.1 | 3 | 6 | 6 | 18 | 0 | 0 |
| Fruit and Vegetable Canning | 139.5 | 4 | 4 | 6 | 18 | 0 | 0 |
| Peanut Butter | 226.3 | 3 | 5 | 5 | 13 | 0 | 0 |
| Cheese | 280.3 | 2 | 2 | 5 | 12 | 0 | 0 |
| Salad Dressing | 291.8 | 4 | 6 | 5 | 12 | 0 | 0 |
| Evaporated Milk | 306.5 | 3 | 5 | 4 | 12 | 0 | 0 |
| Biscuits and Crackers | 736.1 | 0 | 3 | 1 | 5 | 0 | 0 |
| Gelatin Desserts | 817.6 | 1 | 3 | 1 | 4 | 0 | 0 |
| Cereal Preparation | 1,989.3 | 1 | 2 | 1 | 2 | 0 | 0 |
| Margarine | 1,083.3 | 0 | 1 | 1 | 3 | 0 | 0 |

Source: Computed from *Moody's Industrial Manual* (various editions) and miscellaneous sources.

  * These are the sales of the smallest chain to have integrated into a particular industry in the year it integrated.
  † Computed by assuming that all chains which had 1940 or 1957 sales (in adjusted prices) greater than the smallest chain entering an industry were also large enough to have integrated.

brands. And if they become large enough to sell the output of an efficient-sized plant under their own brand, they are in the position of being able to integrate into such industries by either buying a going concern or by building their own plant. Thus the main determinants of whether a chain can integrate into a particular field are (1) the development of its own brand and (2) the expansion to a size adequate to operate and utilize the output of efficient-sized plants manufacturing various products.

### Motives for Integration Into Manufacturing

There are technical, market structure, and miscellaneous reasons chains integrate into manufacturing.

Our hypothesis explains ownership integration in terms of the market structure of vertically related industries. Applied to grocery retailing, this hypothesis states that retailers have the greatest incentive to integrate into those grocery manufacturing industries in which sellers have the greatest amount of market power in selling their products.

This hypothesis was tested by correlating statistically the market concentration ratios of various grocery manufacturing industries with an index of chain integration into these industries. This latter index was a ratio (percent) of actual chain integrators to potential chain integrators. This correlation indicated a highly significant statistical relationship between the market concentration of various food industries and the extent to which chains integrated into them.[4]

Analysis of the integration experience of large chains in the last several years further supports this hypothesis. Chains definitely are integrating into the most concentrated grocery manufacturing industries at a higher rate than into the less concentrated ones.

### Nonownership Integration

Chains may enjoy many advantages of vertical integration without actually entering, through ownership, vertically related industries. The unifying economic result of these less complete forms of integration is that certain decisions of chains and their suppliers are made jointly rather than individually; that is, firms in different stages of the marketing system coordinate certain of their operations through formal or informal agreements rather than rely on open markets—and the prices generated therein—to coordinate their operations. This can be achieved through specification buying and private labeling by chains.

As early as 1930, about 45 percent of all grocery chains sold

---

[4] The correlation coefficient is .88, which is significant at the 1 percent level.

some groceries under their own brands. By 1958, most chains in all size categories sold some groceries under their own brands. Even independents operating from one to three supermarkets sold under their own labels about 5 percent of their dry groceries, and about 12 percent of the dry grocery sales of retailers operating from 11 to 100 stores were of their own brands. It is estimated that as much as 50 percent of the food sales of some very large chains are of their own brands.

The basic motive underlying chain use of private labels is that doing so increases their profits. Brands or labels are one form of product differentiation and, when such differentiation is pronounced, firms are able to follow selling policies which are partially independent of other firms. When retailers buy from manufacturers with market power built on successful product differentiation, chains have an incentive to integrate into such industries. But chains have an incentive to develop their own brand even for products not produced by firms with market power. By developing their own brands for such products, they may achieve some "original" market advantage.

There is an important distinction between retailer branding of products produced by firms in oligopolistic market structures and in competitive ones. In an oligopolistic market, retailers may prefer, or are forced, to produce the product in their own plant. But in a competitive market, they generally prefer to buy it from existing producers. The reason for this is that firms operating in competitive industries are likely to earn lower returns than chains. Consequently, chains may enjoy the advantages of selling a differentiated product bought from firms which do not enjoy market power based on product differentiation.

Once chains develop their own labels, they almost inevitably embark on a policy of specification buying. For once they no longer buy on a brand basis; they must prescribe physical specifications for their product. And since they have a vital interest in maintaining consumer acceptance of their private brands, their specifications will be designed to assure them of an adequate product.

### Vertical Mergers of Grocery Chains

During 1940–58, grocery retailers made at least 81 vertical acquisitions into grocery manufacturing, of which the 20 largest chains made 68.

Between 1948 and 1958, voluntary chains also acquired eight manufacturing plants and cooperative chains acquired two manufacturing plants.

The greatest number of vertical mergers were made during World War II, when 34 mergers occurred during 1943–45.

Analysis of these vertical mergers reveals that chains used mergers extensively to enter new fields. However, once they had entered a new field, chains customarily grew by internal means.

These findings suggest that chains used vertical mergers in preference to internal growth because they provided the easiest means of overcoming the technical and managerial barriers to entry.

### Entry of Grocery Wholesalers and Manufacturers Into Retailing

Although grocery retailers had integrated into manufacturing for over 50 years, a recent development significant to market structure has been the integration of grocery suppliers into grocery retailing. Since 1948, five grocery manufacturing firms have acquired control of 40 retail firms with sales of $1.1 billion at the time of purchase (Table 1.11). Moreover, in 1948–58, nine grocery wholesalers acquired 131 retail stores with combined 1958 sales of $63.2 million. In addition, several manufacturers and wholesalers expanded into grocery retailing through internal growth.

Although complete data of these developments are not available, it is estimated that, by 1958, grocery manufacturers and grocery wholesalers controlled chain grocery outlets with sales of at least $1.5 billion, or about 8 percent of the total sales of all chains with 11 or more stores.

TABLE 1.11

GROCERY RETAILERS ACQUIRED BY GROCERY MANUFACTURERS,
GROCERY WHOLESALERS, AND NONGROCERY FIRMS, 1948–58

| Nature of Acquiring Firms | Number of Acquiring Firms | Number Acquired Retail Firms* | Number of Retail Stores Acquired | Sales of Acquired Retailers in Year of Acquisition |
|---|---|---|---|---|
| | | | | (millions) |
| Grocery Manufacturers | 5† | 40 | 1,420 | $1,109.6 |
| Grocery Wholesalers‡ | 9 | ‡ | 131 | 63.2 |
| Nongrocery Firms | 5 | 16 | 308 | 445.6 |
| Total | 19 | 56 | 1,859 | $1,617.2 |

Source: *Supermarket News, Moody's Industrials, Progressive Grocer.*

\* This table includes stores acquired by chains subsequent to the latter's acquisition by grocery manufacturers and nongrocery firms. Ten acquisitions with combined sales of $886 million shown in this table do not appear in Table 1.6.

† Consolidated Foods, which acquired three chains during 1948–58, is listed as a manufacturer although its wholesale and manufacturing operations are of about the same magnitude.

‡ These data are based on the *Economic Inquiry Into Food Marketing, Interim Report,* Federal Trade Commission (Washington, 1959). The source did not report the number of acquired firms.

Moreover, there reportedly are various, subtler financial ties between chains and manufacturers. These may involve loans or other financial assistance from manufacturers to chains, or outright selling of chain shelf and display space to suppliers.

The developments of the last decade indicate a significant reaction to past vertical integration in food distribution. And if the trend of food manufacturer and wholesaler integration into retailing continues, food manufacturers will soon control more of food retailing than retailers control of food manufacturing.

In addition to the horizontal and vertical mergers, between 1940 and 1958, at least 16 grocery firms with combined sales of $446 million were acquired by five firms not previously engaged in any phase of the grocery industry. These mergers, which might appropriately be called conglomerate mergers, did not have any immediate effect on the degree of either horizontal or vertical structure of grocery retailing.

## IMPLICATIONS OF CHANGING MARKET STRUCTURE FOR COMPETITIVE BEHAVIOR AND INDUSTRIAL PERFORMANCE

### Implications of Local Market Structure

The structure of local markets in grocery retailing approximates oligopoly models. Typically, relatively few large firms account for the bulk of sales, with a fringe of small independent firms accounting for the remainder. Moreover, the existing rivals often enjoy considerable spatial separation, so that very large cities actually consist of a number of submarkets rather than a single large one.

Economic theory suggests that when the number of sellers in the relevant market is small, or where a few firms account for a considerable share of sales, rivals tend to behave in an interdependent manner.[5] Market structures of small numbers of rivals tend to create an atmosphere and opportunity conducive to outright collusion.

(But even in the absence of collusion, firms may agree tacitly to avoid price competition, although still engaging in a variety of nonprice forms. In grocery retailing, nonprice competition may assume the form of product and/or service differentiation and extensive local advertising. This does not mean that all the symptoms of price competition disappear or that some products will not be

---

[5] See Edward H. Chamberlain, *The Theory of Monopolistic Competition* (Cambridge: Harvard Univ. Press, 1933); Joan Robinson, *Economics of Imperfect Competition* (London: Macmillan Co., Ltd., 1933); William H. Nicholls, *Imperfect Competition Within the Agricultural Industries* (Ames: Iowa State College Press, 1941); and William Fellner, *Competition Among the Few* (New York: Alfred A. Knopf, Inc., 1949).

priced near, at, or below costs. Such pricing may become a common part of a package of special inducements to encourage customers to shop in a particular store. But intensive price competition would not be expected to prevail in local markets in grocery retailing if sales are concentrated in a few firms, except where large horizontally integrated firms choose to operate their stores in a particular city below costs in order to enter a new market or to expand their market share.)

If entry into a market is very easy, high profits would encourage additional entrants, which would tend to diminish existing firms' future profits. To prevent this, existing firms would tend to charge below what short-run market conditions would warrant.

In this respect, (one of the main stimulants to competition in the past decade may have been the geographic expansion of medium and large chains into one another's market areas. This tended to place large, presumably efficient rivals in competition with one another. To the extent mergers are used to enter one another's market, this tends to minimize the price and nonprice rivalry which would ordinarily result as one large firm tries to enter another's market through internal growth. Thus, while many retail mergers may not have increased market concentration greatly, they may well have reduced considerable potential rivalry among large chains.)

Moreover, if local market structures become more concentrated, we may expect a further decline in price competition, although nonprice competition may actually increase. Economic experience in other industries indicates that nonprice competition—especially advertising and selling efforts—often becomes more intensive as concentration and differentiation increase. There is evidence that this development is under way in grocery retailing.

According to internal revenue records, corporate food retailers' advertising expenses increase from $49 million in 1947 to $233 million in 1957, or from .48 percent of their sales to .92 percent of sales. Between 1947 and 1952, advertising expenditures as a percent of sales remained relatively stable. But between 1952 and 1957, they increased from .54 percent to .92 percent, or by three-fourths in just five years.[6]

(A key determinant of future market structure and competitive behavior in local markets is the success with which affiliated independents are able to achieve the economies of corporate chains, and the extent to which small- and medium-sized corporate chains are able to survive and grow.)

---

[6] During 1947–56, all areas of retail trade increased their advertising expenditures as a percent of their sales by only 10 percent, and between 1952 and 1956 by only .1 percent.

The extent to which small and medium chains continue to offer competition to large chains will largely depend on the extent to which large chains continue to use mergers in their expansion. If the 20 largest chains average as many acquisitions during 1959–67 as they did annually during 1955–58, by the end of 1967 they will have acquired stores with sales greater than the total sales of the 770 other chains with four or more stores operating in the beginning of 1958.[7]

No attempt has been made to develop any empirical evidence of competitive behavior at the local level to determine whether it currently approximates that which economic theory suggests. But conversations with retailers suggest that retailers think largely in terms of nonprice rivalry with other chains, and casual observation suggests that currently such nonprice rivalry is extremely keen in many areas.

### Implications of Absolute Size

The market power conferred on firms as a result of their absolute size, rather than just their relative size in particular markets, has not been incorporated in most theories of competitive behavior. However, the absolute size of firms influences greatly the kind of competitive practices they are able to follow in particular markets. As Edwards points out, a firm that "operates across many markets need not regard a particular market as a separate unit for purposes of determining business policy. . . . It may possess power in a particular market not only by virtue of its place in the organization of that market but also by virtue of the scope and character of its activities elsewhere. It may be able to exploit, extend, or defend its power by tactics other than those that are traditionally associated with the idea of monopoly."[8]

This concept of the market advantages conferred by large size seems to have important implications for competitive behavior in local retail grocery markets. Even though a very large regional or national chain may not have the largest sales in a particular local market, it may nonetheless be a much more important factor in the market than its local sales alone suggest. Because of its ability to sustain losses in a particular market out of its operations elsewhere, it has the potential power to expand its market share at the expense of other firms. Moreover, once it has established its position in a market, it may be able to induce local retailers to follow

---

[7] Since 1960, the merger pace in grocery retailing has slowed considerably from that of 1955–58.

[8] Corwin Edwards, "Conglomerate Bigness as a Source of Power," *Business Concentration and Price Policy*, Nat. Bur. of Econ. Res. (Princeton Univ. Press, 1955).

its pricing policy because of its potential ability to engage successfully in any price wars which might develop should others not follow its lead. Edwards states it succinctly when he says, "The large
company is in a position to hurt without being hurt."

There is some evidence that the large size of some chains has
permitted them to follow the practices that Edwards suggests. The
record in the A & P case cited many instances in which company
units operated at a loss over long periods, e.g., Boston and Prov-
idence from 1934 through 1941; Toledo, 1932–38; Indianapolis,
1932–35 and 1937–38; Detroit and Cincinnati, 1932–37.[9]

In a recent antitrust case involving Safeway Stores, the country's second largest grocery chain, the Department of Justice charged
that Safeway operated some of its districts below costs for the
purpose of discouraging competition.[10] Safeway pleaded *nolo
contendere* and was fined.

Edwards cites another market characteristic of very big firms
which may have important implications for competitive behavior in
local markets. He points out the differences in competitive at-
titudes which emerge when large firms come into contact with one
another in many local markets. As Edwards puts it:

> The interests of great enterprises are likely to touch at many points,
> and it would be possible for each to mobilize at any one of these
> points a considerable aggregate of resources. The anticipated gain
> to such a concern from unmitigated competitive attack upon another
> large enterprise at one point of contact is likely to be slight as com-
> pared with the possible loss from retaliatory action by that enterprise
> at many other points of contact. . . . Hence there is an incentive to
> live and let live, to cultivate a cooperative spirit, and to recognize
> priorities of interest in the hope of reciprocal recognition.[11]

This conception of competitive conduct among large firms has
important implications for the future, as well as relevance today.
As grocery chains become larger and meet one another in more and
more markets, we might expect the emergence of a "live and let
live" policy, which Edwards implies results from such industrial
characteristics.

### Implications of Regional and National Market Structure

Market structure theory suggests that the relative market power
of firms derives from their relative share of particular markets,

---

[9] See Robert F. Lanzillotti, "Pricing Objectives in Large Companies: Reply," *American Economic Review* (Sept. 1959), pp. 679–82, for other examples of
A & P's policy in this respect.

[10] *U.S. vs. Safeway Stores, Inc.,* U.S. District Court for the Northern District
of Texas, Dec. 7, 1957.

[11] Edwards, *op. cit.*

overall market concentration, the extent of their product differentiation, the degree to which other firms can enter their markets, and the structure of markets from which they buy their inputs and to which they sell their outputs.

On the buying side of grocery retailing, the relevant market typically is much larger than it is in selling. In some products, such as many canned fruits and vegetables, concentrated milk, and butter, retailers buy and manufacturers sell in essentially national markets. But in some products, such as fluid milk, bread, and locally produced fruits and vegetables, the relevant markets vary from essentially local markets to rather large regional ones.

For products sold nationally or in large regional markets, the structure of the buying side of grocery retailing appears to be characterized by a fairly large number of large- and medium-sized chains or affiliations of independents, and a very large number of smaller firms. Economic theory suggests that such market structures severely limit interdependent pricing behavior; that is, this large number of firms would encourage very many buyers to behave as if their individual market behavior had an insignificant effect on market conditions. Even A & P, which purchases about 11 percent of all products sold through grocery retailers, does not buy enough of products sold in national markets to control arbitrarily the general price level received by suppliers of such products.

Caution must be exercised in interpreting the implications of certain market conduct of large chains as *prima facie* evidence that they have market power in buying. It is frequently observed that a large chain acts as a price leader in certain supply markets. Care must be taken, however, in determining the exact type of price leadership exercised by such a chain.

It is the author's judgment that the price leadership policies most likely to emerge on the buying side of grocery retailing conform to the "barometric" type[12] of price leadership. The theoretical explanation of this kind of price leadership is that the leader is chosen or accepted because of his superior ability to assess market conditions. As Stigler puts it, the barometric firm "commands adherence of rivals to his price only because, and to the extent that, his price reflects market conditions with tolerable promptness."[13]

The price which the barometric price leader sets may be competitive, monopolistic, or somewhere in between. Thus, it is possible to have a competitive or monopolistic barometric price leader.

---

[12] Jesse Markham, "The Nature and Significance of Price Leadership," *American Economic Review* (Dec. 1951), pp. 891–905.

[13] George Stigler, "The Kinky Oligopoly Demand Curve and Rigid Prices," *Journal of Political Economy* (Oct. 1947), p. 446.

To discover which type exists in a particular industry requires thorough investigation. However, certain types of market structure are most conducive to competitive behavior and others to monopolistic, and certain patterns of action may be taken as implicit evidence of competitive pricing.

The leading structural determinant of the type of barometric price leader which emerges is the number and size distribution of firms. If the leader has too many rivals to make some fairly well disciplined form of collusion or tacit understanding workable, he may be forced to indicate prices near or at competitive levels. A more profitable price (to the leader) would be in constant danger of being shaded by some of his rivals because they felt their individual actions had an insignificant effect on the general price level.

On strictly market structure grounds, the price leadership practiced in buying products sold in national and large regional markets seems to be essentially the competitive barometric type.[14] However, as markets become smaller, the market structure of grocery retailing may become conducive to a less competitive type of barometric price leader. However, more empirical work is needed to determine the forms of price leaderships actually practiced by grocery retailers in different markets.

The remainder of this chapter shall (1) deal with the theoretical implications which this has for competitive behavior in grocery retailing and manufacturing and (2) test empirically some of these implications.

## Market Position of Retailers vs. Manufacturers

The grocery manufacturing industries are considerably more concentrated in national markets than is grocery retailing. In 1954, there were 38,476 firms in the 49 industries manufacturing food and related products.[15] Thus, there were fewer firms in *all* the food and related products manufacturing industries than in grocery retailing, with its over 200,000 firms.

In 1954, market concentration at the national level, measured in terms of the four largest firms, was greater in 41 (83 percent) of these 49 grocery manufacturing industries than it was in grocery re-

---

[14] See the following reference for an attempt to determine empirically the kind of barometric price leadership followed among California tomato processors. Norman R. Collins, Willard F. Mueller, and Eleanor M. Birch, *Grower-Processor Integration in the California Processing Tomato Industry*, Calif. Exp. Sta. Bul. 768 (Oct. 1959), pp. 54–59.

[15] These included all the firms in the *Census of Manufactures* listed as producing food and kindred products, tobacco products, soap, and salt. *Concentration in American Industry*, Report of the Subcommittee on Antitrust and Monopoly, 85th Cong. (Washington, 1957), pp. 41 ff.

tailing. Similarly, in 1954, the 20 largest grocery retailers accounted for just under 32 percent of all grocery store purchases. But in 47 of the 49 grocery manufacturing industries, the 20 largest firms accounted for over 32 percent of their industry's sales and, in 29 of the 49 industries (59 percent), the 20 largest manufacturers accounted for over 70 percent of their industry's sales.

Grocery manufacturing industries generally are considerably more concentrated in selling than are grocery retailers in buying. Moreover, these comparisons tend to understate the relative differences in concentration between these industries. First, many grocery manufacturers sell significant quantities of their products to other than grocery retailers, sometimes directly to consumers (e.g., home-delivered milk), to institutional buyers (e.g., canned vegetables, dairy and meat products to restaurants and military installations), to other types of food stores (e.g., meat to meat markets and flour to retail bake shops), and to other food manufacturers (e.g., sugar to confectioneries, fruit canners, and ice cream makers).

In 1954, grocery stores accounted for about 86.4 percent of all food stores' sales. Manufacturers' sales to other than food retailers are quite substantial in some items. It is the author's judgment that, in 1954, the 20 largest chains accounted for about 25 percent or less of the outlets (expressed in dollars) of the total sales of grocery manufacturers.

Furthermore, because the industry classifications used are very broad, market concentration in particular *products* produced in these industries often is considerably greater. For example, while the four largest canners account for 28 percent of all canned fruits and vegetable products, the four largest soup makers account for 89 percent of all canned soup sales.

What is the significance of this high degree of market concentration in most food manufacturing industries? On the basis of market structure theory, we would expect that such structures give sellers some discretion over their selling policies. The extent of such discretion would vary considerably from industry to industry.

Significantly, the buying side of grocery retailing is considerably less concentrated than all but a handful of food manufacturing industries. Since the 20 largest grocery chains account for only 36 percent of all grocery store purchases, the buying side of grocery retailing clearly falls into Bain's definition of an industry with "low grade" concentration.[16]

The above comparisons are based on market concentration in national markets. Actually, of course, some grocery suppliers operate in essentially regional markets. In such markets, both processor

---

[16] Joe Bain, *Industrial Organization* (New York: John Wiley & Sons, Inc., 1959), pp. 131–32.

and retailer market concentration ratios are higher than the above. But, as a generalization, we may assume that food processing industries are more concentrated than grocery retailing in both regional and national markets. Moreover, in most manufactured food products, the relevant market is essentially a national or very large regional market; hence, the above concentration ratios are fairly good indicators of relative market concentration.

Based solely on the relative degree of market concentration in grocery buying and selling, economic theory suggests that, in most industries, the balance of bargaining power would rest with manufacturers; but that, in the less concentrated industries, the largest chains would be able to induce suppliers to grant them discriminatory prices—in the absence of effective enforcement of the Robinson-Patman Act. But if such price discrimination were extended to more and more buyers, it would soon become so commonplace that it would force a readjustment in prices quoted to all buyers. Hence, in the less concentrated manufacturing industries, large retailers might have little market advantage in their dealings with grocery manufacturers.

## Vertical Integration and Private Labeling by Retailers

Relative market concentration data suggest that, in most products, grocery manufacturers have much more market power in selling than retailers have in buying. However, relative market concentration is only one factor influencing the relative market power of buyers and sellers. Vertical integration by grocery retailers is another factor. On the basis of economic theory and empirical evidence, it is concluded that the primary reasons for retailer integration into manufacturing are to be found in the market structure of grocery manufacturing.

Since many grocery manufacturing industries are highly concentrated, and insofar as this results in market power which, in turn, results in relatively high manufacturing profits, chains have an incentive to integrate into such industries. Moreover, insofar as the high concentration and profits of such industry result from product differentiation based on high advertising expenditures, chains with acceptable brands of their own may be able to save some of these advertising expenses should they make the product themselves.

Both of these reasons, especially the first, act as strong stimulants to chain integration into manufacturing; the second advantage, saving of advertising expenditures, may be enjoyed by chains without actually making their own products, by simply placing their brand on products made by others.

If the above hypothesis is a primary explanation of chain integration, we would expect the greatest relative amount of chain integration into those manufacturing industries with the greatest amount of market power. Empirical analysis of chain integration supports this hypothesis. Although other factors also encourage chain integration, the analysis of its implications for competitive behavior dealt mainly with market structure-motivated vertical integration.

Grocery retailers have integrated into manufacturing in two ways: (1) by actually operating their own manufacturing plants and (2) by developing their own labels. Let us consider the impact of each type of integration on market structure and industrial performance.

### Implications of Chain Manufacturing

Traditionally, retailers specialized in the retailing function, food processors specialized in manufacturing, and retailers and processors dealt with one another through intermediary firms performing the wholesaling function. Although their local market structure gave retailers some power in selling, in buying they were at a relative disadvantage in their dealings with grocery manufacturers, whether they bought from firms directly or through wholesalers.

Often the main source of high concentration in grocery manufacturing was that some firms had successfully differentiated their products; this made it difficult for other manufacturing firms to enter such industries. But as grocery retailers developed their own brands and became large enough to sell under their brands the output of an efficient-sized manufacturing plant making a particular product, they found it relatively easy to integrate into such a product. In other words, they were able to overcome the product differentiation barrier to entry which kept many other potential entrants out.

As more and more chains become large enough to integrate into particular products, their integration may begin to significantly affect the number and market shares of firms making such products. As a result, we would expect that extensive chain integration into manufacturing, or even extensive potential integration, would have the effect of making the affected manufacturing industry behave more competitively than market concentration data alone suggest.

However, on strictly theoretical grounds,[17] integration by chains into manufacturing would not necessarily drive prices all the way

---

[17] For an excellent theoretical discussion of the importance of product differentiation as a barrier to entry and the effects of barriers to entry on industrial performance, see Joe S. Bain, *Barriers to New Competition* (Cambridge: Harvard Univ. Press, 1956), Chap. 1.

down to competitive levels; for once earnings of grocery manufacturers fell to the point where earnings on marginal investments of chains in grocery manufacturing were less than additional investments in grocery retailing, chains would no longer have an incentive to integrate into grocery manufacturing. Thus, the entry-forestalling price of grocery manufacturers would tend to be something above competitive levels as long as grocery chains' earnings were above competitive levels.

Data developed in this study, as to the extent of actual and potential vertical integration by chains into leading grocery manufacturing industries, demonstrate that there has been a pronounced change in the importance of the vertical integration variable of market structure since 1940 (see Table 1.10). The significant point to remember is that this structural change has come about because of the increase in the absolute horizontal size of many chains during 1940–58, and is not due to market power resulting from increased market concentration. This increased horizontal integration of many chains has given them the ability to do what a few decades ago only a few large chains could accomplish.

### Implications of Private Label Selling by Chains

When chains become large enough to develop their own brands, they are able to integrate into food manufacturing. But they may gain some, or all, of the advantages of actually integrating into manufacturing by having food manufacturers pack their products under chain labels. When this is done, chains, in effect, have integrated into grocery manufacturing; now their private label products are in competition with products sold under manufacturers' brands.

Such "integration" into manufacturing would change the structure of the manufacturing industry. If, as the author believes, the main source of market power in most food manufacturing industries is successful product differentiation, firms selling to chains on a private label basis may not have much market power on such sales since they are selling undifferentiated products. For if manufacturing firms which originally had market power continued to price above competitive levels, they would induce entry of new firms or encourage expansion of those firms which were willing to sell on a private label basis. Entry of new firms would be induced because the main barrier to entry, product differentiation, would not bar the entry of new firms willing to sell on a private label basis.

Actually, entry would not be necessary to bring about competitive results if some firms—most likely small or moderately sized ones—which had not successfully differentiated their products, were willing to sell to chains on a private label basis. But even large manufacturers would sell private label products to chains at near competitive prices if they feared the alternative was that smaller firms would supply the product.

Consequently, it is concluded on the basis of market structure theory that extensive private label selling by grocery manufacturers would encourage very competitive behavior in their sales to chains. And even though concentration in manufacturing remains high in such industries, even the largest firms may lose much of the main source of their original market power—successful product differentiation.

In general, we would expect that the main effect of extensive chain integration into manufacturing, through operating their own plants and/or through partial integration by developing their own brands or labels, would be to change the structure and behavior of manufacturing industries so as to induce them to operate in a much more competitive manner than relative market concentration data suggest. Such behavior would presumably be reflected in profits. Profits of the affected grocery manufacturing industries would decline relative to grocery retailing. Available empirical data support this hypothesis.

Estimating corporate profit rates is a precarious procedure.[18] However, comparison of profits of different industries over time provides a fairly satisfactory indication of *relative* profitability if not of *absolute* profitability. Therefore, comparisons of the earnings in food retailing and in several food manufacturing industries provide a fairly satisfactory indication of the relative changes in profitability of these industries during the period studied.

During 1940–58, there has been a gradual deterioration of earnings in these industries relative to chain earnings. Baking, dairy, and meat packing firms improved their relative profitability significantly during World War II, but thereafter they all lost ground relative to their prewar position.

These findings of the changing relative profitability of these grocery supply industries are consistent with the hypothesis that increasing vertical integration by chains during this period has had the effect of increasing competition in these industries.

The above data, suggesting that grocery manufacturing has become less profitable than food retailing, are consistent with an earlier finding that the relative extent of chain manufacturing was not significantly greater in 1958 than in 1929. Although it is not possible to obtain data of the relative extent of chain manufacturing in various products in the intervening years, it seems probable

---

[18] Joe S. Bain, "Profit Rate as a Measure of Monopoly Power," *Quarterly Journal of Economics* (1940).

that, since the 1930's, some chains have decreased the relative amounts of certain products which they manufacture in their own plants.[19] Certainly the above comparisons of relative profits in manufacturing and retailing indicate that they had an incentive to get out of certain manufacturing industries in favor of buying from others on a private label basis.

There are important exceptions to this generalization. Profits in some manufacturing industries very likely have not been affected adversely by chain integration because not any, or only a few, chains have integrated into them. Also, it is possible that, in certain cases where chains face concentrated market structures, even though manufacturers do not make very large profits, they still are unwilling to sell to chains on a private label basis at prices as low as chains could enjoy if they manufactured the product.

When chains buy in national markets, manufacturing firms are more likely to be willing to sell on a private label basis because the structure of the buying side of retailing results in quite competitive bidding among chains. Thus, a manufacturer has a relatively large number of alternative buyers and may expect to receive something at least approximating long-run competitive prices for his private label products. On the other hand, a manufacturer with only a few potential buyers in a market is placed at a serious bargaining disadvantage if he becomes entirely dependent on one buyer.

Another theoretical implication of the higher earnings in retailing relative to manufacturing is that, while chains have less incentive to integrate into some manufacturing industries today than they did previously, many manufacturers now have a strong profit incentive to integrate into retailing.

Food manufacturers having the greatest incentive and opportunity to integrate into retailing are medium-size, multi-product firms which have not successfully developed differentiated products. The more diversified such firms are, the greater is their incentive to develop captive retail outlets. Therefore, processing firms would have an incentive to diversify, presumably through merger, into various grocery products in order to gain a broader base for such integration. This is exactly what Consolidated Foods did prior to its entry into food retailing on an extensive scale since 1953.[20] Similarly, George Weston Associates acquired control of a number of

[19] Some qualification is needed, since the absolute volume of retail sales has increased greatly due to the addition of more products now sold in stores in contrast to the 1930's.

[20] By 1954, Consolidated had integrated into a full line of canned fruits and vegetables, coffee roasting, baking, dried fruits and nuts, sugar, raisins, frozen foods, tea, and other products. *Moody's Industrials*, 1954. It achieved most of its diversification through merger.

food manufacturing firms prior to and since acquiring control of National Food and Loblaw.

As indicated, by 1958, food wholesalers and manufacturing interests controlled grocery chains with about 8 percent of total grocery chain store sales. This was almost equal to the extent of chain integration into grocery manufacturing. But while extensive chain integration into grocery manufacturing dates from the 1920's, practically all manufacturer integration in grocery retailing occurred since 1950.

To date, very few grocery manufacturers have integrated into retailing but, if many additional ones do so, the entire structure of grocery distribution could be transformed drastically. Moreover, the effect could be cumulative. Some manufacturing firms originally not integrating into retailing might feel compelled to do so for defensive reasons.

The ultimate effect of such integration on industrial performance is not entirely clear. A major determinant of this behavior will be its effect on market concentration in grocery retailing. Extensive manufacturer integration into retailing would not necessarily increase market concentration, unless food manufacturers integrate into retailing by acquiring a number of medium and small chains, as did Consolidated Foods.

It is conceivable, however, that the immediate effect on performance of further manufacturer and wholesaler integration into retailing will be an intensification of rivalry among retailers. If additional large chains are formed, and if they attempt to expand their market position, their expansive behavior will intensify competitive rivalry. This could cut profit margins all around for a time, which would likely place many independents in an even more precarious position than they are today.

The long-run effect on behavior of these structural developments is even more difficult to predict. This is an area which deserves continuing study.

## Concluding Comments on Industrial Performance

We are interested in market structure and competitive behavior because of the belief that these factors influence, in part, the economic and social performance of industries in a market economy. Conceptually, there are many criteria by which industrial performance may be judged, all of which are difficult to measure empirically. For example, one criterion of performance is the profit component of marketing margins. The rationale underlying this criterion is that, if the profit portion of food marketing margins declines, this improves the economic welfare of consumers and farmers.

Certain changes in the structure of food retailing apparently have intensified competition in grocery manufacturing, and consequently have reduced profits in some of these industries. Comparisons indicate a general downward trend in profit margins in these industries since prewar and postwar years. Moreover, profit margins of chains have not increased during the period 1941–58, even though grocery retailers are performing more functions than previously. This suggests that the food retailing industry is also performing in an improved manner compared to prewar years. But this limited evidence is by no means conclusive proof of improved performance. Profit margins may change for many reasons, e.g., changes in marketing technology, which are completely unrelated to competitive behavior and increasing advertising expenditures.

Another important aspect of industrial performance is the effect of recent structural changes on manufacturers' and retailers' promotional expenses. The increasing market concentration of retail grocery sales in local markets has tended to intensify nonprice competition. One major result has been that chains are increasing their promotion efforts. This has been reflected in rising advertising expenditures by grocery retailers and the increased use of trading stamps.

Similarly, many food manufacturers have responded to growing integration and private label selling of chains by expanding their promotion efforts in hopes of improving their consumer franchise. President Charles S. Bridges of Libby, McNeill and Libby, in commenting on the expansion of chain labels, has said, "This obviously has increased the pressure on the advertised brands, necessitating large expenditures for advertising to hold their share of the consumers' business."[21]

The result has been a great expansion of advertising expenses in an industry which already was the country's leader in this field. According to internal revenue records, food manufacturing corporations spent $337 million in 1947, which equaled 1.11 percent of sales. By 1957, food processors spent $808 million on advertising, or equal to 2.03 percent of their sales.[22] Thus, their advertising expenditures, as a percent of their sales, increased by 83 percent in just ten years. This compares with an increase of only 33 percent for all other manufacturing industries.

On the basis of this trend, food processors and retailers spent over $1,250,000,000 on advertising in 1963. And advertising represents only the most obvious selling cost in our modern food distribution system.

---

[21] Quoted in *Food Field Reporter* (Mar. 2, 1959), p. 20.
[22] *Statistics of Income*, U.S. Treas. Dept. Int. Rev. Serv.

Evidence on nonadvertising promotional cost is scanty, and is usually buried in broad, vaguely defined categories of a firm's operating statement.[23] For example, some food manufacturers spend considerable amounts on point-of-sale promotion which may not show up as advertising expenses. Similarly, entertainment and other miscellaneous expenses incurred by salesmen are not recorded among advertising expenses. Also, much that is officially classified as product development costs may actually involve only superficial product and packaging changes aimed at increasing consumer acceptance of an otherwise unchanged product. It is not unreasonable to expect that nonadvertising promotional efforts of many food processors are as great or greater than their advertising expenses.

Why all this concern over the size of selling expenditures? Clearly, all selling efforts do not involve social waste of resources. Many are informational in character; in a private enterprise economy, this is a means of informing potential buyers of the availability, prices, and quality of your wares. However, today much, and perhaps most, advertising by food processors and an increasing amount by food retailers is concerned with persuading rather than informing the consumer.[24]

In judging advertising as a component of industrial performance, it is of more than passing interest to compare its magnitude with the size of expenditures for research. After all, these are alternative forms of competition; in truth, a growing number of economists have come to believe that the main and most fruitful competition in modern American capitalism is the drive to develop better products and processes.

One measure of this performance characteristic is the amount of resources firms devote to research aimed at product and process discovery and development. In 1956, food and kindred products manufacturers spent an estimated $76 million on research,[25] equaling about .2 percent of their total sales. This compared with 1956 advertising expenditures of about $800 million. Thus, food manufacturers spent $10 for advertising for every $1 spent on research. In 1960, food manufacturers spent an estimated $96 million on research[26] compared to nearly $1 billion on advertising.

---

[23] For example, the Quaker Oats Company spent $49,166,990 on "selling, general and administrative expenses" in 1957. This equaled 16.3 percent of its total sales—up from 14.3 percent in 1950. The bulk of these expenses very likely represents selling expenses of one kind or another.

[24] Even in food retailing, advertising effort is losing much of its informational value. Increasing amounts of newspaper space are being devoted to persuasive rather than informational advertising. Today, most full-page newspaper ads list price and other information on only about 50 items. This represents less than 1 percent of the items handled in modern supermarkets.

[25] *Business Plans, 1957–60*, McGraw-Hill, Dept. of Econ., p. 12.

[26] *Ibid.*

These facts suggest that, when measured against the advertising component of industrial performance, some of the recent changes in the market structure of grocery retailing have tended to lower rather than raise the level of industrial performance.

These comments are not intended to demonstrate empirically whether the net result of the recent structural changes in retailing has been to raise or lower the level of performance of the food industries. More thorough analysis is required of the criteria mentioned here and, of course, these are only two of many criteria. Additional performance criteria must be tested before a conclusive answer can be given to the question, "Are the current and prospective market structures of grocery retailing encouraging desirable industrial performance?" Among the most important aspects of performance requiring study are the effects of recent structural changes on manufacturers' and retailers' efforts to make real or superficial product innovations, and on other aspects of their production and marketing efficiency.

Although an exhaustive study of the performance of the grocery retailing industry is not presented, economic theory buttressed by industrial experience in other industries warrants this generalization: the future performance of grocery retailing will depend, in large part, on the extent to which market concentration continues to increase, especially at the local level.

One of the leading structural elements causing intense rivalry among retailers in local markets in recent years has been the efforts of large chains to enter one another's markets. But there is a question whether society can be certain that this cause for rivalry will continue indefinitely. If market concentration increases and big chains meet as rivals in many markets, their appetite for aggressive competitive rivalry may diminish.

It is more difficult to predict when market structure will have changed enough to permit and encourage such performance than to predict that it will occur. Much will depend upon public policy toward maintaining competitive market structures through placing certain restraints on growth via merger by large retailers, and upon the environment created to assist small firms in operating more efficiently.

# 2

# THE MEAT INDUSTRY[1]

## WILLARD F. WILLIAMS[2]

MEAT PACKING was one of the first of the major agricultural industries to develop an organization characterized by dominant, large-scale, vertically and horizontally integrated firms. In the process it acquired an image that has persisted through more than half a century of change. In many quarters, the industry still is viewed as one in which a few monolithic firms and remaining small, locally oriented companies enjoy unusually favorable competitive circumstances, being faced on the one side by large numbers of small livestock producers and on the other by innumerable small retail meat markets. Conditions, however, have changed greatly since the early 1920's when Congress and others were so vitally concerned with large-scale organization in meat packing. Significant changes in structure have appeared throughout all sectors of the red meat industry since World War II, and marketing patterns and practices have been altered dramatically. The changes are not confined to meat packing; meat packers, never exclusively responsible for meat distribution, do not occupy so prominent a position in the red meat industry as they once did.

## THE ECONOMIC ENVIRONMENT

Interest and concern with respect to any particular industry or industry sector of the economy—by business participants and society alike—center primarily on economic performance.[3] More particularly, interest centers in the progress of performance through time. But economic performance and changes in it are determined

---

[1] Derived partially from Willard F. Williams and Thomas T. Stout, *Economics of the Livestock-Meat Industry* (New York: Macmillan Co., 1964). See particularly Chaps. 14–17, 22, and 25.

[2] Professor and Head of the Department of Agricultural Economics, Texas Technological College, Lubbock, Texas.

[3] Business participants are included here because economic performance, as ordinarily defined, embraces profits and other measures of entrepreneurial success.

by all relevant factors of economic significance rather than by a few which might be conveniently classified as structural dimensions or conduct. In general, changes in economic performance are determined by (1) the multi-faceted aspects of economic environment and industry character including economic characteristics of the firms, products, and productive resources in that industry and (2) the competitive strategy or conduct of the individual firms in adjusting to *changes* in economic environment and industry character. Since organizational characteristics of the industry—structural attributes—are a part of the economic environment within which individual firms operate, these are important and must be given detailed consideration. Equally important, however, are other environmental factors and economic characteristics. With respect to the meat industry, these include demand and supply characteristics of industry products, the technological environment and technical input-output relationships, institutional environment, and conditions of entry to and egress from the industry. For convenience here, discussion of demand and supply characteristics precede the description of structure which is followed by consideration of other specified aspects of environment or industry character.

## General Characteristics

The meat industry is a heterogeneous collection of enterprises and functions tied together by common product interests, competition in buying or selling, and a variety of economic conditions and forces. Included as sectors of the industry are livestock slaughterers or meat packers, meat processors, transportation agencies, commercial storage firms and warehouses, packinghouse branches which are nonslaughtering processing and sales branches of packers, many different types of "independent" wholesale meat distributors, meat brokers, retail stores and meat markets, and other retail distributors.[4]

Meat packing is a process of dissembly involving many operations that are not easily mechanized. Raw material costs represent nearly three-fourths of the meat packer's sales dollar while labor costs account for almost half of the remainder.[5] The industry has relatively little control over the volume, type, or quality of raw materials offered to it and these are subject to shrink and loss of weight. In addition, fresh meats have never lent themselves well to uniform packaging, standardization, and branding. The industry

---

[4] Emphasis is placed here upon meat packing and processing and wholesale distribution including procurement activities of retailers.

[5] American Meat Institute, *Financial Facts About the Meat Packing Industry, 1963* (Chicago, 1963).

constantly is faced with problems associated with perishability and the inherent offensiveness of slaughter.

Significant regional differences are found in structure and in marketing practices. There are many different types of meat packers, processors, and distributors, and these are widely distributed geographically. In some areas and sectors of the industry, the progress of change is far advanced, while in others it has been retarded by institutional forces and factors.

### Demand and Supply Characteristics

The attention consumers give to prices is matched today by consumer insistence upon service, quality, and uniformity. These, together with a steadily rising population, increasing per capita incomes, and changed buying habits, have generated a combination of forces which have placed considerable pressure upon retailers and other industry sectors for adjustments. Resulting structural changes at retail are well documented elsewhere.[6]

Sparked by sharp increases in demand for beef, United States demand for red meat has been rising. Elasticity of consumer demand for meat at −.6 to −.7 is relatively high compared with averages for all foods, but it appears that the demand for meat is becoming more inelastic. Elasticity coefficients for individual species are slightly higher, but it generally is agreed that demand for beef and pork is inelastic while demand for veal and lamb is elastic. Cross elasticities of demand among the various species are relatively high.[7]

While numerous factors affect changes through time in per capita demand for meat, the influence of per capita income is most significant. Although meat consumption usually is positively associated with income this is not always true of all meats. Per capita consumption of beef, veal, and lamb generally rises sharply with income. Pork consumption, much less affected, seems to be positively associated with income only in areas such as the West where per capita consumption of pork is low. It is possible that relative differences in economic performance of the beef and pork sectors of the industry during recent years are largely explained by differences between these two meats in income elasticity. Income elasticity also may explain some of the differences between the beef

[6] W. F. Mueller and Leon Garoian, *Changes in the Market Structure of Grocery Retailing* (Madison: Univ. of Wis. Press, 1961). Also, see Williams and Stout, *op. cit.*, Chap. 16.

[7] G. E. Brandow, *Interrelations Among Demands for Farm Products and Implications for Control of Market Supply*, Penn. State Univ. Bul. 680 (Aug. 1961); Harold F. Breimyer, *Demand and Prices for Meat*, U.S.D.A. Tech. Bul. 1253 (Washington, Dec. 1961); and Williams and Stout, *op. cit.*, Chap. 22.

and pork sectors in market structure and in competitive strategy.[8]

The elasticity of the supply function for slaughter livestock and meat is much greater between years or production periods than within them. The few data and other information available for recent periods suggest that both beef and pork production are highly responsive through time to prices. Beef production also appears to respond significantly and positively to population increases and to changes in per capita incomes of consumers, i.e., to shifts in demand functions for meat.

Increases in relative importance of large, specialized, and commercialized livestock-producing units in the United States appear to have contributed to recent increases in the elasticity of the supply response. Related or additional factors include (1) better quality animals and improved techniques of production, (2) larger calf, lamb, and pig crops per breeding unit, and (3) increased feeding, more year-round feeding, and improved feeding techniques. The appearance and rapid growth of commercial drylot feeding of cattle has tended toward an increase in the elasticity of the short-term supply response in beef.[9] Development of the commercial cattle feeding industry, partially a result of changes in consumer demand and in structure of the retail food sector, has affected structure, conduct, and performance of the meat industry.[10]

## Industry Structure and Changes in Structural Characteristics

Structure of the meat industry has changed radically in each of several dimensions.[11] Medium-volume, independently owned, commercial packers and meat distributors have grown rapidly in

---

[8] See Brandow, *op. cit.;* Breimeyer, *op. cit.;* and Williams and Stout, *op. cit.,* Chap. 22.

[9] However, coefficients based on historical data necessarily reflect the influence of a relatively long period of secular growth in feedlot production. Recent experience suggests that, when cattle prices are falling, feedlot placements and marketings may be quite unresponsive to price changes. Such experience also suggests that commercial drylot cattle feeding may have provided the beef industry with an additional source of price instability.

[10] E. R. Swanson, "Supply Response and the Feed-Livestock Economy," *Agricultural Supply Functions,* (Ames: Iowa State Univ. Press, 1961), Chap. 15; A. A. Harlow, *Factors Affecting the Price and Supply of Hogs,* U.S.D.A. Tech. Bul. 1274 (Washington, Dec. 1962); and Breimeyer, *op. cit.*

[11] These dimensions, for reasons deeply rooted in the philosophy of the author, are confined to physical organizational characteristics. They include (1) number, (2) size and size distribution, (3) type and type distribution, and (4) geographic location. "Type," in turn, includes organizational differences associated with differences in nature and degree of specialization, integration, product differentiation, legal form, and/or other attributes of firms that distinguish them as to type. This definition is considered more defensible and more consistent with the warning given by Bain against a broad, inclusive definition of "market structure" than those ordinarily adopted, including Bain's own definition. See J. S. Bain, *Industrial Organization* (New York: John Wiley & Sons, Inc., 1959), pp. 8–9.

number and size while many of the small, locally oriented firms have disappeared or grown larger. The nation's major packing firms, the "national" packers, have declined relatively in importance and both functional and organizational characteristics of many of these firms have changed. Concentration in wholesale meat distribution as well as in fresh meat packing has declined, specialization and production according to specification has increased, and some packers have vertically integrated into livestock feeding and other activities. Location of the slaughter industry has shifted regionally and, within regions, the packing industry has become highly decentralized.

*Numbers and Sizes of Meat Packers and Processors.* Numbers of meat packing plants engaged primarily in slaughter have trended cyclically upward in this country, according to census data, since before the turn of the century (Table 2.1). They rose gradually to a peak in 1889 when the large corporate packers were forming, dropped during the next decade, and then rose to a new peak during and after World War I. These plant numbers dropped to a new low for the century during the depression of the thirties, rose sharply to new highs during World War II, and have continued to rise. More gradual increases since 1939 are indicated for numbers of plants engaged primarily in processing.

Data of the U.S. Department of Agriculture indicate that, in contrast with the total, numbers of *commercial* meat packing plants—those slaughtering 300,000 or more live-weight pounds of livestock annually—dropped only about 3 percent during the decade of the 1950's. Diverse changes by type, however, were recorded. Numbers of "Federally Inspected Slaughtering" (F.I.S.) plants and the larger nonfederally inspected plants—those handling two million or more live-weight pounds of livestock annually—rose sharply during 1950–55. Continued increases during 1955–60 were achieved by F.I.S. plants. A reduction of more than 17 percent for the decade in numbers of the smaller (local) commercial plants suggests that many of these firms have either grown larger or have been dissolved.[12]

Indications of changes through time in the average size of meat packing plants in the United States differ depending upon the data source and the measure of size employed. Average deflated shipments per plant have changed little since the first decade of the century and much the same is true of meat processing plants for the period since 1947 (Table 2.1). With the principal exception of the depression years during the 1930's, average numbers of workers per plant (another measure of average size) have dropped almost

---

[12] Williams and Stout, *op. cit.*, pp. 345–52, where significant regional differences also are indicated.

TABLE 2.1

MEAT PACKING AND PROCESSING PLANTS: NUMBER AND RELATED DATA, SELECTED
CENSUS YEARS, 1889–1958

| Census Year | Plants | Production Workers | | Value of Shipments* | | | | Value Added | |
|---|---|---|---|---|---|---|---|---|---|
| | | | | Actual | | Deflated† | | | |
| | | Total | Per plant | Total | Per plant | Total | Per plant | Total | Per plant |
| | (no.) | (1,000) | (no.) | (mil. dol.) | (thous. dol.) | (mil. dol.) | (thous. dol.) | (mil. dol.) | (thous. dol.) |
| Meat packing plants | | | | | | | | | |
| 1889 | 1,118 | 117 | 104.7 | 562 | 502.7 | …‡ | …‡ | 81 | 72.5 |
| 1899 | 882 | 68 | 77.1 | 784 | 888.9 | …‡ | …‡ | 102 | 115.6 |
| 1904 | 929 | 74 | 79.7 | 914 | 983.9 | …‡ | …‡ | 108 | 116.3 |
| 1909 | 1,221 | 88 | 72.1 | 1,355 | 1,109.7 | …‡ | …‡ | 164 | 134.3 |
| 1914 | 1,279 | 99 | 77.4 | 1,652 | 1,291.6 | 4,214.3 | 3,295.0 | 210 | 164.2 |
| 1919 | 1,304 | 161 | 123.5 | 4,246 | 3,256.1 | 5,429.7 | 4,163.9 | 463 | 355.1 |
| 1925 | 1,269 | 120 | 94.6 | 3,050 | 2,403.5 | 5,276.8 | 4,158.2 | 425 | 334.9 |
| 1929 | 1,277 | 123 | 96.3 | 3,435 | 2,689.9 | 5,871.8 | 4,598.1 | 461 | 361.0 |
| 1935 | 1,223 | 117 | 95.7 | 2,362 | 1,931.3 | 4,533.6 | 3,707.0 | 332 | 271.5 |
| 1939 | 1,392 | 115 | 82.6 | 2,540 | 1,824.7 | 5,866.1 | 4,214.5 | 404 | 290.2 |
| 1947 | 2,154 | 167 | 77.5 | 8,970 | 4,164.3 | 9,134.4 | 4,240.7 | 977 | 453.6 |
| 1954 | 2,367 | 168 | 71.0 | 10,265§ | 4,336.7§ | 9,748.3§ | 4,118.4§ | 1,397 | 590.2 |
| 1958 | 2,801 | 151 | 53.9 | 11,962§ | 4,270.6 | 10,786.3§ | 3,850.9§ | 1,747 | 623.7 |
| Meat processing (prepared meat) plants | | | | | | | | | |
| 1939 | 1,197 | 18 | 15.0 | …‡ | …‡ | …‡ | …‡ | 64 | 53.5 |
| 1947 | 1,264 | 34 | 26.9 | 1,601 | 1,266.6 | 1,630.3 | 1,289.8 | 235 | 185.9 |
| 1954 | 1,316 | 34 | 25.8 | 1,551 | 1,178.6 | 1,472.9 | 1,119.2 | 338 | 256.8 |
| 1958 | 1,494 | 36 | 24.1 | 2,066 | 1,382.9 | 1,862.9 | 1,246.9 | 442 | 295.9 |

Sources: *Census of Manufactures,* Bureau of Census, U.S. Department of Commerce for census years indicated.
* Defined as "Value of Production" prior to 1947.
† Total value of shipments divided by BLS Wholesale Price Index for Processed Foods (1947–49 = 100).
‡ Not available.
§ Includes resale of finished products purchased.

steadily since the early 1920's. This downtrend appears to have accelerated in recent years (Table 2.1).[13] Substantial increases in productivity of labor in meat packing and processing are suggested. Value added per plant, according to Table 2.1, has trended upward sharply and, as indicated by Table 2.2, it was small firms with not more than four employees that made the most striking in-

---

[13] Since these changes reflect the growing influence of technology including automation and improvements in the productivity of labor, changes in plant numbers arrayed according to numbers of employees, as provided by Census data, are not particularly appropriate measures of size (Table 2.3). Many plants within each employment size group in 1954 had slipped by 1958 to the next lower employment size interval despite substantial increases in their meat output; some may have slipped several intervals.

TABLE 2.2

PERCENTAGE CHANGES IN SELECTED MEASURES OF MEAT PACKING NUMBERS
AND VALUE ADDED BY EMPLOYMENT SIZE, UNITED STATES, 1954–58

| Employment Size (employees) | Est. 1958 | Percentage Changes, 1954–58 | | |
|---|---|---|---|---|
| | | Number of est. | Value added | Value added per plant |
| | *(no.)* | | *(percent)* | |
| 1–4 | 1054 | 38.7 | 171.4 | 96.0 |
| 5–9 | 387 | 10.9 | 69.6 | 51.4 |
| 10–19 | 383 | 17.8 | 44.8 | 22.8 |
| 20–49 | 456 | 8.6 | 37.7 | 26.6 |
| 50–99 | 212 | 2.4 | 21.7 | 19.4 |
| 100–249 | 156 | 3.3 | 24.0 | 20.1 |
| 250–499 | 75 | 8.7 | 52.1 | 39.9 |
| 500–999 | 38 | −7.3 | 3.6 | 11.8 |
| 1000–2499 | 30 | 3.4 | 68.7 | 63.1 |
| 2500+ | 10 | −37.5 | −11.7 | 41.3 |
| Total | 2801 | 18.3 | 25.3 | 5.9 |

Source: *Census of Manufactures,* Bureau of Census, U.S. Department of Commerce.

creases during 1954–58 in plant numbers, value added, and value added per plant.[14]

Federally inspected slaughtering plants accounted for about 82 percent of the total commercial red meat production in 1962 compared with about 75 percent in 1940. The average volume of red meat production per F.I.S. plant, however, was about the same in these two years. By species, little trend during 1940–60 was evident, but large year-to-year and cyclical variations in average volume per F.I.S. plant were indicated.[15] Average production per plant by other commercial firms has been rising. Total production of pork by these other plants has remained about constant but their output of beef rose nearly 50 percent during 1940–62 and increased about one-third during 1950–60. With a slight drop in numbers of nonfederally inspected commercial plants, average annual per plant production by these packers rose from 1.5 million to nearly 2 million pounds.

***Number and Sizes of Wholesale Meat Distributors.*** Development of the refrigerator car after 1870 permitted the national packers to establish "packinghouse branches" or "branch houses" at distant

---

[14] While value added is a reasonably accurate measure of changes in the dollar value of marketing services provided by the meat packing industry, it is affected by changes in per unit prices of these services. Prices of marketing services, like other prices, are influenced by inflationary or deflationary tendencies.

[15] *Livestock and Meat Statistics,* Agr. Mkg. Serv., Stat. Bul. 333 (Washington, July 1963), pp. 147–49.

points. These houses served as geographical extensions of their processing and wholesaling departments at parent packing plants. By 1929, branch house sales accounted for almost half of the total sales by all commercial packers.

Growth since 1929 in number and business volumes of "independent wholesale meat distributors" together with sharp reductions in numbers and sales of branch houses is one of the distinctive changes in structural features of the wholesale meat sector of the industry. Even today, however, meat wholesaling consists primarily of sales activities by packers including truck and railcar routes, distribution through packer-owned branch houses and processing facilities, and direct sales to retailers. In 1958, meat packers and their branches made nearly two-thirds of the total sales to retail outlets (Table 2.3). But large numbers of small independent meat dealers also had appeared by the 1920's in the large cities of the Northeast and the Far West. Independent wholesale distributors have developed to include a variety of firms ranging widely in size and function. In general, these are non-slaughtering firms still located primarily in deficit area metropolitan centers and engaged primarily in fresh meat distribution and in performance of increasingly specialized marketing services.

TABLE 2.3

ESTIMATED MARKET SHARES BY WHOLESALE MEAT DISTRIBUTORS, PREPARED MEAT PLANTS, AND MEAT PACKERS, UNITED STATES, 1958

| Item | 1958 | Percentage Distribution of Value of Shipments by Packers | | |
|---|---|---|---|---|
| | | 1948 | 1954 | 1958 |
| | *(thous. dollars)* | | *(percent)* | |
| Wholesale Distributors | | | | |
| Merchants wholesalers (net sales)* | 2,462,157 | 16.9 | 20.0 | 21.3 |
| Packinghouse branches (net sales)† | 2,050,020 | 29.5 | 25.0 | 17.7 |
| Subtotal | 4,512,177 | 46.4 | 45.0 | 39.0 |
| Prepared meat plants (value of receipts)‡ | 1,624,199 | 15.2 | 11.0 | 14.1 |
| Meat packers, direct§ | 5,423,707 | 38.4 | 44.0 | 46.9 |
| Total‖ | 11,560,083 | 100.0 | 100.0 | 100.0 |

Source: "Wholesale Trade," *Census of Business and Census of Manufactures,* Bureau of Census, U.S. Department of Commerce, for selected census years, and other sources.

* Dollar sales minus operating expenses, profits (assumed) at 1.5 percent of dollar sales, and sales to other wholesalers.

† Dollar sales minus operating expenses and profits (assumed) at 1.5 percent of dollar sales.

‡ Value of shipments minus value added.

§ Value of shipments by packers minus preceding items.

‖ Value of shipments by packers which excludes interplant transfers and sale value of items purchased for resale.

While the percentage of meat volume handled by all non-slaughtering distributors has declined, the independent wholesaler has improved his position with respect to total volume sold as well as to the volume distributed by branch houses (Table 2.3). Numbers of independent wholesalers doubled and their aggregate (deflated) sales volume rose nearly two and one-half times during 1929–58 (Table 2.4). At the same time, more than half of the packinghouse branches disappeared and sales volume of these establishments fell about 48 percent. While the annual sales volume of the average independent meat wholesaler was less than one-fifth as large as the average volume of the typical branch house in 1958, averaged deflated per plant sales of wholesalers have been rising much more rapidly (Table 2.4). The role of meat brokers diminished rather sharply after 1929 until after World War II.[16]

**Concentration in Meat Packing and Processing.** By 1916, five leading firms accounted for more than half of the commercial slaughter

TABLE 2.4

Meat Wholesalers and Distributors: Numbers and Sales, 1958, and Percentage Changes in Numbers and Deflated Sales Values, Selected Periods, United States

| Item | 1958 | Percentage Changes* | | |
|---|---|---|---|---|
| | | 1929–58 | 1948–58 | 1954–58 |
| | *(number)* | | *(percent)* | |
| Number | | | | |
| Ind. wholesalers | 4459 | 100.4 | 39.3 | 2.3 |
| Branch houses | 520 | —55.1 | —31.2 | —21.7 |
| Brokers | 153 | 17.7 | 163.8 | 57.7 |
| Total | 5132 | 46.1 | 27.9 | 0.3 |
| Total Sales | *(mil. dol.)* | | *(percent)* | |
| Ind. wholesalers | 3879 | 146.1 | 100.7 | 14.9 |
| Branch houses | 2303 | —47.6 | —16.1 | —27.4 |
| Brokers | 606 | 165.3 | 8.5 | —1.2 |
| Total | 6788 | 9.5 | 29.6 | —5.3 |
| Sales Per Plant | *(thous. dol.)* | | *(percent)* | |
| Ind. wholesalers | 807 | 22.9 | 44.0 | 12.3 |
| Branch houses | 4429 | 16.7 | 21.9 | —7.5 |
| Brokers | 3960 | 125.4 | 58.9 | —37.4 |

Source: "Wholesale Trade," *U.S. Census of Business,* Bureau of Census, U.S. Department of Commerce, selected issues.

* Percentage changes refer to values deflated by an unpublished U.S.D.A. index of wholesale red meat prices.

---

[16] Significant regional differences in numbers and relative importance of branch houses and independent wholesalers, as well as in meat packers and processors, are apparent in the available data. These differences result in notable regional differences in organizational structure, marketing practices, and industry performance. For more detailed discussion, see Williams and Stout, *op. cit.,* Chaps. 14 and 15.

TABLE 2.5

PERCENTAGES OF TOTAL COMMERCIAL SLAUGHTER ACCOUNTED FOR BY THE FOUR
LEADING MEAT PACKERS BY SPECIES FOR SPECIFIED YEARS, UNITED STATES

| Year | Percentages of Commercial Slaughter Accounted For by the Four Leading Firms* | | | |
|------|--------|--------|--------------------|------|
|      | Cattle | Calves | Sheep and lambs | Hogs |
|      | *(percent)* | | | |
| 1908† | 44.8 | 23.2 | 54.2 | 43.0 |
| 1916† | 53.9 | 32.1 | 70.2 | 50.8 |
| 1919† | 53.6 | 42.3 | 72.0 | 52.7 |
| 1924 | 50.5 | 40.1 | 66.4 | 44.7 |
| 1929 | 49.9 | 46.9 | 70.7 | 40.2 |
| 1935 | 46.6 | 46.3 | 70.5 | 41.4 |
| 1947 | 38.3 | 39.6 | 67.8 | 40.4 |
| 1955 | 30.8 | 34.7 | 58.5 | 36.4 |

Source: 1908–35 computed from *Agricultural Income Inquiry*, Federal Trade Commission, Part 1, *Farm Products*, U.S. Gov't. Printing Office, 1937, p. 198; and 1947–55 from *Unfair Trade Practices in the Meat Industry*, United States Senate, Hearings Before the Senate Subcommittee on Antitrust and Monopoly of the Committee on the Judiciary, U.S. Gov't. Printing Office, May 10, 1957, pp. 261–65.

* Includes Swift, Armour, Wilson, and Cudahy for each of the years shown.
† Includes Morris and Company acquired by Armour in 1923.

of cattle and hogs, nearly a third of the commercial calf slaughter, and 70 percent of the sheep and lamb slaughter (Table 2.5).[17] Since that time, however, market shares of the dominant firms have declined.

As percentages of total commercial slaughter, cattle and hog slaughter by the four largest firms dropped significantly during the period 1916–35. The aggregate position of these firms in sheep and lamb slaughter, however, was maintained almost unchanged during this period and their share of the calf slaughter increased relatively.

After 1935, the four leading firms lost ground rather steadily in each of the four species (Table 2.5). Their relative losses were greater for cattle and sheep than for calves and hogs. Each of the four was severely affected. Cudahy initiated a program of adjustment during the early 1950's which included the closing or dismantling of plants at various locations. By 1955, packing plant numbers of this firm had dropped from 12 in 1950 to 7, and both Wilson and Armour were reorganizing their operations. Armour closed plants at many locations, including the East and West Coast areas, reducing numbers to about 27 in 1962 compared with 40 in 1950. Wilson, with 7 plants in 1950, dropped one and modernized several others. Branch house numbers of Armour, Wilson, and Cudahy also fell sharply. During 1950–62, Cudahy closed or sold

---

[17] The five include Morris and Co., acquired by Armour and Co. in 1923.

54 of the firm's 65 branch houses, Wilson disposed of 66 of the company's 116 branch plants, and Armour's packinghouse branches dropped in number from 256 to 148.[18]

With these changes, adjustments appeared in relative positions of the top 10 firms. In terms of total net sales, Wilson retained the third ranking position but, by 1962, Cudahy had fallen to seventh. Morrell had moved up to fourth with Hygrade fifth and Hormel sixth.[19]

Although Swift and Company, the largest of the four, probably was least affected, packing plant numbers of the firm fell from about 56 in 1950 to 48 in 1962 and several were rebuilt or modernized. In addition, Swift handled sharply reduced percentages of the cattle, calves, and hogs slaughtered in 1956–58 compared with 1934–37. On the other hand, absolute levels of slaughter by the company in each of these species remained nearly unchanged and branch house numbers of the firm fell little, if any. With reductions in total industry slaughter of sheep and lambs, Swift has almost maintained its position in the slaughter of this species. Slaughter of sheep and lambs by Armour (formerly a close competitor of Swift with regard to volume) has dropped to about half of the volume accounted for by Swift. The two were responsible for more than half of the total commercial sheep and lamb slaughter in the postwar period to 1955. In 1958, the two firms still accounted for about 45 percent of the commercial sheep and lamb slaughter, about one-fourth of the commercial slaughter of calves and hogs, and about 22 percent of the cattle.[20]

Most recently the larger national packers have established new, modern plants at a number of locations and have placed considerable emphasis upon product innovation and development. Some have renegotiated labor contracts in plants at various points in the South and have succeeded in establishing wage scales more competitive with those paid by the larger, independent packers in that region. In addition, they have acquired, through contract or otherwise, a number of additional "captive" plants in the South.[21]

[18] *Moody's Industrials.*

[19] *Ibid.*

[20] See percentages reported in *Post Trial Brief of Armour and Co.*, U.S. District Court for the Northern District of Illinois, Eastern Division, U.S. v. Swift and Co., Armour and Co., Wilson and Co., and Cudahy and Co., 58C 613, filed Chicago Fed. Court 3/8/60 (LaSalle St. Press, Chicago 10), p. 3; data for largest firm in 1934–37 and 1956–58 reported in *Post Trial Brief of Swift and Co.*, in the same case. Data for both firms in 1946–55 from U.S. Senate, *Unfair Trade Practices in the Meat Industry*, Hearing before the Subcommittee on Anti-Trust and Monopoly of the Committee on the Judiciary (Washington, May 10, 1957), pp. 261–65.

[21] These, of course, are not included by available sources as plants owned or operated by the firm under consideration.

In effect, they simply acquired the labor contracts of a few firms that were experiencing financial difficulties. The extent to which these developments have effected or likely will effect concentration in the meat industry is a matter for speculation. Available data suggest, however, that concentration ratios have continued to fall. A comparison of net sales data for nine national packers as reported by *Moody's Industrials* with estimates by the American Meat Institute of total industry sales suggests percentages for these firms of 63.5 percent in 1950 compared with 59.1 percent in 1957 and 51.2 percent in 1963. This decline has taken place despite inclusion of data in national packer sales of nonmeat items such as leather and other by-products, chemicals, poultry and dairy products, some produce, and sports equipment.[22]

The aggregate data obscure many vital questions and issues. More detailed information by species, by type of firm, by area, or by type of meat might reveal significantly large sectors of the industry in which concentration is increasing. It might be possible, for instance, to construct a case for a high and increasing level of concentration in prepared and processed meats.

*Specialization in the Meat Industry.* A marked tendency toward specialization within the industry has persisted since the turn of the century. With the development of large-volume carlot buyers, the related advent at the retail level of detailed specifications, improvements in transportation and communication, and shifts in location of the packing industry to principal areas of production, the tendency toward specialization among packers and other suppliers has accelerated. Specialization results in organizational arrangements which reduce costs and, at the same time, tend to restrict or confine the competitive environment of the firm. More complete knowledge of the structure of the meat industry will require more complete information on nature and degree of specialization.

*Specialization Among Meat Packers.* Most of the national packers have been concentrating more heavily upon processing. Prepared and processed meats consist primarily of branded, prepackaged items. A national system of distribution offers economies in advertising and advantages in the merchandising of such items. While conclusive data are not available, fragmentary information suggests that the nation's largest packers are now primarily meat processors and manufacturers. Concentration among firms formerly ranking fifth to tenth largest increased to some extent during 1947–55. Most of this reflected increased emphasis of these firms

---

[22] Income from nonmeat products, according to the American Meat Institute, represented about 22 percent of total net income in 1963. See *Financial Facts About the Meat Packing Industry, 1963, op. cit.*

on hogs and processed meats.[23]  While these firms are small so far as numbers of meat packing plants are concerned, they are large in terms of volume. Their numerous branches are processing plants primarily. The group includes several youthful, well-organized, and vigorously growing firms which have confined their slaughtering establishments to strategic Corn Belt locations while emphasizing processing and distribution elsewhere. At the same time, independent meat processing plants typically are small and the deflated sales volume of all such firms rose relatively little during 1947–58 (Table 2.1).

√ Independent packers, generally speaking, have largely stripped themselves of functions other than slaughtering and processing. In many areas, these firms, particularly those concerned primarily with beef, have tended to leave the production of sausage and other prepared or manufactured meats to the national packers and to the processing specialists.[24]

Increased levels of specialization by species or class of meat are indicated by census and U.S.D.A. data.[25]  Increased percentages of the nation's F.I.S. plants handle cattle while sharply reduced percentages slaughter calves, hogs, or sheep and lambs (Table 2.6).

TABLE 2.6

FEDERALLY INSPECTED MEAT PACKING PLANTS: NUMBER CONDUCTING SLAUGHTER AND PERCENTAGES HANDLING EACH SPECIES, SELECTED YEARS, 1930–63, UNITED STATES

| Year | F.I.S. Plants Conducting Slaughter | Species Slaughtered by Establishments Conducting Slaughter | | | |
|---|---|---|---|---|---|
| | | Cattle | Calves | Hogs | Lambs |
| | (number) | (percent) | | | |
| 1930 | 319 | 77.7 | 78.7 | 74.9 | 65.2 |
| 1940 | 308 | 82.8 | 81.8 | 73.4 | 65.9 |
| 1950 | 456 | 84.0 | 67.1 | 57.9 | 44.1 |
| 1960 | 527 | 92.4 | 60.9 | 51.0 | 41.0 |
| 1962 | 552 | 88.6 | 54.7 | 46.4 | 37.0 |
| 1963 | 570 | 86.3 | 49.5 | 46.1 | 38.2 |

Source: *Livestock and Meat Statistics, 1957,* Agricultural Marketing Service, U.S.D.A. Stat. Bul. No. 230 (July 1958 and annual supplements), inc. Stat. Bul. No. 333 (July 1963 and supplements).

---

[23] Willard F. Williams "Structural Changes in the Meat Wholesaling Industry," *Journal of Farm Economics,* Vol. XL, No. 2 (May 1958), pp. 322–29.

[24] This, however, is not generally true for the South and the nation's "sausage belt" running through Oklahoma, northern Texas, Arkansas, southern Kansas and Missouri and on eastward through Kentucky and Tennessee or of the larger independent hog slaughterers in the Corn Belt.

[25] In general, these data tend to underestimate specialization. For instance, they include among multi-species plants those that slaughter even a few animals of one or more species on a custom basis for local farmers. Slaughter data on a firm heavily engaged in production of prepared or processed meats do not distinguish between slaughter of cows, sows, or ewes for this purpose and the slaughter of animals for fresh meat distribution.

Relatively large numbers of plants in all regions and 40 to 50 percent of the F.I.S. plants in the North Central region specialize exclusively in cattle, calves, or both. Less than one-fourth of the F.I.S. packers and fewer than one-third of all larger commercial meat packers now handle all three species.[26]

According to census data, sharply increased levels of specialization appeared between 1948 and 1958 for fresh beef, fresh veal, sausage and other prepared meats, and pork. In 1958, fresh beef was the primary product in 45 percent of the nation's meat packing plants and, of these, 52 percent were specialized to the extent of 75 percent or more of their shipments. Meat processing plants also are rather highly specialized and the degree of specialization is increasing.[27]

Some specialization is taking place even within species. Today, many independent packers slaughter steers or heifers only, while others specialize in cows. Some scale their operations to handle only the particular grades or within-grade qualities which meet the detailed specifications of particular large-volume buyers.

The phenomenon of the "shipper-type" packer has become more common. This usually is an independent packer slaughtering a particular grade or class of one species on a volume basis, located in a principal supply area, and shipping to large-volume intermediate handlers or large retail accounts wherever they may be located. Shipper-type packers offset relatively high transport costs with lower plant costs associated with specialized equipment and large volume and with relatively low merchandising costs per unit of product marketed. They usually ship in carcass form and engage in little or no processing.

*Specialization Among Wholesale Distributors.* To an increasing extent, packinghouse branches are specializing in processing and in prepared and branded meat items. Independent wholesale meat distributors are specialized along various lines. Types include (1) "hotel or restaurant supply houses" or "purveyors" specializing, as implied, in distribution of meat to public or private dining establishments or institutions, (2) "wholesalers" including "beef breakers" which are relatively large firms operating on a volume or carlot basis, (3) "jobbers," relatively small firms specializing primarily in sales to small retail stores and restaurants, (4) "boners," principally engaged in removing bones and sinew from beef carcasses and in selling the meat to processing plants, retailers, and the military, and (5) "frozen meat handlers" specializing in chip steaks, veal patties, quick frozen cuts, or other frozen meat products. The peddler or

[26] *Number of Livestock Slaughtering Plants, March 1, 1960,* Agr. Mkg. Serv., U.S.D.A. (Washington, August 1960).
[27] See Williams and Stout, *op. cit.,* pp. 358–60, for details.

"truck jobber" can be classified as a sixth type and there are others. Little data exist regarding relative importance of these various types.[28] Hotel supply houses and jobbers probably are most common. A few beef breakers are found in most of the larger cities. These firms generally sell on a volume basis to any and all types of buyers including retail chains. They frequently sell relatively large quantities of beef to hotel supply houses and other types of independent wholesalers.[29]

*Integration by Meat Packers.* Most meat packers are integrated to one extent or another. Either directly or through branch houses, packers provide two-thirds of the meat wholesaling services and, as indicated, they perform much of the processing. In addition, the national packers are horizontally integrated through ownership or lease of many packing plants, processing plants, and branch houses. These and other packers are vertically integrated through ownership of livestock on feed, feedlots, concentration yards, transportation facilities, and by-product plants.

The extent of packer feeding of cattle and sheep has risen sharply since about 1955 (Table 2.7). In addition, many packers have continuing informal arrangements with feedlots. Such arrangements often are made to secure a steady supply of the particular grades and weights desired. Packers fed about 40,000 hogs in 1963, an insignificant number compared with total numbers fed or slaughtered. Cattle feeding by retail food chains, never large, had dropped to the point in 1962 that numbers fed by chains would barely fill one large, modern feedlot. A sharp increase, however, was experienced in 1963 (Table 2.7).

Packer integration into feeding is most important in the principal areas of commercial livestock feeding. A survey in 1958 indicated that in the 11 western states, nearly 600,000 head of the cattle on feed were owned or controlled by packers. This represents about 16 percent of the total feedlot marketings in these states during 1958.[30] Packer feeding of cattle is most important in California where it represented nearly one-fourth of the total numbers fed in 1963. The second most important state in this respect is Texas where packer-owned cattle accounted for about 16 percent

---

[28] For some additional detail, see Willard F. Williams, Earl K. Bowen, and Frank C. Genovese, *Economic Effects of U.S. Grades for Beef*, Mkg. Res. Rept. 298, Agr. Mkg. Serv., U.S.D.A. (Washington, June 1959), Chaps. 2 and 5.

[29] A relatively large volume of sales among the various types of independent wholesale meat distributors suggests that census sales data for these firms include much double counting.

[30] Allen B. Richards, "Cattle Feeding and Packing Are Closely Integrated in the West," *Western Meat Industry* (Sept. 1959), pp. 11–17.

TABLE 2.7

NUMBERS OF LIVESTOCK FED 30 DAYS OR MORE BY MEAT PACKERS AND
RETAIL FOOD CHAINS BY SPECIES, 1954–63

| Year | Packers Ten largest | Packers Other | Packers Total | Retail Food Chains | Percentage of Total Numbers Fed* Packers | Chains | Numbers Packers | Chains |
|---|---|---|---|---|---|---|---|---|
| | *(number)* | *(number)* | *(number)* | *(number)* | *(percent)* | | | |
| | | | Cattle and Calves | | | | | |
| 1954† | 156,478 | 329,648 | 486,126 | ...‡ | 5.6 | ...‡ | 157§ | ...§ |
| 1955† | 142,853 | 333,634 | 476,487 | ...‡ | 4.9 | ...‡ | 153§ | ...‡ |
| 1956 | 163,972 | 304,354 | 468,326 | 54,455 | 4.6 | 0.5 | 149§ | 3 |
| 1957 | 159,092 | 373,017 | 532,109 | 25,567 | 5.2 | 0.2 | 143§ | 3 |
| 1958 | 217,596 | 491,991 | 709,587 | 19,518 | 6.7 | 0.1 | 168§ | 3 |
| 1959 | 158,030 | 428,277 | 586,307 | 30,679 | 4.9 | 0.2 | 149§ | 3 |
| 1960 | 262,491 | 567,032 | 829,523 | 27,234 | 6.4 | 0.1 | 156§ | 4 |
| 1961 | 313,600 | 566,600 | 880,200 | 39,000 | 6.4 | 0.1 | 199§ | 4 |
| 1962 | 316,200 | 639,700 | 955,900 | 25,500 | 6.4 | 0.1 | 205§ | 2 |
| 1963 | 414,100 | 706,700 | 1,120,800 | 54,800 | 7.4 | 0.1 | 198§ | 5 |
| | | | Sheep | | | | | |
| 1954 | 1,201,109 | 36,486 | 1,237,595 | ... | 27.8 | ... | 19 | ... |
| 1955 | 520,364 | 12,783 | 533,147 | ... | 12.5 | ... | 26 | ... |
| 1956 | 661,242 | 62,459 | 723,701 | ... | 16.8 | ... | 16 | ... |
| 1957 | 648,362 | 19,023 | 667,385 | ... | 16.5 | ... | 19 | ... |
| 1958 | 601,561 | 42,034 | 712,595 | ... | 15.8 | ... | 23 | ... |
| 1959 | 670,248 | 31,396 | 701,644 | ... | 16.2 | ... | 24 | ... |
| 1960 | 758,508 | 67,270 | 825,778 | ... | 19.4 | ... | 24 | ... |
| 1961 | 524,200 | 80,400 | 604,600 | 1,000 | 14.2 | ... | 26 | ... |
| 1962 | 510,400 | 40,300 | 550,700 | ... | 15.2 | ... | 26 | ... |
| 1963 | 581,200 | 60,900 | 642,100 | 100 | 15.8 | ... | 27 | 1 |

Source: 1954–55 compiled from *P. and S. Docket*, PS-16, Packers and Stockyards Division, U.S.D.A.; 1956 compiled from *P. and S. Docket*, PS-48, Apr. 5, 1961, Packers and Stockyards Division; 1957–60 compiled from *Packers and Stockyards Résumé*, Vol. I, No. 7, Dec. 1, 1963, p. 8, Packers and Stockyards Division; 1961–63 compiled from *Packers and Stockyards Résumé*, Vol. II, No. 2, Dec. 11, 1964, Packers and Stockyards Division.

* Total numbers of cattle and calves fed represent 26 major feeding states estimated for 1954–62. Percentages for lamb represent percentages of numbers on feed January 1 for each year.
† Does not include calves.
‡ Not available.
§ Does not include additional packers, if any, feeding calves.

of the total in 1963. Comparable percentages for other western states averaged about 6.0 percent.[31]

The incidence of interlocking directorates among major firms in the meat industry apparently has dropped sharply since the Federal Trade Commission investigation in 1918. At that time a number of intercorporate connections among the larger national packers were uncovered. In a later investigation, for 1946, no such connections of any significance were found within the meat industry.[32]

[31] *Packers and Stockyards Résumé*, U.S.D.A., Packers and Stockyards Div., Vol. II, No. 2 (Washington, Dec. 11, 1964).
[32] Whitney, *Antitrust Policies* (New York: The Twentieth Century Fund, 1958), pp. 71–72.

## Technological Environment and Technical Characteristics

The meat industry, like others, has been vitally affected by the rapidly changing technological environment in which it operates. Since meat is a highly perishable product, the factors of distance and time affect location of meat packing and processing plants as well as distribution patterns and practices. Three general types of technological innovation in the United States—improvements in transportation, communication, and refrigeration, including intransit refrigeration—have reduced the importance to the meat industry of perishability and of time and distance. In large measure, these three have transformed a nation of many small, isolated, and independent livestock supply areas and markets for meat into one large, interrelated, and close-knit economy. Additional innovations such as containerizing offer the promise of continuing new sources of economies in distribution.

Internally, increases in output per man-hour in the meat industry relative to increases achieved by other large industries are small.[33] Nevertheless, numerous technological improvements have been made available to the industry during recent years. In the meat industry, as elsewhere, automation has become increasingly apparent.

While changes in structure and procurement practices at retail have eliminated many of the advantages formerly associated with multi-species packing plants, significant internal economies of scale apparently are available to the more specialized plants. Logan and King found, for example, that synthesized slaughter costs per head (for California) drop from $9.48 in a one-bed conventional beef slaughtering plant at an output of 17 head per hour to $7.28 in an "on the rail" conveyorized plant at an output of 120 head per hour.[34] These may arise from various sources with increases in scale including improved management, superior adaptability of labor and capital resources, or access to lower cost technology. However, internal economies of scale in meat packing frequently are offset by two sources of scale-associated diseconomies. In areas of less densely populated slaughter livestock supplies, significantly large diseconomies of scale in procurement may be encountered. Similarly, in low density areas of human population, diseconomies of scale in distribution may exist. Since beef production is more widely and less densely distributed than hog production, net economies of scale in beef are relatively small, and existing cost advantages of scale apparently are achieved at a significantly smaller

[33] William H. Waldorf, *Output of Factories Processing Food Products in the United States, 1909–58*, U.S.D.A. Tech. Bul. 1223 (Washington, Sept. 1960).
[34] Samuel H. Logan and Gordon A. King, *Economies of Scale in Beef Slaughter Plants*, Calif. Agr. Exp. Sta. Res. Rept. 260 (Berkeley, Dec. 1962), p. 114.

volume in beef packing plants than in pork packing and processing plants. A priori observations suggest that scale economies in lamb slaughtering and distribution are substantial.

## Institutional Environment

The meat industry has been subjected to constant surveillance and periodic investigation since before the turn of the century. History of the industry in this respect is well documented elsewhere.[35] Among the currently effective public regulations and services that provide a significant portion of the economic environment of the industry and which affect industry structure and competition and, therefore, performance, are the following:

1. The Consent Decree imposed in 1920 which places certain prohibitions and restraints upon four of the largest packers.
2. The Packers and Stockyards Act of 1921 which until recently has affected the meat industry relatively little.
3. Federal and State meat inspection regulations which have affected structure, including plant location, and competitive strategy through a number of different avenues.
4. Uniform United States grade standards for beef, calf, and lamb, official grading services, and operational use of these standards and services by the industry also have had a variety of effects.
5. Development and widespread use of public and private marketing information services.
6. State and Interstate Commerce Commission regulations on the transportation industry which have affected plant location, distribution patterns, and competitive strategy in the meat industry.

Effects upon competitive environment of expanded marketing information programs and adoption of official carcass grade standards have been substantial. These institutional innovations along with improved means of communication increased the general level of economic knowledge in the industry and, in addition, tended to equalize this knowledge among buyers and sellers. The latter effect may have been the more significant. Packers (the national packers particularly) already were well informed. The current economic knowledge of producers, retailers, and others regarding quality and factors affecting supply and demand by quality classes appears to have improved considerably and relatively in recent years.

---

[35] See Simon Whitney, *op. cit.*, Chap. 2; and Williams and Stout, *op. cit.*, Chap. 25.

Operational use by the industry of official grade standards provided retailers with ready-made, widely accepted, and influential merchandising tools. In addition, grades and grading sharply reduced the value to the national packers of their private brands on fresh meat. They strongly supported forces that were causing a decline in relative importance of packinghouse branches and encouraged many independent packers to grow in volume by providing these firms with national rather than strictly local or regional markets. Furthermore, they may have contributed to the demise of the smallest locally oriented packers and distributors and materially aided the forces that were shifting the location of slaughter away from principal consumption areas of concentrated population. Grading also provided independent wholesalers with an improved competitive climate. Some, for instance, found they could specialize in handling the types and qualities of beef in the upper grades that packers could not sell on a graded carcass basis to large-volume retailers.

The F.I.S. regulations on meat for interstate shipment include detailed requirements on plant layout, restrictions on types and quantities of cost-reducing ingredients that may be added to sausage and other products, and specifications regarding the extent to which the processed weight of hams, bacon, and other cured or processed meat items may exceed the original weight through the addition of curing solution. With several principal exceptions, state and local inspection requirements, where these exist, generally are much more liberal and less carefully enforced. The F.I.S. regulations, therefore, provide nonfederally inspected packers, processors, and distributors, located primarily in deficit areas outside the Corn Belt, with a measure of protection.

Regional differences in structure and competitive environment also arise out of regional differences in unionization of labor in meat packing and processing. For instance, national packers with uniform wage contracts experience considerable difficulty in competing in the South and elsewhere with nonunion plants. Unionized plants are disadvantageously affected by work-week guarantees and agreements impairing flexibility in use of labor as well as by wage rate differences.

The division of responsibility between the Federal Trade Commission and the Packers and Stockyards Division of the U.S. Department of Agriculture for antitrust regulation of the meat industry was not fully determined until 1958 with an amendment to the Packers and Stockyards Act. In addition, funds allocated to the P and S Division for administration of the Act as it applied to the meat industry were extremely limited. With clarification of the law and an internal reorganization, the Division has more aggressively regulated meat industry trade practices at the meat packer and wholesaler levels. Retail meat trade practices now lie more exclusively within the jurisdiction of F.T.C.

## Conditions of Entry and Egress

"Condition of entry" is considered here as a *measure* which helps to describe the interindustry economic environment with respect to the industry in question and potential entrants. As an interindustry measure, condition of entry is affected by a variety of factors. Some are structural while others, such as legal or institutional barriers, are exogenous and still others classify as conduct or competitive strategy. That "condition of entry" affects conduct and performance is unquestioned and it, therefore, must be taken into account.

The meat packing industry apparently can no longer be characterized accurately as one having a few exceptionally large, dominant, and well-protected firms together with a large and ineffectively competitive fringe of very small firms. Entry and exit barriers to meat packing—to cattle slaughtering in particular—are low. Recent data show that of 494 F.I.S. packing plants in 1947, 198 had been discontinued and 97 were operating under different ownership in 1963. Only 199 still were operating under the same name while 269 new F.I.S. plants had been added to the industry.[36] Most of these were primarily beef packing plants.

Neither economies of scale nor product differentiation are effective deterrents to entry to the slaughter and distribution of beef. "Absolute cost" advantages, if any, appear to rest with the relatively large, single-plant, independent firms. Among a variety of other effects, structural changes at retail and use by the industry of official grade standards reduced barriers to entry. In beef packing, this is true also of many technological innovations which were adapted for use in small plants.

Entry barriers to pork packing and processing and prepared meat production are more imposing and, in some respects, have increased. In contrast to beef, hogs generally are disassembled at the packing plant and large portions of the hog generally are processed. It is in disassembly and processing that mechanization and automation have become most evident. Some types of newer equipment simply are beyond the means of small, independent plants. In addition, national packer brands and standardized packaging practices on processed pork and prepared meats gradually have become more widely accepted by retailers and consumers. On the other hand, the more moderate and less rigidly enforced state and local meat

---

[36] Agr. Mkg. Serv., U.S.D.A.

inspection requirements and access in some areas to nonunion labor tend to modify effects of these and other factors on entry barriers and to increase barriers to egress from pork packing and meat processing. Regional differences in tastes and preferences add to these effects.

Entry barriers to sheep and lamb slaughter probably are the most imposing of those found in the meat industry. These arise out of economies of scale, the seasonal and localized nature of production, contract control of live lamb marketings, and the nature of demand for lamb together with preferred access to wholesale and retail outlets for lamb.

## COMPETITIVE CONDUCT

Within any specified economic environment, it is human conduct through establishment of firm policies and practices that produces changes in structure, market power relationships, and economic performance. Marketing firms compete with one another on several different planes or directions. On a horizontal plane, they compete with other similar firms—with firms offering similar services to buyers or those using the same or similar resources—for differential cost, price, volume or quality advantages, or in terms of services offered. Business firms also compete on a vertical plane, as do retail chains and meat packers, for advantages or power in establishing the terms of trade. These two planes of competition are closely interrelated. The nature of horizontally competitive relationships at one level *relative to* those at adjacent levels often determine the vertical distribution of market power. Firms in an industry or industry segment also compete in another dimension with firms or potential firms outside the industry for access to factors and plant capacity. The nature of the power developed through this competition partially determines the nature of restrictions or limitations on entry to or exit from the industry.

In the livestock and meat industry, market power relationships in each of these dimensions have changed markedly in recent years. With changes in structure and procurement practices at retail, structural changes at the producer level and in livestock marketing practices, the advent of new technology, and a restricted institutional environment, competitive adjustments in the meat industry were inevitable.

### Meat Supplier-Retailer Competition

Food retailers gradually have become less restricted in their abilities to specify the terms of trade for the meat industry. Mass buying for horizontally integrated units, vertical integration, use of uniform grade standards and detailed product specifications, improvements in transportation, communication, and refrigeration and other factors greatly improved alternatives available to retailers in buying. At the same time, these factors, together with a rapidly falling number of retail outlets, greatly reduced alternatives available to packers and other suppliers in selling. As food retailers increased the average size of their retail units and formed themselves into corporate chains, voluntary groups, or cooperative organizations, they tended to (1) become more impersonal in their dealings with suppliers by increasing the extent of buying according to grades and specifications, (2) support and reinforce the growing consumer demand for quality and uniformity, as this pleased customers and facilitated advertising and quality control programs, (3) reach out much farther for their supplies of meat and other commodities, (4) seek out specialized, dependable, larger volume, year-round suppliers, and (5) change their pricing methods and procedures. While horizontally integrated retailers are attracted to the dependable and specialized large-volume sources, they generally have avoided tying themselves to one or a few suppliers.

The relative rise in bargaining power of retailers is evident in the "offer and acceptance" or "bid" system of procurement that has become prevalent in most areas where purchases by food chains are important. In this system, suppliers make offers to buyers in which they specify quantities and prices. Retailers formerly shopped the meat coolers of suppliers and made offers which the packer or other supplier either accepted or rejected. The acceptance or rejection usually was immediate. In the newer bid system, the retailer prefers to receive all offers before any acceptances are made. He frequently refuses to bargain or to provide the supplier with opportunity to revise his bid; he simply accepts or does not accept. This provides the retailer with maximum opportunity to exploit positions of suppliers that may be heavily burdened with meat and of those that cannot afford rejection. It is fair to say, however, that retailers usually operate in such systems with considerable care and discretion. In the final analysis, the supplier and his goodwill are essential to the retailer.

In some respects, the changes at retail and in transportation were disadvantageous to both exceptionally small, local packers and exceptionally large packing firms. Distribution systems of both were geared to the needs of small, independent retail stores, meat markets, and dining establishments. In contrast, medium-volume independent packers in position to specialize and to concentrate upon specified requirements of supermarkets and integrated retailer organizations realized new opportunities. In addition, these packers found themselves with a national market for their product and nationally recognized certificates of quality in the form of official grade marks.

Faced with relative reductions in volume, rapidly disappearing numbers of branch houses, and low or negative profits, counter strategy by many of the national packers logically might have been expected. It appears in retrospect, however, that national packers generally did not fully recognize implications of the changing competitive environment until about 1955 and even then attributed their plight primarily to old or antiquated plants, high labor costs, and other factors. In general, the focus of attention in the meat packing industry still was upon procurement and upon relationships with respect to position of the firm in certain livestock markets, numbers of slaughter livestock purchased, plant volume, and related per unit costs.

More aggressive price competition in selling probably was considered by larger packers. But standardization of beef quality in terms of official uniform grades and detailed retailer specifications, high elasticity of the supply response for beef, and ease of entry in cattle slaughtering had rendered markets for beef highly competitive. Selling costs of many major packers were relatively high. In addition, retailers were fully as interested in quality, uniformity, and services as in prices.

While the pork and processed meat sectors also were highly competitive, these offered more attractive opportunities. Here, packer brands still were important and barriers to entry were more imposing. Accordingly, several of the national packers introduced new and more aggressive merchandising programs on pork and processed meat items; newer and more attractive packages and containers were developed; and increased emphasis was placed upon price and service competition. Obstacles and opposition were encountered, however, in many of these programs. "Specials," "tie-in sales," and merchandising gimmicks involving first one brand and then another were not particularly conducive to development of strong brand loyalties. In addition, significant regional differences in tastes with respect to processed pork and prepared meat items and access by competitors to nonunion labor, fortified by lax state and local meat inspection regulations, made it difficult in many instances for national packers to meet local competition.

Various means were employed by federally inspected packers to modify or circumvent the federal regulations. These included the further decentralization of the processing function by national packers and arrangements of various types with local processors. Such efforts were partially responsible for the widely publicized ham-pumping controversy of the early 1960's. Some relaxation in the federal regulations was achieved. Difficulties in competing with nonunion packing plant labor led to alternative devices such as (1) expanded or continued operation of branch houses in some areas of the South and (2) arrangements for capturing the labor cost structures of independent packing plants.

Since meats are the leading item sold in retail grocery stores, it would appear that meat packers have more incentive than suppliers of other food products to integrate into the food retailing field. Meat packers, however, generally have considered this strategy either as not feasible or as impractical. One relevant factor in this respect is the 1920 Consent Decree entered into by five (now four) major packers. According to the decree, Swift, Armour, Wilson, and Cudahy are prohibited forever from operating retail stores. Others probably are deterred to some extent by (1) the resentment which customer retailers undoubtedly would express as a result of the packer's intrusion into retailing and (2) cost and merchandising advantages offered by specialization. The capital investment required for establishment of a nationally integrated system of retail stores may have been another factor. While capital requirements might have been overcome through the leasing of supermarket meat departments, the trend has been in the opposite direction. About 1948, both chain and independent retail grocery firms began to cancel leases on their meat departments and to operate these departments themselves. More aggressive merchandising and procurement policies were introduced by retailers at this time.

## Meat Packer-Livestock Supplier Competition

Livestock marketing patterns and practices as well as pricing methods and procedures in buying and selling livestock have been described and analyzed elsewhere.[37] Two points of emphasis for consideration here are (1) the changed position of the meat packer in buying and (2) remaining opportunities for inefficient or exploitive pricing in the process of buying slaughter livestock.

In the decentralized system of livestock marketing that has developed in the United States, opportunities for inefficient and/or exploitive pricing practices have increased in some ways and decreased in others. Whatever else might be said about terminal markets, these markets, when they were used almost exclusively in marketing livestock, did provide producers with a measure of protection in selling. Commission agents at these markets generally were knowledgeable and capable. While questions were raised from time to time regarding the stable or inflexible positions of

[37] See Williams and Stout, op. cit.; A. D. H. Kaplan, J. B. Dirlam, and R. F. Lanzillotti, Pricing in Big Business (Washington: The Brookings Institutions, 1958), pp. 40–47, and elsewhere.

certain packers in particular markets and the proportions acquired
by one or a few packers,[38] it generally is agreed that these normally
were not results of outright collusion. Partly in the search for an
improved bargaining climate, many packers moved their buying
operations to the country.[39] Here, they were faced with large numbers of relatively uninformed producers. In country selling today,
producers are protected to some extent by aggressive competition
among packers. In addition, improved and more timely marketing
information, more widespread distribution of this information, use
of grades and standards in buying and selling livestock, the development of commercial feedlots, and the appearance of larger-volume
commercial producers have improved bargaining positions of producers.

Inefficient, inequitable, and exploitive pricing remains, nevertheless, as an important aspect of conduct in buying and selling
livestock. The most convenient and least expensive but least accurate way of pricing livestock is to sell by the head. In this method,
weight, grade, and yield, all of which are relevant pricing factors,
must be estimated. The most accurate of the methods considered
practicable is sale on a carcass grade and weight basis. But this
method often is considered inconvenient, as identification throughout the process of slaughter is required and special facilities and
detailed records are necessary. The grade and weight method also
is slightly more expensive and generally is opposed by those having
vested interests in livestock marketing facilities. A recent report
indicates that in 1961 the following percentages of commercial
slaughter were handled by packers on a "grade and yield" basis:
cattle, 4.2; calves, 1.8; hogs, 2.2; and sheep, 3.6[40] While these percentages are small, they probably represent substantial increases for
recent years.

As a compromise, most slaughter livestock are sold on a live-
weight basis with grade and yield estimated. While it frequently
is argued that a high degree of accuracy is attained in live grading,
research studies have shown that, even with 100 percent accuracy
in live grading, pricing errors due to errors in estimates of yield
normally are substantial.[41] Most hogs still are sold on a weight
basis with little or no consideration given to grade or yield.

---

[38] See William H. Nicholls, *Imperfect Competition Within Agricultural In-
dustries* (Ames: Iowa State College Press, 1941); Clair Wilcox, *Competition and
Monopoly in American Industry,* TNEC Monograph 21 (1941), pp. 181–58; and
Whitney, *op. cit.,* pp. 77–85.

[39] Many other factors, of course, were involved.

[40] *Packers and Stockyards Résumé,* Packers and Stockyards Div., U.S.D.A.,
Vol. I, No. 3 (Sept. 1, 1963), p. 7.

[41] Gerald Engelman, A. A. Dowell, and R. E. Olson, *Relative Accuracy of
Pricing Butcher Hogs on Foot and Carcass Weight and Grade,* Minn. Agr. Exp.
Sta. Tech. Bul. 208 (Minneapolis, June 1953).

The widespread practice of applying a "pencil shrink" at country points also is a source of inefficient pricing and, to a degree, reflects the market power position of livestock producers. Estimated shrink frequently is taken into consideration in the base price before the "pencil shrink" is applied. In addition, pencil shrink percentages often became excessive.

Generally speaking, however, packers themselves do not reap the benefits of inefficient or exploitive pricing practices. When such practices become widespread, no packer gains relative to another and in an aggressive competitive environment they are forced to pass any net advantages along to retailers. This leaves producers worse off and packers in no better position than if more equitable pricing practices were adopted.

## Competition Among Meat Packers

With little opportunity either in buying or in selling to capture and retain economic advantages, the nation's major packers have been forced to seek other avenues of strategic conduct. Several sought refuge under the more effective entry barriers to pork processing. Attentions of most shifted to operating costs and efficiency. Large numbers of old or inefficient plants were sold, closed, or remodeled. Emphasis upon automation increased sharply and several plants reorganized managerial lines of authority.

Research and new product innovation received renewed attention. In new product innovation, however, four of the largest firms were again partially blocked by the Consent Decree which prohibited them from handling a specified list of 144 commodities. It was partially for this reason that, in 1958, these packers again initiated legal action for modification of the Consent Decree. But, again, they were unsuccessful. Several have succeeded, however, in developing many new products and in gaining entry to or expanding nonfood lines of production.

The plight of the nation's larger meat packers is not now as serious as preceding comments may have suggested. By 1963, most were firmly reorganized or reoriented on a sound financial basis and some were growing both absolutely and relatively. While the branch house system has been profoundly affected by technological developments and other factors, improved means of transportation have greatly enlarged the radius within which packers can distribute directly from their slaughtering plants. Several have invaded traditional functional areas of the independent meat wholesaler by more aggressively soliciting hotel and restaurant accounts and providing additional fabricating and processing services. New technology has been adopted that can not be employed economically by all small or antiquated packing plants.

## MEAT INDUSTRY PERFORMANCE

Economic performance of the meat industry apparently has been reasonably satisfactory and has improved to some extent. The industry has become more highly competitive. While many factors contributed to a more competitive economic environment, the principal underlying forces probably were (1) changes in consumer demand with increased emphasis upon service, quality, and uniformity as well as prices, (2) technological innovations in transportation, communication, and refrigeration together with adaptation of in-plant technology for use in small plants, and (3) a variety of institutional forces which increased the level and improved the uniformity of relevant economic knowledge in the industry. Higher degrees of specialization and commercialization in production of slaughter livestock also contributed significantly.

Through adjustments and competitive strategy of firms in the industry, these forces have been reflected in structural changes and in new or altered marketing practices. Structural adjustments at retail and changes in procurement practices of retailers introduced additional motivating forces for change in meat packing, processing, and distribution. Firms not strategically postured for immediate adjustments—the national packers and their packinghouse branches along with local butchers—were most disadvantageously affected. Concentration ratios declined, economic positions of the larger independent packers and distributors improved, and competition on a cost, price, and service basis increased.

Retailers reaped relative increases in market power to the extent that in a vertical sense competition may have been impaired. At particular locations and in certain situations, some exploitation of the meat packers' weakened bargaining power position may have taken place.[42] Some types of specialization and technology may have tended toward a reduction or relaxation in horizontal competition. Specialization often tends to reduce numbers of competitors and to heighten barriers to entry.

The competitive nature of the industry is reflected in industry margins and profits. Marketing margins on beef, pork, and lamb rose substantially during the period 1949–63 (from $.21 per pound on pork in 1949 to $.29 in 1963, from $.20 to $.36 on beef, and from $.23 to more than $.35 on lamb). These increases, however, are attributed primarily to increases in per unit prices of marketing services and to additional marketing services. In addition, most of the rise can be assigned to the retail sector. During this same period, wholesale-retail retailer margins rose about 60 percent on

---

[42] See, for instance, Willard F. Williams, and Edward Uvacek, *Pricing and Competition on Beef in Los Angeles*, Mkg. Res. Rept. 413, Mkg. Econ. Res. Div., U.S.D.A. (Washington, 1960).

pork and lamb and 42 percent on beef. A rather large apparent increase in farm-wholesale (packer) margins on beef from $.05 to $.09 per pound is the result primarily of statistical adjustments in the data to allow for a significant increase in the average dressing percentage.[43]

The ratio of sales to assets in the meat packing industry, a measure of "turnover," averages more than five to one. This compares with an average sales-to-assets ratio of 1.4 in 1960 for major durable and nondurable manufacturing corporations. Net earnings of meat packers, nevertheless, remain notoriously low when expressed as percentages either of stockholders' equities or of sales. They rose relatively during World War II but, in the decade of the 50's, they again dropped to establish approximately the prewar relationship with other industries. In 1962, earnings-to-assets ratios of 21 packers were 5.4 percent compared with 11.6 percent for 61 retail food chains and 11.7 percent for 132 other companies representing several other food industries. During the same year, these ratios averaged 3.0 percent for 9 national packers, 4.9 percent for 23 regional packers, 6.2 percent for 40 sectional packers, and 5.2 percent for 26 local packers. Similar patterns are indicated by ratios of earnings to sales and earnings to net worth.[44]

Progress in the meat industry clearly is evident. The industry has successfully handled at reasonable prices and costs the rising volume of products and services required by an increasing population with more money to spend. All sectors have made giant organizational and technological strides in adjusting to emerging facts of business life. Increased emphasis has been placed upon both technical and economic research, upon merchandising, and upon new product innovation. But problems also are evident and continued adjustments are likely.

Continued low earnings and other recent developments may have set the stage for a new era of growth and dominance by the national packers with a reversal in the current trend in concentration ratios. Entry barriers to pork packing and meat processing, new emphasis on product innovation, the gradual rise in relative importance of packer brands on packaged meat products, specialization, and other factors are improving competitive situations of some national packers. Concentration in the prepared or processed meat sector of the industry may rise to the point that it becomes a matter of public interest. More integration by packers into livestock or feed production and livestock feeding is a distinct possi-

---

[43] *The Marketing and Transportation Situation*, U.S.D.A., E.R.S. (Washington, recent issue).

[44] American Meat Institute, *Financial Facts About the Meat Packing Industry, 1960*.

bility. Increasingly, packers may feel forced to integrate into feedlot production to assure themselves of livestock supplies meeting increasingly detailed retailer specifications and to retain market power. Increased feeding of cattle or hogs by packers could lead, in turn, to packer contracts with producers for feeder calves and pigs and, further, to contract production. Organization by packers for more effective merchandising and for integration into the hotel and restaurant supply sector could limit or reduce the role of independent wholesale meat distributors.

Relatively high barriers to egress and excess capacity have plagued the industry for many years and, according to industry economists, will not soon be remedied.[45] A recent study reports rated capacity of packing plants in the United States as 55,000 hogs and 15,000 cattle per hour. On this basis, and assuming a 40-hour average week, annual average utilization for the period 1950–60 varied between 53 percent and 86 percent for cattle and between 57 percent and 71 percent for hogs. Averages for the 11-year period are 73 percent for cattle and 65 percent for hogs. Many plants, however, operate more than 40 hours per week. Some maintain two or more shifts. But the figures also are affected by many small nonunion plants which slaughter during the morning period and utilize kill-floor labor in the afternoon to process meat..[46] It must be recognized, however, that the meat packing sector is required to maintain much "extra" capacity by wide seasonal and cyclical variations in production. In one sense, this is a public service provided mainly by the larger packers. In another, however, it represents inefficiency in pricing as well as in production and marketing.

Needed adjustments include continuing improvements in marketing information, in the official grade standards for both livestock and meat, and in state and local meat inspection requirements. The regulations governing transportation of meat and livestock, including transportation rate structures, are a tangle. Inequities and diseconomies are apparent. Further clarification of the role and functions of the Packers and Stockyards Division in relation to the meat industry is needed.

In working toward further improvements in performance, industry leaders and public policy makers likely will be faced with a continuing and classical dilemma. Adjustments by individual firms, as in the meat industry, leading to changes in structure and marketing practices are introduced for the primary purpose of improving operational efficiency through scale economies and other

---

[45] *The National Provisioner*, 56th Ann. AMI Conv. Rept. Issue (Sept. 30, 1961), pp. 52 ff.

[46] See American Meat Institute, *Financial Facts About the Meat Packing Industry, 1962*, for capacity data on F.I.S. plants for May 1963.

means, or of improving prices and returns by enlarging merchandising "opportunities" in available or constructed havens of restricted competition. Improvements in pricing efficiency and competition usually are fewer and less effective, and frequently can be achieved only at the expense of higher costs and reduced levels of operational efficiency. Many of the more serious marketing problems currently faced by the industry, therefore, are those in the area of prices, pricing efficiency, and competition. Although his position has improved, the livestock producer still has little bargaining power in selling either at markets or on his own farm. Pricing methods throughout the industry are inexact and inefficient, often leading to misallocations of both resources and finished products. Solution of these problems will require acceptable compromises between the divergent goals of operational efficiency and opportunity, on the one hand, and competitive pricing efficiency on the other.

# THE BROILER
# CHICKEN INDUSTRY

3

## EWELL P. ROY[1]

THE U.S. DEPARTMENT OF AGRICULTURE first began assembling statistics on broiler chicken[2] production in 1934. At that time, broilers were produced mainly in Delaware, Maryland, and Virginia. It was not a year-round operation, but mainly a one-batch growout during the winter to utilize the farmer's labor and facilities during an otherwise idle period. Not too many changes occurred in the broiler industry until World War II. Because of rationing of red meats during the war, broiler chicken production was encouraged by the government and the public as a means of alleviating the meat shortage. Although price ceilings were imposed on chicken meat by the Office of Price Administration, prices were high enough to attract many newcomers into the industry.

Between 1945 and 1949, broiler chicken output expanded very little. In fact, output in 1948 was about the same as for 1945. In 1948, farmers received 36 cents per pound, the highest price broiler chickens ever reached at the farm level. At this price, profits in broiler production were unusually large.

In 1949, broiler output jumped to 513 million but prices fell 7.8 cents down to 28.2 cents per pound live. Production increases followed in subsequent years even though prices at the farm declined. This expansion, despite falling prices, was made possible because various cost-reducing technologies were applied rapidly throughout the whole United States. The development of contract

---

[1] Professor, Department of Agricultural Economics and Agribusiness, Louisiana State University, Baton Rouge, Louisiana.
[2] A broiler is defined as a young chicken (usually 8 to 12 weeks of age) of either sex, that is tender meated with soft, pliable, smooth-textured skin and flexible breastbone cartilage. Broilers are sometimes referred to as "fryers" or "frying chickens."

farming and vertical integration expedited the adoption of these technologies (Table 3.1). Economies associated with larger scale operations were also a factor.

Broiler chickens represent about a $1 billion enterprise at the farm level. The farm values constitute about 50 percent of the retail price paid for broiler chickens. Thus, the retail value of broiler chickens is about $2 billion annually. The cash income from all

TABLE 3.1

COMMERCIAL BROILERS: PRODUCTION, AVERAGE LIVE WEIGHT, PRICE PER POUND, AND VALUE OF PRODUCTION, 1934 TO DATE

| Year | Production Number | Production Pounds (live) | Average Live Weight, Per Bird | Average Price Received by Producers, Per Pound, Live Weight | Value of Production |
|---|---|---|---|---|---|
| | (millions) | | (pounds) | (cents) | (million dollars) |
| 1934 | 34 | 97 | 2.8 | 19.3 | 19 |
| 1935 | 43 | 123 | 2.9 | 20.0 | 25 |
| 1936 | 53 | 152 | 2.9 | 20.6 | 31 |
| 1937 | 68 | 196 | 2.9 | 21.4 | 42 |
| 1938 | 82 | 239 | 2.9 | 19.0 | 46 |
| 1939 | 106 | 307 | 2.9 | 17.0 | 52 |
| 1940 | 143 | 413 | 2.9 | 17.3 | 72 |
| 1941 | 192 | 559 | 2.9 | 18.4 | 103 |
| 1942 | 228 | 674 | 3.0 | 22.9 | 155 |
| 1943 | 285 | 833 | 2.9 | 28.6 | 238 |
| 1944 | 274 | 818 | 3.0 | 28.8 | 235 |
| 1945 | 366 | 1,107 | 3.0 | 29.5 | 327 |
| 1946 | 293 | 884 | 3.0 | 32.7 | 289 |
| 1947 | 310 | 936 | 3.0 | 32.3 | 302 |
| 1948 | 371 | 1,127 | 3.0 | 36.0 | 405 |
| 1949 | 513 | 1,570 | 3.1 | 28.2 | 443 |
| 1950 | 631 | 1,945 | 3.1 | 27.4 | 533 |
| 1951 | 789 | 2,415 | 3.1 | 28.5 | 689 |
| 1952 | 861 | 2,624 | 3.0 | 28.8 | 756 |
| 1953 | 947 | 2,904 | 3.1 | 27.1 | 786 |
| 1954 | 1,048 | 3,236 | 3.1 | 23.1 | 747 |
| 1955 | 1,092 | 3,350 | 3.1 | 25.2 | 844 |
| 1956 | 1,344 | 4,270 | 3.2 | 19.6 | 838 |
| 1957 | 1,448 | 4,683 | 3.2 | 18.9 | 886 |
| 1958 | 1,660 | 5,431 | 3.3 | 18.5 | 1,002 |
| 1959 | 1,737 | 5,763 | 3.3 | 16.1 | 925 |
| 1960 | 1,795 | 6,017 | 3.3 | 16.9 | 1,014 |
| 1961 | 1,993 | 6,841 | 3.4 | 13.9 | 949 |
| 1962 | 2,026 | 6,919 | 3.4 | 15.2 | 1,051 |
| 1963 | 2,104 | 7,284 | 3.5 | 14.6 | 1,064 |
| 1964 | 2,161 | 7,524 | 3.5 | 14.2 | 1,071 |

Source: U.S.D.A., Washington, D.C. Annual Reports.

farm marketings is about $35 billion. Therefore, broiler chickens comprise about 3 percent of the total cash farm income for the United States.

## DELINEATION OF THE MARKET PROBLEM

Broiler production and other related phases of the industry constitute a large and complex area of study. For example, in the broiler chicken industry, there are about 10,000 feed mills and mixers and 25,000 feed dealers, 4,500 chick hatcheries, 26,000 commercial broiler growers, 320 commercial broiler processing plants, and 285,000 retail food stores. In most instances, these segments are integrated either through contract, ownership, or both. This is most frequently at the grower-dealer level (Figure 3.1).

This chapter is concerned primarily with end-product marketing or that of dressed-drawn broiler chickens. This area of study involves primarily the commercial broiler processing plants and retail food stores which sell the bulk of all broilers produced and processed.

## MARKET STRUCTURE

### Integration at the Growing Level

In recent years, feed dealers, hatcherymen, and processors have become increasingly integrated into joint horizontal and vertical combines. These integrated ventures have absorbed the broiler growing segment to an increasing degree. It is estimated that about 57 percent of the broiler producers are on contract with integrated contractors. In addition, about 18 percent of the growers are producing broilers on account with their cooperatives; 20 percent of them are growing broilers on farms operated by integrators; and 5 percent of the growers are operating independently. Thus, about 95 percent of broiler producers are engaged in some type of economic integration.

Growers and contractors negotiate contracts mostly from brood to brood. There is almost no group bargaining by growers with contractors. Contracts are standardized among a particular integrator and his growers; therefore, the grower either accepts or rejects the contract as offered to him. The more prominent types of grower-contract plans are known as (1) open account, (2) open account—no loss, (3) guaranteed price, (4) profit sharing, (5) flat fee, (6) feed conversion, (7) point spread, (8) joint risk, and (9) combination plans. The plan currently in greatest use is the flat fee with some type of efficiency bonus such as for feed conversion.[3]

---

[3] E. P. Roy, *Contract Farming, U.S.A.* (Danville, Ill.: Interstate Printers & Publishers, Inc., 1963), p. 28.

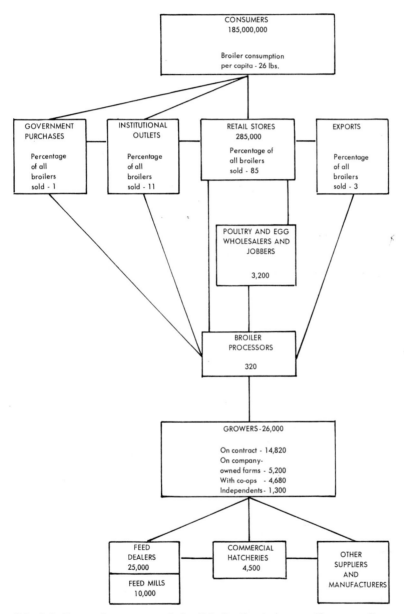

FIG. 3.1—Economic structure of the U.S. broiler industry. (Courtesy, Dept. of Agr. Econ., L.S.U., Baton Rouge, La.)

Previous to integrative developments, the processor under an independent broiler growing structure did not know precisely when, where, and how his broiler supplies were to be obtained. When broilers were offered, perhaps a few days before they were ready for market, the processor scheduled them into his processing program although he was never positive of the day the broilers would be delivered. Upon delivery, the processor would pay the grower a price based upon some terminal market or wholesale "live poultry" quotation. Processors had no connection with or financial interest in broilers from a production standpoint.

## Location of Production and Consumption Areas

Associated with the rise of economic integration was a shift in broiler production from the Delmarva area to the economically poorer southern states, especially to Georgia, North Carolina, Alabama, Texas, Mississippi, and Arkansas (Figure 3.2).

Broiler contracting has been a major feature of production in the southern United States. Other broiler areas, such as the Northeast (excepting Maine), Middle West, and Far West, have had less contracting and have lagged in broiler production over the last few years. In 1940, Georgia was a small broiler producing state, while Delaware was the major producing state. Maryland and Virginia were the only two other states with over 10 million broiler production. In 1945 the top eight states were in the order of production: Delaware, Maryland, Georgia, California, Virginia, North Carolina, Arkansas, and Texas. In 1964, the top eight states were Georgia, Arkansas, Alabama, North Carolina, Mississippi, Texas, Maryland, and Delaware.

The primary markets for broiler chickens are the large urban centers such as New York, Philadelphia, Boston, Cleveland, Atlanta, Pittsburgh, Chicago, St. Louis, New Orleans, Houston, Dallas, Los Angeles, San Francisco, and Detroit (Figure 3.2).

Broiler consumption per capita is greatest among low-income families. Lower income groups spend more of their incomes for broiler chickens than for beef because of the former's economy in meal planning (Figure 3.3). Some studies have shown that the frequency of chicken consumption tends to decrease as incomes, job levels, and education increase.[4]

## Characteristics of Processor-Sellers

Broiler chicken processors are usually vertically integrated with one or more of the following: chick hatcheries, feed mills, feed

---

[4] H. V. Courtenay and R. E. Branson, *Consumers' Image of Broilers*, Tex. Agr. Exp. Sta. Bul. B-989 (College Station, Apr. 1962).

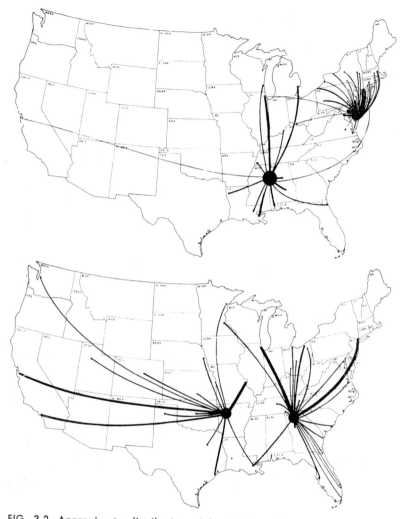

FIG. 3.2—Approximate distribution of broiler-fryers from major areas to major cities in 1961.

dealers, and growout operations. Processors represent the terminal or end point of "production" integration.

Rogers reports:

In processing, the extent of integration appears to be a function of firm size, although precise knowledge regarding this relationship is limited.

CENTS PER POUND

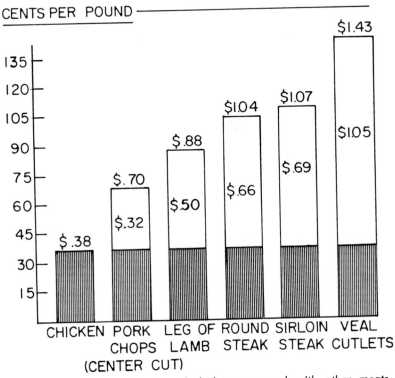

FIG. 3.3—Average retail price of chicken compared with other meats, United States, 1961. (Courtesy, **Broiler Industry**, Sea Isle City, N.J., Apr. 1962.)

If we ignore for the moment the producer-processor tie-in, where growing is of major importance, and other farming operations, then it is readily apparent that large plants tend to be more highly integrated than other size groups. This relates to the combination of assembling, processing, and distributing poultry with extensive contract growing, experimental and breeding operations, large-scale hatching, and large-scale handling of eggs, feed, and supplies.[5]

Processors receive live birds, slaughter and prepare them in ready-to-cook form. About 74 percent of the broilers slaughtered are ice-packed whole birds, 15 percent are fresh cut up, and 11 percent are frozen. The birds are sold primarily in straight truckload lots to large volume distributors such as wholesale receivers and the regional and national chain store organizations.

### Degree of Horizontal Integration

One indication of horizontal integration at the processing level is the number of plants operated as branches of the parent firm. A

[5] G. B. Rogers *et al.*, *Characteristics of the Processing Industry*, N.H. Agr. Exp. Sta. Bul. 444 (Durham, Sept. 1957), p. 31.

limited study in three southern states showed that, out of 64 plants enumerated, 22 or about one-third were branch plants while 42 were single-plant firms.[6] The largest number of broiler processing plants owned by one firm is 12, out of a total of 320 plants in the United States.

## Degree of Vertical Integration

Of 19 large-scale feed milling companies examined by the Small Business Committee, the following vertical expansion into broiler processing was noted:[7]

| Year | Number of Feed Companies Engaged in Processing | Volume of Birds (number) (000,000) | Percent of U.S. Total |
|------|-----------------------------------------------|-----------------------------------|----------------------|
| 1959 | 6 | 103.6 | 6.0 |
| 1960 | 8 | 119.9 | 6.7 |
| 1961 | 7 | 151.0 | 7.6 |

In the southern United States, processors procure their broilers mainly from feed dealer contractors and/or from their own production-controlled operations. In Delmarva, the Middle West, and the Pacific states, there are less close-knit procurement operations.

Rogers found that under the price and cost relationships in his study, direct contracting between the plant and the grower was the most profitable method of plant procurement because of the advantages of coordinating supply with processing. Buying broilers live on the open market was least profitable. Three-way contracting and a combination of buying on the open market and direct contracting fell between the two extremes.[8]

## Number, Size, and Location of Processing Plants

While the data on poultry dressing plants are not always comparable due to various definitions of "plants," the trend in numbers of plants is indicated by data in Table 3.2. The number of "commercial" slaughtering plants has been definitely declining. It is estimated that one-half of the nation's broiler processing plants dress 90 percent of the U.S. broilers; also, that 10 plants dress 12 percent of the total U.S. output; 35 plants dress 34 percent, and 87 of the plants dress 64 percent of the total.

The data shown in Table 3.3 indicate that the South Atlantic and South Central regions account for 60 percent of the broiler

[6] Southern Regional Poultry Committee, *Annual Report* (1962).

[7] *Small Business Problems in the Poultry Industry*, U.S. House of Representatives Rept. 2566 (Washington, 1963), pp. 15–16.

[8] G. B. Rogers, *Relative Profitability of Alternative Procurement, Production and Selling Programs for Broiler Processors*, E.R.S. Rept. 516 (Washington, Jan. 1962), p. iii.

TABLE 3.2

NUMBER AND SIZE OF POULTRY PROCESSING PLANTS, U.S.A., 1939–63

| Year | Number of All Poultry | | Main Type of Poultry Processed | No. of Commercial Processing Plants* |
| | Processor firms | Processing plants | | |
| --- | --- | --- | --- | --- |
| 1939† | N.A. | 765 | Fowl | N.A. |
| 1947‡ | 330 | 553 | Fowl, broilers | N.A. |
| 1954‡ | 1,189 | 1,309 | Fowl, broilers | N.A. |
| 1956§ | N.A. | 2,230 | Fowl, broilers | 691 |
| 1958‡ | 1,041 | 1,233 | Fowl, broilers | N.A. |
| 1958§ | N.A. | N.A. | Fowl, broilers | 594 |
| 1961‖ | N.A. | N.A. | Broilers | 397 |
| 1962‡‡ | N.A. | N.A. | Broilers | 320 |
| 1963** | N.A. | 968 | Fowl, broilers | N.A. |

* A "commercial" plant is one which processes at least 30,000 pounds of live poultry per week.
† Allen B. Paul, *Economic Structure of the Food Processing Industries,* Illinois Agricultural Experiment Station Report FT-5 (Urbana, 1940), p. 9.
‡ *Marketing and Transportation Situation,* U.S.D.A. (Washington, Feb. 1962), Table 8.
§ Fred Faber, *Commercial Poultry Slaughter Plants,* Agricultural Marketing Service Report 379 (Washington, 1960).
‖ A. D. Thompson and M. Planting, *Credit and Economic Aspects of the Broiler Industry,* Farm Credit Administration (Washington, July 1963), Table 8.
‡‡ *Broiler Industry* (Sea Isle City, N.J.: Garden State Publishing Co., May 1963).
** *1963 Census of Manufactures,* U.S. Department of Commerce, Bureau of the Census (Washington, March 1965).

processing plants and 81 percent of the output. Plants in those regions are generally much larger than those in other parts of the United States.

There are now fewer but larger plants, with increased concentration of processing plants in the South. Competition has forced closing of many smaller, less efficient plants. Larger capacity plants have been built in the Western and North Central states, although the number of plants has declined in these areas. Production in other areas has not grown as much as in the South with the result that these other areas have a smaller share of the market.

### Economies of Scale

For plants processing from 150 to 10,000 broilers per hour, the cost savings from the smallest to the largest is 2.2 cents per pound live (Figure 3.4). Although the decline in average unit cost between successively larger plants may appear relatively small, total savings would be large. This is important in examining the implications of small differences in unit costs to individual firms and to the marketing system.[9]

In recent years, those plants processing over 10,000 birds per hour have been operating mostly at a 12,000 bird per hour rate although a few are even larger. This is mainly because plants are

[9] G. B. Rogers and E. T. Bardwell, *Economies of Scale in Chicken Processing,* N.H. Agr. Exp. Sta. Bul. 459 (Durham, Apr. 1959), p. 15.

TABLE 3.3

NUMBER OF BROILER PROCESSING PLANTS AND BROILERS SLAUGHTERED, BY REGIONS,
U.S.A., 1962

| Region | Number of Plants | Total Quantity Slaughtered | Quantity Slaughtered Per Plant |
|---|---|---|---|
| | | *(thousands of pounds)* | |
| New England | 16 | 302,032 | 18,877 |
| Middle Atlantic | 26 | 273,236 | 10,509 |
| East North Central | 44 | 165,812 | 3,768 |
| West North Central | 6 | 36,429 | 6,072 |
| South Atlantic | 89 | 2,383,516 | 26,781 |
| East South Central | 44 | 1,132,088 | 25,729 |
| West South Central | 59 | 1,134,692 | 19,232 |
| Western | 20 | 144,229 | 7,211 |
| Subtotal | 304 | 5,572,034 | 18,329 |
| Plants not disclosed | 16 | 197,405 | 12,338 |
| Grand total | 320 | 5,769,439 | 18,030 |

| Region | Percent of Total | | Percent of Average Plant |
|---|---|---|---|
| New England | 5.0 | 5.2 | 104.7 |
| Middle Atlantic | 8.1 | 4.7 | 58.3 |
| East North Central | 13.8 | 2.9 | 20.9 |
| West North Central | 1.9 | .6 | 33.7 |
| South Atlantic | 27.8 | 41.3 | 148.5 |
| East South Central | 13.8 | 19.6 | 142.7 |
| West South Central | 18.4 | 19.7 | 106.7 |
| Western | 6.2 | 2.5 | 40.0 |
| Subtotal | 95.0 | 96.5 | 101.7 |
| Plants not disclosed | 5.0 | 3.5 | 68.4 |
| Grand total | 100.0 | 100.0 | 100.0 |

Source: *Broiler Industry* (Sea Isle City, N.J.: Garden State Publishing Co.,
May 1963), p. 40.

limited by inspection procedures to 80 or 90 birds per minute.
However, unit cost reductions beyond 12,000 birds per hour are
not believed to be too significant.

## Entry and Exit

It is getting more difficult for newcomers to enter the broiler
processing industry. The reason is not due to processing economics
or technology alone, but to the need for incorporating a complex
combination of hatching, feeding, and growing-out programs with
processing. It is, of course, much easier for existing integrators to
add processing to their integrated "combine" than it is for a newcomer to enter the processing phase. A newcomer to broiler processing would have some difficulty in developing integrated broiler
production to supply his plant. He might, of course, develop con-

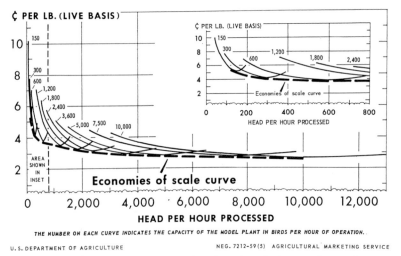

FIG. 3.4—Broiler processing costs related to size of plant and use of capacity, based on ten model plants.

tractual arrangements with integrators having no processing plants. Such integrators are now rather few in number. The exits of processing firms who were operating independently have been numerous. Exit has consisted of bankruptcy, merging, and outright sale. Exit has become costly because of increased investments. Also, some firms have been forced to operate at a loss in an effort to meet competition and strive for survival. Much of the competition at below-cost prices has been in the form of *staying power* of firms.

A survey by *Feedstuffs* of 117 broiler industry leaders throughout the United States on the merger question yielded these results:

> Nearly 100 of these indicated that there would likely be more feed and/or poultry mergers, to one degree or another. Of these, at least 46 felt that there was a definite or strong possibility that the broiler industry in particular would be dominated by 25 or so firms.[10]

### Federal Inspection Versus Noninspection

Young chickens slaughtered under mandatory federal inspection for wholesomeness began January 1, 1959. The wholesomeness inspection program is causing some competitive situations which in themselves are not wholesome. About 85 percent of the broilers processed in the United States are federally inspected although percentages by state vary greatly. For example, in states where broiler production is not an important industry, there is less federal

---

[10] Roger Berglund, "The Urge To Merge," *Feedstuffs* (Minneapolis, Dec. 29, 1962), p. 10.

inspection because plants in those states are not apt to move dressed broilers across state lines. Yet, the fact that these plants in low-producing areas have no federal inspection may cause them to lose some chain store markets which often demand federally inspected broilers. The nonfederally inspected broilers are then offered at lower prices to nonchain stores and other outlets.

In states where broiler production is high, about 88 percent of the broilers are federally inspected. However, the remaining 12 percent represents a large amount of nonfederally inspected broilers. Some of this nonfederally inspected poultry sells at lower prices both live and eviscerated and thus undercuts the price structure and reduces prices for all broilers. Smaller chain stores in one city may "loss-leader" nonfederally inspected broilers and cause similar retaliatory moves by larger food stores.

## Buyers of Eviscerated Broilers

Eviscerated broilers have at least four general market outlets: (1) institutional food markets (cafes, restaurants, hospitals, schools, etc.), (2) export trade, (3) government purchases (for school lunches), and (4) retail food stores.

Institutional outlets at the retail level account for $210 million poultry meat sales annually, primarily broilers. Broiler exports amounted to about $48 million in 1962 and government purchases, $18 million. Retail food stores account for the balance of sales valued at retail at about $1.6 billion.

## Retail Food Stores

There are at least three types of retail food stores: (1) chain stores which conduct about 40 percent of the retail food business, (2) affiliated independent stores (with some wholesaler either proprietary or co-op) which conduct about 45 percent, and (3) unaffiliated independents which conduct the remainder or about 15 percent. The principal outlets for broilers are the chain stores and affiliated independents.

## Structure of Food Store Markets

Local food store markets vary greatly in the United States. Some local markets are heavily populated with stores operated by national chains; other markets have a predominance of independent stores and voluntary and co-op chains. The penetration of national chain food stores is certainly not uniform from market to market. For this reason, many smaller broiler processors have survived longer than the economies of scale would indicate. These smaller processors may sell uninspected broilers in these local markets, perform various services for retailers, and provide a flexibility in operation which larger processors cannot meet.

## Concentration in Food Store Markets

Cairns has made a careful study of concentration of food stores by regions. Although most of the broiler processing capacity is centered in the South Atlantic and South Central states, broiler sales are made principally in the New England, Middle Atlantic, East North Central, and Pacific regions. In these latter regions, food store concentration is higher than the national average, especially in the New England and Middle Atlantic regions.[11]

Mueller and Garoian report:

> The share of the grocery business of the four largest chains has remained relatively constant from 1940 to 1958 at about 22–23%. However, the share of the 5th to 20th ranking chains has increased dramatically from 6.2% to 13.3% in the same period. Although on the national level the coverage is much less, the study estimated that in 133 cities the two largest retailers in each of these cities averaged over 40% of the grocery business in the city.[12]

## Buying by Chains

Branson reports the following buying policies among chains:

> Under specification buying, national chains can procure on an offer and bid basis. Bids are received by the buyers and procurement follows on a price basis. As much as possible, the requirements are filled by the lowest bidder. If his supply is not sufficient, the balance needed is bought from the next lowest bidder and on up the price array until the full need is met.
>
> Regional and local chains present a more varied picture. Generally their central policies are geared directly to gaining a competitive advantage over their national rivals. This appears most commonly in more stress placed on the quality and variety of nationally advertised brands of canned goods, fruits and vegetables, poultry and meats, and wider use of hardware, drug and cosmetic and clothing departments within stores.
>
> Policies of the regional and local chains are formulated loosely and are difficult to document. Policy handbooks, such as used by national chains, do not exist. Commodity buyers, under this system, have much more latitude in decision making if not outright policy determination responsibilities. In fact, one frequently gains the impression that at the top level each department—grocery, fruits and vegetables and meats and poultry, which is the most common three-way grouping—operates as though it is a separate firm in a holding company type of framework. Each buying department makes its own decisions regarding procurement, pricing, displays and even advertising down to the

---

[11] J. P. Cairns, *Acquisitions, Concentration and Vertical Integration in Food Retailing*, Johns Hopkins Univ. Ph.D. thesis (Baltimore, 1960).

[12] W. F. Mueller and Leon Garoian, *Changes in the Market Structure of Grocery Retailing*, Wis. Agr. Exp. Sta. Rept. 5 (Madison, 1960).

nature of the copy to be used. With this variation in top level management between national and regional or local chains, it is not surprising that buying practices assumed diverse forms.

All chains, irrespective of their organization structure for buying, use the folowing criteria in supplier selection: (1) quality of product; (2) deliverable quantity per week or order period; (3) ability to furnish a continuous supply during the season involved; (4) price consistent with the quality of the product and market condition; (5) ability to fit into company merchandising policies; and (6) ability to contribute toward attainment of overall policy objectives of the chain.[13]

## Store Sales of Broilers

Depending upon the size of city and number of chains in it, chain food stores will sell from about half to three-fourths of the broilers retailed in a given city. An average supermarket may sell 1,500 broiler chickens weekly, mostly on the weekend.[14]

Jamison reports:

One major northern California chain with annual sales approximately equal to many of the larger Los Angeles chains uses about 200,000 broilers for a weekend special. Processor volume information obtained in this study shows that such an order would require the total weekly output of the three largest California processors.[15]

Smith found in Baltimore and Washington, D.C.:

Eighty-seven per cent of the fryer volume was handled by chain stores and 13 per cent by independents and corner groceries.

In Baltimore, independent stores sold an average of 154 pounds of chicken per week while chain stores averaged 2,045 pounds per store. In Washington the comparison was 205 pounds for independents and 1,473 pounds for chain stores. It was found that 31 per cent of all stores in the two-city area sold less than 50 pounds of chicken per store each week and 33 per cent sold more than 1,550 pounds.[16]

## Food Stores Processing Broilers

According to *Food Engineering*, of the top 20 retail food chains only two are integrated into broiler processing for at least a majority of their supplies.[17]

---

[13] R. E. Branson, *Buying Practices of Major Food Handlers*, A.S.A.W. paper (College Station, Tex., Feb. 6, 1961).

[14] J. C. Maness and E. P. Roy, *Broiler Business* (Cullman, Ala.: Watt Publ. Co., May 1963), p. 38.

[15] John Jamison, *Grower-Processor Coordination*, Calif. Agr. Exp. Sta. Rept. 239 (Berkeley, Dec. 1960), p. 15.

[16] H. D. Smith, *Poultry Processing and Marketing* (Mount Morris, Ill.: Watt Publ. Co., Feb. 1962), p. 40.

[17] *Food Engineering* (Philadelphia: Chilton and Co., Oct. 1960).

Broiler processors in 1958 had total shipments valued at $1.713 billion while chain food stores which integrated broiler processing had shipments valued at only $8.6 million. It is clear, therefore, that chain food store integration backwards into broiler chicken processing has been meager.

## MARKET CONDUCT

### Pricing System for Broilers

Hughes has commented on the overall efficiency of the broiler pricing system as follows:

> Day-to-day and week-to-week price fluctuations, arising from competitive bartering, are more extreme than for many other farm and most nonfarm commodities. Live values are determined by the demand for and supply of eviscerated birds, and this demand is influenced by supply and the availability of competitive meats.
>
> Simply stated, local prices for live and eviscerated birds usually are fairly well in line with the national level. The Georgia market, because of top volume and nearness to other production areas, reflects the national market and is the strongest price level determinant.
>
> However, no area can stand alone. If the price for live birds should rise, say, to 1 cent above the national figure, the price of eviscerated birds, because of offal losses, would rise 1⅓ cents. Under such circumstances, sales may slacken and exert downward pressure on the price.
>
> Conversely, a live price at 1 cent below the national level may lead either to the withholding of live birds by growers or increased shipments of eviscerated birds to far-away markets, or both. The reduction in supply soon buoys up the sagging price level.[18]

*Processors' Live Broiler Prices.* Processors who own or control their own birds have a problem of allocating a "price" for the live broilers taken into their plants. This is important because they must have some idea of the live broiler price in order to bargain with food buyers over the prices for dressed broilers.

Those processors not directly owning or controlling broilers may buy at auction and/or from live haulers or shippers. They may use both Urner-Barry price quotations and the U.S.D.A. Market News Reports.

*Decline of Terminal Live Poultry Markets.* The New York and Chicago live poultry markets which dominated the scene for many years have become less important. In addition, the "farm" prices

---

[18] Charles Hughes, *Armour's Analysis* (Chicago: Armour & Co., Dec. 1960), pp. 6–7.

for broilers quoted in various production areas are also losing their significance. As broiler production becomes more processor integrated, there will be less need to set a "farm" price because few market transactions or exchanges between buyers and sellers occur or will occur at the farm level.[19]

*Live Broiler Auctions.* The live broiler auctions such as those in Delmarva, Texas, and in other states represent the last vestiges of live broiler markets. These auctions at which processor-buyers and feed integrators sell and buy broilers provide some yardstick with which to measure live broiler values. Although auctions do not handle a large percentage of the broilers, they represent the main valid "transaction" price between sellers and buyers of live broilers. If vertical integration continues, the future of broiler auctions appears dismal because no live broiler transactions will occur.[20]

## Stores' Pricing Policies: Buying Eviscerated Broilers

*Buying by Formula.* It has become customary for some chain food stores to establish a base price by use of formulas. Chain buyers know that a live broiler shrinks about 27 percent upon evisceration. For example, a 3.50-pound live broiler becomes a 2.56-pound eviscerated broiler. If live broilers are selling for 15 cents per pound, the broiler cost to processors is $.525. Dividing $.525 by 2.56 pounds yields a dressed product cost of about $.205 per pound. Then, by applying an estimated cost for processing, given the size of plant, the chain buyers can arrive at an f.o.b. plant cost for their broilers plus transportation to their stores. The chain store buyer can thus use this base price from which bargaining can proceed with the processor—perhaps up, perhaps down. If broilers are in heavy supply (as they usually are) the chain store buyer may refuse to pay more than the variable costs of the processor. In short-run cases, the price may be driven even lower.

It is reported that one chain's formula is "the live market plus 5.25 cents per pound (dressed weight) based on a 73 percent yield, f.o.b. plant."[21] Another chain's formula is reported to be "133 percent of the live market price plus processing cost plus freight."[22]

*Centralized Buying.* Some chains continue to further centralize their buying of poultry meat. This gives them greater command over price negotiations with processors. Their market requirements also spell concern for smaller processors. Food stores

[19] *Small Business Problems in the Poultry Industry, Part III,* Staff, Small Business Committee, U.S. House of Representatives (Washington, 1962), p. 373.

[20] E. P. Roy, "Live Broiler Auctions," *Broiler Producer* (Chicago, Mar. 1960).

[21] *Broiler Industry* (Sea Isle City, N.J.: Garden State Publ. Co., May 1963), p. 8.

[22] *Southeastern Poultry Times* (Gainesville, Ga., Mar. 21, 1962), p. 4.

may require fresh whole chicken, frozen chicken, cut-up whole, parts, and other forms of chicken. Plants that are too small cannot efficiently accommodate such requirements. Also, by consolidating their buying, chains can get a wider range of price offers by processors into one central office. This gives them leverage in pinpointing the lowest price offer among processors.[23]

## Stores' Pricing Policies: Selling Broilers

Gray reports:

> Retail prices are determined by competition as well as by direct cost elements. In any given time period, prices for frying chickens in a particular store or group of stores of a major retailer may be set largely by administered pricing policies of the retailer. These policies, however, are influenced by prices and practices of competing independent and chain store retailers in various cities and local areas. This type of pricing policy would be in contrast to retail prices determined on the basis of costs of production plus transportation and other costs of marketing to get the fryers to retail stores and ready for sale to consumers. Presumably, however, retail selling prices over an extended period of time would be sufficient to equal buying prices plus marketing charges. Comparisons of newspaper prices featured in different cities by national or regional firms indicate that factors other than direct costs were important determinants of retail price.[24]

Prices set by the chain food stores on frying chickens are determined on a "zone" basis corresponding to the administrative offices for a given group of stores. If a food chain has an administrative district located in the Washington, D.C.-Baltimore area, then broiler prices in all stores in that chain's district will be uniform for a weekend. The same holds true for a co-op chain which has member stores in a given locality, especially when newspaper ads are used on a "pool" basis. No store in the co-op group can deviate from the "pool" ad price quoted.

## Competitive Practices Among Firms

This section deals with attempts by firms to strengthen their competitive position in relation to other firms.

*Product Differentiation.* Product differentiation of whole broiler chickens in retail food stores is very weak. It consists primarily of advertising "federally inspected" chickens as opposed to chickens that are "state" and/or "city" inspected or noninspected for wholesomeness. Differentiation of chickens on the basis of

---

[23] *Broiler Industry* (Sea Isle City, N.J.: Garden State Publ. Co., Feb. 1963), p. 6.
[24] Leo Gray, *Retail Price Specials for Frying Chickens*, E.R.S. Rept. 101 (Washington, Jan. 1963), p. 5.

grade is not too strong. Although broilers of A, B, and C grades do exist, few are retailed under such designations.

Store differentiation on cut-up, tray-packed chicken is more widespread than for whole broilers. Because most of the cut-up chickens are packaged in the store, this allows retailers an opportunity to insert and advertise their own brand names on such packs of chicken. Product differentiation, nevertheless, is still weak even in those instances. However, retailers do have an opportunity to cut up the lower cost B-grade chickens, for example, and sell them at regular retail prices plus charges for cutting up and tray packing. Broiler chickens may be downgraded from A to B on the basis of a single defect although B-grade chickens are a wholesome product.

Processors are attempting, in some markets, to perform the cutting and packaging at their plants. Some retailers do not favor this as it reduces their branding opportunities. Some retailers prefer for processors to cut up chicken in bulk and let the retailers do the packaging in their own stores.

Frozen broilers have not been a big factor in retail markets largely due to consumers' resistance and retailers' reluctance to stock and sell them. Frozen chickens are favored by processors because it would mean longer shelf life, less price competition, and more opportunity for hedging in the futures market. Branding and product differentiation on frozen chickens are more readily accomplished than with ice-packed chicken.

One chain store consultant has expressed the preferences of retailers for branded poultry:

> Retailers want more branded products in poultry. Look around the food industry and you will find that any time you have a product which is sold unbranded, you have a product on which there is more price-slashing. (Broilers, for example). And why? Because price is the only method available for differentiating your product from someone else's. Put a brand on it, though, and you relieve some of this pressure.[25]

Grading provisions for broilers are still voluntary and optional for each processor. Grading of eviscerated broilers at plants into A, B, and C grades has not been widespread but it is increasing. It is difficult to satisfactorily retail a product such as chicken with a B- or C-grade label. Therefore, it has been more common to sell broilers either without a grade designation or as grade A with a wholesomeness inspection tag if the processor of broilers so qualifies. There are, however, some stores that cater to people seeking undergrades and in those stores the B and C grades move well.

---

[25] C. C. Bowes, *Poultry Processing and Marketing* (Mount Morris, Ill.: Watt Publ. Co., Feb. 1963), p. 24.

*Price Discrimination: Loss-Leaders.* Probably the main competitive device used in retailing broiler chickens has been that of "loss-leaders." A loss-leader may be defined as a product which is retailed by firms for less than their cost of procuring and handling the product in its normal scope of operations. Contrary to popular belief, food stores will not generally retail broilers for less than what they paid the city receiver-distributor or processor. Generally, the "loss" comes in not marking up the price of chickens to cover retail handling costs.

A 12-month study of broiler loss-leaders in Baton Rouge, Louisiana, showed that national food chains sponsored loss-leader sales somewhat less frequently than did local food chains. Food stores affiliated with co-op wholesalers rarely conducted loss-leader sales. Unaffiliated and independently operated food stores used price specials more frequently than did all other stores.[26]

A study by Gray reached conclusions similar to the Baton Rouge study:

1. In Washington, D.C., independent retailers often were the first firms to advertise price specials on fryers.

2. Fryer specials apparently were not always initiated by retailers, but often suggested by wholesalers and processors, who offered price discounts for volume purchases.

3. More fryers were sold on an annual basis as a result of special sales than might have been sold without sales promotion.

4. When retailers featured fryers, prices generally were about 30 per cent lower than prices during nonsale periods, and weekly volumes averaged nearly 4 times as large. In the week after a special, volume was generally about 25 per cent smaller than in the week before a special.[27]

Why do stores loss-leader broilers? The answer is generally the same—to attract customers into the store. One store owner reported:

We have found poultry specials to be one of our best drawing cards. During opening week at our new store we sold nearly 30,000 pounds of fryers at about 4¢ a pound below our cost. Similar sales are held every few weeks with nearly that much being sold at each of our four stores. A promotion like this means that we just about break even in the entire meat department during that period. However, the extra store traffic makes it worthwhile. Although we have on oc-

---

[26] E. P. Roy, *Poultry Processing and Marketing* (Mount Morris, Ill.: Watt Publ. Co., Nov. 1959).

[27] Leo Gray, *op. cit.*

casion featured fryers at as much as 8¢ a pound below their cost, specials usually are timed to coincide with a market surplus.[28]

Saunders and Stoddard in their Maine study concluded that loss-leader sales were losing some of their effectiveness.

Fryer specials had little effect on store traffic. The number of people who shopped during weeks when fryers were offered at reduced prices were practically the same as when fryers were sold at regular markups.

Although more fryers were sold during fryer specials, the dollar return from fryers was less than when regular markups were taken. Apparently, as frying chicken has become more plentiful and less expensive, it also has become less a luxury item.

If this is the case, we could expect consumers to be less responsive to changes in fryer prices in the future than they have been in the past.[29]

**Dual Pricing.** Some industry spokesmen claim that while the food stores do conduct loss-leaders, they will raise margins extremely high in weeks subsequent to loss-leader sales. The following view, though somewhat exaggerated, is widely held:

"Here is an outline of the current picture, and it isn't a pretty one—a chain is getting ready for a major broiler sale. It canvasses the sources of supply asking not what is the price but proclaiming how much it will give. The producers resist, but broilers may not be kept too long, and the supply mounts. Finally, someone sells. Thus, a market is created and the young chickens go into distribution at prices that mean little more than cost recovery for the producers and straight loss for the chains.

"We said the chains, for the news that one of the major outfits has gotten broilers at this price cannot be kept secret and soon everyone is getting the price forced by the one or two.

"Finally, the big broiler sale breaks on Thursday at a price equal to invoice and sometimes even less. The public rushes to buy, filling their freezers and refrigerators with an inventory that will last 2 or 3 weeks, by which time a new broiler sale will be staged and the process repeated.

"Next Monday, after the sale, the chains, done with their price orgy, mark up the chickens to exorbitant heights, anywhere from 35 to 49 cents a pound, in an effort to recoup their losses. The result is that demand falls flat. Broiler movement is next to nothing and supplies begin to pile up in the warehouses of the proces-

---

[28] *Poultry and Eggs Weekly* (Kansas City, Mo., Sept. 12, 1959), p. 18.
[29] Richard Saunders and Everett Stoddard, *Effects of Fryer Specials*, Maine Agr. Exp. Sta. Bul. 643 (Orono, Maine, Sept. 1960), pp. 12–13.

sors. The stage is being set for a repeat of the profitless performance."[30]

In defense of chain store pricing policies, one executive has
stated:

> Under situations like this, broiler producers and processors keep con-
> stant pressure on retailers to take their products at giveaway prices in
> order to get rid of it. The only way to move this much of an over-
> supply is through special sales which usually generate purchases 2 to
> 4 times normal sales. Generally a series of such specials will clear the
> market and allow prices to return to acceptable levels. But when the
> industry continues week after week, even in the face of prices below
> cost of production, to maintain increases in production far beyond
> increases in population, there is little the retailer can do to help the
> situation.[31]

*Advertising and Promotion.* Newspapers serve as the main advertising media for broiler chickens. Broiler chickens are more
often advertised when sold as loss-leaders.

One Louisiana study indicated that advertising broilers was
closely correlated with size of store, volume of poultry sales, and
loss-leader selling. Small food stores seldom make use of broiler
promotion and advertising. Larger food stores used newspaper ads
primarily, plus store window ads and pennants or posters to conduct their advertising. Radio-TV was not utilized very much by
anyone.[32]

Little evidence exists of "co-op ad" allowances given by processors to retailers. Neither do processors assist greatly in retail store
promotions. Whatever industry promotion assistance is given usually comes from agencies such as the Poultry and Egg National
Board and National Broiler Council.

*Overt Price Fixing.* There are probably few if any overt price-fixing schemes in broiler transactions. The closest overt scheme comes
from the chain stores' use of buying formulas. These may become
so well known and definitive that each chain knows how the other
will buy. From these overt formulas, however, negotiations and
bargaining with broiler processors occur.

*Agreements Not To Compete.* There are probably no definitive
agreements among processors or stores not to compete. The skillful
manner of staging loss-leader sales is cause for suspicion that some
type of agreements in some local areas may exist.

*Trade Association Activities.* In the southeastern United States,

[30] *Report on Small Business Problems in the Food Industry* (Washington,
1961), p. 81.
[31] *Small Business Problems in the Poultry Industry, Part II, op. cit.,* p. 467.
[32] James C. Maness, *Retail Poultry Meat Merchandising,* D.A.E. Res. Rept.
322, La. Agr. Exp. Sta. (Baton Rouge, La., Aug. 1963).

certain trade associations comprised of broiler processors are attempting to set up a clearinghouse of market and price information to counteract chain store buying policies:

> The Georgia processors' association swaps information among its 22 members daily as an aid in determining broiler supply and market demands. It also acts as a clearinghouse, when one plant is short and another long on supply, through a daily network phone system.

> This feature alone has put many a processor in a position to help move another's distress merchandise at higher prices, because he could help find a market.

> The Georgia processors' information system works this way: Each Tuesday a phone call is placed by the association's executive secretary to all association members. Each member reports what his situation is and what he thinks the demand will be. The information is kept confidential and no single processor knows what the other is reporting.

> These Tuesday reports are consolidated at the office in Gainesville and the results are reported back to the processing plants on Wednesday. Processors use this information in dealing with buyers on Thursday, the big selling day. A Friday phone call lets processors know exactly what happened on Thursday and how the market went.[33]

*Price Concessions.* One industry man has commented that processors taught chain stores how to feature price specials:

> Back in the National Broiler Council, which most of us fellows contribute to, when we begin to get stuck on chickens, to hunt up markets, they went to the chainstores and told them: "Here we have got a lot of chickens coming over so and so; you will have to help us move them in a few weeks." And I think actually we taught them ourselves the very way of merchandising—that we created the atmosphere for them. They developed—they ran specials on them to help us clean them up at that time and through that process they discovered what fine leaders they were, and now they have gone a step further and they have run a little further possibly than we members of the National Broiler Council wanted.[34]

One witness claimed price concessions were worked as follows:

> There have been instances which are extremely hard to prove where there has been evidence of collusion between the retailer and the processor which has resulted in a price that is offered to only one chain of stores. The processor will then attempt to make up his losses by offering other retailers fryers at a higher price.[35]

[33] *Broiler Industry* (Sea Isle City, N.J.: Garden State Publ. Co., Aug. 1963), p. 24.

[34] *Small Business Problems in the Poultry Industry, Part III, op. cit.,* p. 460.

[35] *Poultry and Egg Prices* (Washington, 1959), p. 312.

*General Price Competition.* A chain store spokesman has summarized the broiler price situation as follows:

> The thing that retailers are concerned about is the price they pay for an item in relation to the price paid for the same item by the competitors. Thus it is the relative price and not the absolute price that concerns them most.

> Understanding of this one fact is tremendously important and explains why retailers—in their own way—are just as disturbed over wild build-ups in poultry supplies as are producers. Retailers are devoted to a firm market price at which producers earn a fair profit because they know that under these conditions they aren't going to be underbought by their competitors. If the poultry industry can get itself into this condition, it will earn the eternal gratitude of every food retailer, as well as reasonable profits.[36]

## MARKET PERFORMANCE

### Decline in Costs, Prices, and Margins

The decline in costs of production and prices received for broilers are well-known facts in the broiler industry. Complaints of those in the industry are usually aimed at these very facts, namely, that economies in improved efficiencies have not been retained by those in the industry but, instead, have been passed to others (mainly the consumer of chickens).

During the past decade, the retail price of ready-to-cook broiler-

TABLE 3.4

FRYING CHICKENS: RETAIL PRICE, FARM VALUE, FARM-RETAIL SPREAD, AND FARMER'S SHARE OF THE RETAIL PRICE, U.S.A., 1952–62

| Year | Retail Price Per Pound* | Farm Value Eviscerated* | Farm Value Live | Farm-Retail Spread* | Farmer's Share of Retail Value* |
|---|---|---|---|---|---|
| | *(cents per pound)* | | | | *(percent)* |
| 1952 | 60.0 | 39.7 | 28.8 | 20.3 | 66 |
| 1953 | 58.5 | 37.0 | 27.1 | 21.5 | 63 |
| 1954 | 52.8 | 31.6 | 23.1 | 21.2 | 60 |
| 1955 | 54.8 | 34.6 | 25.2 | 20.2 | 63 |
| 1956 | 47.8 | 26.9 | 19.6 | 20.9 | 56 |
| 1957 | 46.7 | 25.9 | 18.9 | 20.8 | 55 |
| 1958 | 46.1 | 25.4 | 18.5 | 20.7 | 55 |
| 1959 | 42.0 | 22.0 | 16.1 | 20.0 | 52 |
| 1960 | 42.7 | 23.1 | 16.9 | 19.6 | 54 |
| 1961 | 38.5 | 19.3 | 13.9 | 19.2 | 50 |
| 1962 | 40.7 | 20.8 | 15.2 | 19.9 | 51 |

Source: Economic Research Service, U.S.D.A., Washington, D.C.
* On eviscerated basis.

[36] Clarence Adamy, *Poultry Processing and Marketing* (Mount Morris, Ill.: Watt Publ. Co., Sept. 1963), p. 21.

fryers has dropped 35 percent. During the same period, reductions in processing costs, excluding shrinkage and grading losses, have ranged from 33 to 50 percent. The price of live broilers at the farm dropped from 28.8 cents per pound in 1952 to 14.4 cents in 1963. The farm share of the retail price dropped from 66 percent in 1952 to 51 percent in 1962 (Table 3.4).

However, with the advent of integration by processors into the broiler-growing phase and other associated enterprises, the processors' prices as a percentage of the consumer prices for chickens have been relatively stable. The retailers' margins in absolute and relative terms have changed less than those for processors (Table 3.5).

## Level of Profits

Generally, the level of profits per broiler for growers and handlers was very attractive in the years during and after World War II and up to about 1958. Beginning in 1959 and up to the present, profit levels have been thinned. Examples of thinning profit levels are well known and are indicated by the decline of independent broiler growing, increased merger among processing firms, exit of General Mills and other firms from the broiler field, decrease in flow of new capital into broiler operations, tightening of credit extension, increases in bankruptcies and substantial sentiment for some type of government intervention in order to restore profit levels.

## Sales and Promotion Costs

Sales and promotion costs by retailers in differentiating broiler chickens are very small. The primary emphasis in sales and promo-

TABLE 3.5

CHANGES IN PROCESSORS' AND RETAILERS' MARGINS ON BROILER CHICKENS, U.S.A., 1957–62

| Year | Processors' Selling Price* | Retailers' Margins | Consumer Price | Processors' Share of Consumer Price | Retailers' Share of Consumer Price |
|---|---|---|---|---|---|
| | (cents per pound) | | | (percent) | |
| 1957 | 35.1 | 11.6 | 46.7 | 75.2 | 24.8 |
| 1958 | 34.3 | 11.8 | 46.1 | 74.4 | 25.6 |
| 1959 | 31.2 | 10.8 | 42.0 | 74.3 | 25.7 |
| 1960 | 32.7 | 10.0 | 42.7 | 76.6 | 23.4 |
| 1961 | 28.5 | 10.0 | 38.5 | 74.0 | 26.0 |
| 1962 | 30.0 | 10.7 | 40.7 | 73.7 | 26.3 |

Source: Adapted from *Developments in Marketing Spreads for Agricultural Products in 1961*, Economic Research Service Report 14 (Washington, 1962), p. 14; and *Marketing Spreads for Eggs and Frying Chickens in the U.S. and Selected Cities*, Economic Research Service Report 105 (Washington, Feb. 1963).
* Farm value plus intermediary margins up to retail level.

tion efforts is on "price," namely, "loss-leaders." Television, radio, and magazine promotions are infrequent. The primary media used are newspapers, especially urban dailies. Broiler processors incur relatively small sales and promotion costs in differentiating and in selling their products. Sales and promotion costs constitute an infinitesimal portion of total costs.

## Technology and Innovations

*Processing.* Technological developments and innovations in the processing phase have been both numerous and rapid such as (1) shift from New York dressed to evisceration, (2) continuous chiller processes, (3) automatic in-plant conveying equipment, (4) "feather" and "offal" flow-away, (5) the efficient utilization of processing by-products and wastes, (6) improved defeathering equipment, (7) better plant layouts, (8) machines designed to cut up poultry, (9) electronic machines designed to weigh, segregate, and package poultry parts, (10) the near perfection of chicken-deboning machines, (11) the freeze-drying of poultry meats, and (12) the expansion of further processed poultry meat products or convenience foods.

*Retailing.* There have been many innovations in broiler retailing such as (1) offering broiler parts and cut-up whole chicken, (2) multiple broiler packaging, (3) development of frozen chicken retailing, (4) trend away from bulk cutting up of broilers in stores (less efficient) to processors (more efficient), (5) selling "all breasts," "all thighs," etc., as packaged parts, (6) offering a varied assortment of new chicken products and packages, and (7) more consumer education on use of chickens.

Some of the new broiler meat products that have been developed and are being retailed are half-chicken, chicken and dumplings, boned chicken breast, boned chicken with noodles, chicken broth, and chicken with rice. Some poultry specialty products include boned chicken fricassee, chicken à la king, chicken sticks, chicken pies, barbecued chicken, precooked fried chicken, precooked boned chicken, chicken bologna, chicken hot dogs, chicken tamales, broasted chickens, chicken rolls, smoked chicken, boil-in-bag chicken, diced chicken, chicken croquettes and fillets, chicken-and-gravy plastic pouches, and chicken patties, among others.

## Quality and Variability of Product

About 85 percent of all broilers in commercial channels are federally inspected. The remainder are inspected by state or local agencies. Because of federal inspection, which began January 1, 1959, the variability in the broiler chicken product has been lessened. However, grading is not mandatory and its use is not presently widespread, but it is gaining.

Regarding grades for broilers, chain food stores and others of substantial size proceed to trade mostly in "Grade A" broilers while other lesser sized retailers may trade in both Grade A and Grade B, and even Grade C in some instances. Often, the consumer has no means of differentiating between Grade A, Grade B, or Grade C birds. Although many plants do grade, and many chains insist on buying on grade, there is nothing to force them to carry the grade marking to the consumer level.

Williams concludes that buying and selling on a U.S. grade basis (for beef) contributes to mass buying on a specification basis and to the "offer and acceptance" system of buying. These developments put much greater stress on *price* competition which weakens product differentiation by packers and processors. He concludes that the observed results of federal beef grades and grading would likewise apply to similar commodities (broilers, in our case).[37]

## Excess Capacity and Overhead Costs

There is probably not a great amount of excess capacity in the broiler processing industry when viewed empirically. This is especially true in the South. In many cases, plants run two shifts daily in order to accommodate market demands. Very rarely are broiler processing plants idle for more than a few days at a time. Processing capacity, fortunately, is usually developed as market demands warrant. Independently operated processing capacity has not often developed to split an existing market or an existing volume of broilers.

According to competent studies, overhead or fixed costs in broiler processing comprise 5 percent of total costs and variable costs comprise about 95 percent.[38]

Kohls has said that large Indiana broiler processors operated at about 70 percent of capacity in 1958 compared with a 90 percent rate of capacity in the South.[39]

In New England, Rogers and others found the existence of excess processing capacity. Large plants having considerable investments in growing, hatching, milling and processing plants, and equipment will try to maintain volume at a high level to defray these charges. With smaller plants, these fixed costs are much smaller in magnitude, even though they may be greater per unit of volume than in larger plants.[40]

---

[37] Willard F. Williams, "Impacts of Federal Grading on Market Power," Dept. Agr. Econ. paper (Stillwater, Okla., 1961), p. 9.

[38] Rogers and Bardwell, *op. cit.*

[39] *Small Business Problems in the Poultry Industry, Part III, op. cit.*, p. 363.

[40] Rogers *et al.*, *op. cit.*, p. 48.

## Scale of Plants in Relation to Optimum Scale

In order to achieve a processing cost of under 3 cents per pound (live weight basis), plant capacity per hour needs to be from 3,600 birds per hour on up. This means a minimum annual volume of about 7 million birds, or about 17.5 million pounds eviscerated. Plants smaller than 3,600 birds per hour can still be feasible if the markets served are not too competitive in price.

The Southern Poultry Regional Committee in its classification of 253 broiler processing plants in 1962 found the following:

| Annual Plant Output (million pounds eviscerated) | Number of Plants | Percent of Plants |
|---|---|---|
| Less than 5 | 72 | 28 |
| 5 to 30 | 104 | 41 |
| 30 to 60 | 41 | 16 |
| 60 and more | 36 | 15 |
| Total | 253 | 100 |

Seventy-seven plants or 31 percent of the plants exceeded the minimum optimum scale plant. In addition, 104 other plants or 41 percent of the total had between 5 and 30 million pounds of output. Only 28 percent of the plants had annual outputs of less than 5 million eviscerated pounds.

In other parts of the United States, optimum scale operations would not be as frequent, but many of these smaller plants cater only to local markets.

If we assume that the 2 billion broiler annual output were processed in plants operating 80 hours per week at the rate of 10,000 birds per hour, only 50 plants would be required compared with the 320 plants at present. If the plants were operated on three 8-hour shifts, only 32 plants would be required.

## Competitive Model: Which Kind?

Perfect competition, monopoly, and monopsony are ruled out at the outset as possible competitive models for the broiler processing and food retailing industries.[41, 42]

The model of partial bilateral oligopoly (with competitive fringes and without joint agreement to maximize profits) fits ap-

---

[41] G. L. Mehren, "How Is the Market Made in Integrated Industries?" *National Institute of Animal Agriculture Proceedings* (Lafayette, Ind., Apr. 21, 1958).

[42] W. W. Cochrane, "Super Markets Call the Tune in Farm Marketing," *Co-op Grain Quarterly* (St. Paul, Minn., 1961), pp. 6–7.

propriately the broiler chicken industry.[43] For example, the number of eviscerated broiler buyers and sellers are relatively few. The number of chain store buyers in a particular region of the United States may be less than 50 and sometimes less than 25. These buyers set the tone of the market. The number of processor-sellers in interstate competition is roughly the same as the number of buyers but the former have less market strength. Market shares held by individual oligopolists are not yet pronounced or formidable and are presently unstable. The broiler product sold is standardized with slight product differentiation although attempts at differentiation are increasing. The competitive emphasis is on *price* with the buyers often purchasing broiler chickens by formula. There is price discrimination through loss-leading and dual pricing. This tendency is aggravated by heavy supplies of broilers continually emanating from an industry where the firms are heavily oriented toward *supply* expansion.

*Substantiation of the Model.* A spokesman for the food chains has admitted their superior bargaining power but lays the blame for low broiler prices on producers and processors:

> Much has been said in recent years about the superior marketing power of the chain stores relative to that of producers. We cannot deny that chain stores do have superior marketing powers. But this bargaining power has not been the factor which depressed broiler prices. It has been the adoption of modern technology—including scientific methods—that made it possible to expand broiler production much faster than the increase in demand.[44]

Christensen's recommendation for stabilizing the market involves bolstering the power of producer-processor organizations to equalize the power of chain food stores (countervailing power):

> The broiler processing business will have to assume some control of the market. Sales agencies, bargaining associations, market development associations or highly integrated producer-cooperative associations may provide the desired market control.

> Well designed organizations of that type will be supported vigorously by large retailers. Such organizations have the knowledge, capital and man-power to perform the services which make the mass production and distribution system work efficiently.

> What many producers fail to realize is that market power lies not in manipulating price itself, but in controlling or influencing the factors

---

[43] Joe S. Bain, *Pricing, Distribution and Employment* (New York: Holt and Co., 1953), pp. 269-70.

[44] S. K. Christensen, "What's Ahead in Broiler Marketing," *Broiler Business* (Cullman, Ala., Feb. 1963), p. 32.

which affect price. Market power in a "free market" is acquired through the instrument of organization.[45]

## Overall Market Performance

Overall market performance in the broiler processing-retailing segments has been satisfactory in terms of supplying consumers with an abundant, wholesome product at low cost.

That economic integration in the broiler industry has reduced costs is verified by research experience and observations. Horizontal and vertical integration have eliminated many smaller, inefficient firms with high costs and much instability in operation. It has permitted the maximum exploitation of scientific and technological "know-how" through pooled talents, business acumen, and ample credit. Some entrepreneurial stages in the producing-marketing process have been actually eliminated with a resulting savings in cost and lowering of price to consumers.

## MARKET REMEDIES

Market remedies involve those proposals which contain some promise of correcting the inefficiencies, improving performance, and eliminating abuses in the market system. These remedies may consist of "private" measures taken by those within the industry and/or "public" measures as expressed by executive, legislative, and judicial redress.

In view of the generally efficient performance of the processing and retailing segments of the broiler industry, no large-scale market remedies appear necessary.

However, certain problem areas deserve attention: (1) enforcement of existing laws, (2) supply controls, (3) marketing orders, (4) loss-leaders and dual pricing, (5) price reporting, (6) forward selling, (7) forward pricing, (8) futures market, (9) co-op marketing, and (10) mergers, acquisitions, and integration.

## Enforcement of Existing Laws

The Sherman Act, Clayton Act, Federal Trade Commission Act, and the Packers and Stockyards Act are probably adequate to deal with any and all predatory activities in the broiler industry. While the laws are adequate, it does not always follow that enforcement is adequate.

There is no need to enact further legislation when present legislation is not always vigorously enforced. For example, the Packers and Stockyards Act requires live poultry dealers and handlers (as well as all other persons subject to the Act) to keep accounts and records that fully and correctly disclose all transactions

---

[45] *Ibid.*

involved in their business, to make such records available to the enforcement agencies for examination, to submit general or special reports upon demand, and to testify in response to a subpoena. A more vigorous enforcement of this Act could help rectify some of the market imperfections especially at the grower-processor level.

## Supply Controls

Because of the dispersed structure of the processor-dealer-grower combines, no one integrator can presently control broiler output and hence affect prices. Therefore, some industry men desire some type of supply control legislation which would in effect not only regulate the flow of output but control total output.

While this objective appears a noble one for some integrators, processors, dealers, and growers, it would not be in the best interests of the broiler industry as a whole and for consumers in particular. In the author's opinion, such legislation would tend to crystallize the present integrated structures and prevent any future competition and new entrants. In time, higher broiler prices to consumers would result and any resulting price gains would not necessarily accrue to broiler growers because of their weaker bargaining power. Benefits might accrue primarily to food retailers and broiler integrators.[46]

## Marketing Orders

Instead of a supply control program, the use of marketing orders to regulate the flow of broilers to market may be more helpful and acceptable to growers, contractors, retailers, and consumers. A marketing order program instituted at the broiler hatchery level has distinct possibilities for success. Regulating the flow of broiler-type hatching eggs into incubation would minimize somewhat the complexity of administering an order of this type. The prospects for enacting such an order for broilers appear dim, however, since a related turkey marketing order was disapproved.

## Loss-Leaders and Dual Pricing

Since broiler prices tumbled disastrously in late 1956, chain stores periodically have been blamed for low broiler prices. But each time that Congress has referred complaints to the Justice Department and Federal Trade Commission, their attorneys have found no evidence of illegal action. In effect, they have ruled that overproduction is the culprit, not loss-leaders or dual pricing.

The Congressional investigations of 1961 reinforced such conclusions:

[46] E. P. Roy, "Broilers: Private Business Versus Government," *Broiler Industry* (Sea Isle City, N.J.: Garden State Publ. Co., Dec. 1961), p. 8.

Aside from the issue of loss-leaders, and any anticompetitive arrangements (which have not yet been proven to exist), the chains are business entities and are in business to make a profit. The heart of the problem, as revealed by the evidence presently before the subcommittee, lies in the overproduction which has been created by the broiler industry itself. Chain stores may have taken advantage of the situation, but it is clear that they did not create it.[47]

One means of achieving less frequent loss-leader sales and dual pricing by chain stores is for processors to work together through clearinghouse associations and/or joint sales agencies. However, possible antitrust violations would have to be considered before engaging in such ventures.

### Improving Price Reporting

Broiler price reporting is presently concentrated at the farm level or at transactions between the grower and processor. Since these types of transactions are becoming meaningless (due to vertical integration), other transaction points must be found for meaningful price reporting.

Jackson of Arkansas argues for one transaction point which would either supplement or replace live broiler quotations and accomplish the objective of meaningful broiler price reports, namely, dressed market. He reports:

Many advantages can be cited for discarding live broiler quotations in favor of dressed market reports where most of the transactions take place.

1. When consumers hear of 12 to 15 cent broiler prices, they get a low price image of the product. Dressed market reports would help wipe away the image of low broiler prices.

2. The value of broilers to an integrated firm is determined at the market place—rather than in live market transactions. By converting dressed to live market prices, paying prices for live birds could be based on value at the market place.

3. Quoting only dressed bird prices could put more pressure on those in charge of processor sales. Being in the spotlight on pricing, they might have more incentive to ask for that extra one-fourth or one-half cent per pound.

4. Using only a dressed market quotation would allow an integrated operation to figure from one base. He would not be computing forward from live broiler prices on selling and backwards from the live broiler price on grower settlements. By using a conversion formula, all transactions could be pegged on the dressed market.

---

[47] *Small Business Problems in the Poultry Industry, Part III, op. cit.,* pp. 17–18.

5. Dressed market quotations would lead to more realistic pricing and would pinpoint retailer spreads more accurately.[48]

## Forward Selling

If processors have no prior commitments from prospective buyers before they begin production, they are assuming a very large risk. To avoid selling his processed birds at a loss, or on a very short margin, the processor can develop contacts with prospective purchasers in various markets and can obtain contracts for delivery on specified dates. The contracts usually specify the pricing procedures and allowance for the processing operation.[49]

## Forward Pricing

Another possible market remedy concerns forward or advance pricing. This would involve committing supply—or a portion of it—in advance, at a known price, for a stated period of time. The "price" could include a share-risk arrangement between the processor and the retailer, much as exists between processor and producer.[50]

## Futures Market

A great part of the industry is now interested in determining the possibilities of a futures market. There seems to be an opportunity for the sale of futures contracts for ready-to-cook frozen poultry. If surpluses that could not be marketed readily without a price loss could be sold in this manner, the industry should benefit. It is the thinking that futures contracts will help to stabilize prices and will serve as a hedge against the wholesale price of ready-to-cook, ice-packed poultry. However, a substantial portion of the industry would have to endorse the futures market plan to make it workable.[51]

## Co-op Marketing

Smaller processors could strengthen their market position by forming co-op marketing combinations in order to sell to the chain stores and promote their products more effectively.[52]

---

[48] Hilliard Jackson, "Would Dressed Market Reports Be More Realistic?" *Broiler Business* (Cullman, Ala., Aug. 1962), p. 14.

[49] Barton Westerlund, *Broiler Market Prospects for the Independent Processor*, Univ. of Ark. Small Bus. Rept. (Fayetteville, Ark., 1963), p. 61.

[50] *Broiler Industry* (Sea Isle City, N.J.: Garden State Publ. Co., Jan. 1964), p. 14.

[51] Westerlund, *op. cit.*, p. 63.

[52] Victor Bonnette, "Central Sales and Bargaining Agency for Broilers," *Broiler Industry* (Sea Isle City, N.J.: Garden State Publ. Co., July 1964), pp. 20 and 23.

## Mergers, Acquisitions, and Economic Integration

An accelerating trend toward mergers and acquisitions both at the retail store and processor levels is some cause for concern. If these trends continue unabated, the competitive structure of the broiler industry will shift to a tighter and more complete bilateral oligopoly with considerably greater market imperfection. Present laws to deal with these situations are adequate if they are enforced.

The Small Business Committee of the House of Representatives has projected what some of the more recent trends in the broiler industry may mean:

> For there can be little question that continued integration at the rate witnessed in the past few years will call forth a demand for antitrust enforcement. This will be true, in particular, if market penetration continues in all segments at a corresponding rate of increase, but it will also be true if dominance begins to be witnessed in any single phase. This is obvious since control of processing operations or control of hatcheries, for example, would be an adequate lever for controlling the entire industry. By commanding these segments of the industry, an integrated giant or coterie of integrated giants could foreclose new entry and wash out existing participants. Therefore, members of the industry possessing resources great enough to produce such a situation should be ever on their guard to avoid accumulating the seeds of monopoly power.[53]

---

[53] *Small Business Problems in the Poultry Industry, Part III, op. cit.*, p. 16.

# THE FLUID MILK INDUSTRY

**4**

## JOHN R. MOORE[1]

THE FLUID MILK INDUSTRY is vital to the nation's health and an important source of income to its producers, processors, and distributors. It is the consumer's principal source of calcium and an economic source of protein and fat. Average daily per capita consumption is just under one pint. Sales of milk for all uses provided 14 percent of cash receipts for U.S. farmers in 1963. In 1963, 4,624 fluid milk establishments employed 185,018 men, had a payroll of $1 billion and a value of shipments of $7 billion, well over 1 percent of the gross national product.[2]

### HISTORY

Present fluid milk processing and distribution methods are an outgrowth of urban concentration and technological development. The concentration in population resulted in a decline in the "family" cow and necessitated the development of milk supplies from more distant sources.

Many technological developments helped make the shift from local to more distant areas possible as well as helped provide a better product. Prior to the development of the glass bottle in 1886, milk was sold by distributors who dipped it from horse-drawn carts pulled from door to door.[3] The turn of the century saw the

---

[1] Associate Professor of Agricultural Economics, University of Maryland. The material in this chapter is based on the author's Ph.D. thesis written at the University of Wisconsin under the direction of Dr. Robert L. Clodius and published in part in: John R. Moore and Robert L. Clodius, *Market Structure and Competition in the Dairy Industry*, Res. Bul. 233, Univ. of Wis. Agr. Exp. Sta. (Madison, 1962).

[2] *1963 Census of Manufactures*, Preliminary Report, U.S. Department of Commerce, Bureau of the Census (Washington).

[3] G. M. Beal and H. H. Bakken, *Fluid Milk Marketing* (Madison: Mimir Publishers, Inc., 1956), pp. 41, 42. In fact, dipped milk was sold as late as 1933 in New York City stores. Leland Spencer, *A Half-Century of Significant Developments in the Distribution and Pricing of Market Milk*, A.E. 1039, Dept. of Agr. Econ., Cornell Univ. (Ithaca, 1956), p. 2.

adoption of mechanized refrigeration and pasteurization. This plus the development of railroad tank cars permitted milk to be hauled fairly long distances, but with improvements in roads and trucks, rail shipments have now largely disappeared.

The number of fluid milk processors has been declining for several years, showing a 20.5 percent drop between 1958 and 1963. The decline is due in part to the relatively high volume of sales needed to operate a modern plant efficiently, the declining number of wholesale (retail stores) buyers of fluid milk, the expanding areas of economical distribution by distributors, the importance of brand advertising in expanding sales, and perhaps, to some extent, the use of unfair trade practices.

From a structural point of view, one of the more interesting historical developments in the fluid milk industry has been the growth of eight national dairy chains. In order of decreasing net sales in 1963, they are National Dairy Products Corporation; The Borden Company, Incorporated; Beatrice Foods Company; Carna-

TABLE 4.1

NET SALES OF THE EIGHT LARGEST NATIONAL DAIRIES, 1956–63,* AND 1962 RATE
OF RETURN ON STOCKHOLDERS' INVESTMENT (AFTER TAXES)†

| | Year | | | | 1962 Rate of Return on Stockholders' Investments |
| Company | 1956 | 1960 | 1962 | 1963 | (after taxes) |
| --- | --- | --- | --- | --- | --- |
| | ($ mil.) | ($ mil.) | ($ mil.) | ($ mil.) | percent |
| National Dairy Products Corp. | 1,353 | 1,667 | 1,820 | 1,839 | 10.9 |
| The Borden Co. | 877 | 956 | 1,048 | 1,119 | 10.8 |
| Beatrice Foods Co. | 325 | 443 | 539 | 569 | 10.3 |
| Carnation Co. | 358 | 418 | 437 | 435 | 11.1 |
| Arden Farms Co. | 250 | 365 | 383 | 422 | 4.2 |
| Foremost Dairies | 382 | 438 | 431 | 403 | 6.9 |
| Pet Milk Co. | 176 | 193‡ | 238 | 261 | 6.7 |
| Fairmont Foods Co. | 103 | 97 | 169 | 174 | 8.8 |
| Total | 3,824 | 4,577 | 5,113 | 5,222 | |
| Retail Cost of Dairy Products§ | 9,200 | 10,300 | 10,500 | 10,600 | |
| Retail Cost of Dairy Products as Percent of Eight Dairies' Sales | 41.5 | 44.4 | 48.6 | 49.3 | |

* Net sales figures are from *Moody's Industrial Manual* (New York: Moody's Investment Service, 1964).
† *Report of the Federal Trade Commission on Rates of Return for Identical Companies in Selected Manufacturing Industries, 1940, 1953–62* (Washington: Federal Trade Commission, 1964), p. 37.
‡ Estimated comparable figures were not published because of a change in accounting procedure.
§ From unpublished data from Economic Research Service, U.S.D.A. The retail cost of dairy products overstates the sales of all dairy firms because the majority of their sales are at the wholesale level. This overstatement is partially offset by the fact that many of the larger dairies include their overseas and nondairy sales in their net sales figures. These inaccuracies should be borne in mind when studying the data.

tion Company; Arden Farms Company; Foremost Dairies, Incorporated; Pet Milk Company; and Fairmont Foods Company. In 1963, their sales were about 48.6 percent of all dairy product sales in the United States. (Table 4.1). Their average rates of return after taxes on stockholders' investment in 1962 ranged from 4.2 to 10.9 percent (Table 4.1). It is interesting to note that three of the dairies (Borden, Pet, and Carnation) made their start evaporating milk before the turn of the century, and two (Beatrice and Fairmont) started in the dairy business primarily as butter distributors in Nebraska. The remaining three (National, Foremost, and Arden) have organized since World War I.

Most of the eight dairies have achieved much of their size through mergers. An estimate of the importance of mergers in the growth of six of these before 1948 was made by Weston (Table 4.2). The proportion of their growth due to mergers ranged from 75.4 percent for The Borden Company and 64.4 percent for National Dairy Products Corporation to only 5.4 percent for Pet Milk Company. These estimates are conservative because they attribute all growth due to increasing price levels and all asset growth after the merger to the parent company.

## THE STRUCTURE OF FLUID MILK MARKETS

### Characteristics of Sellers

The market for fluid milk is primarily a local one. Consumers are limited in choice to those brands sold either by home delivery or through retail stores in their trading areas. Prices are usually quite uniform among the various brands within a market, although they do not necessarily coincide with those of neighboring markets. *Number.* The number of fluid milk distributors varies among markets. A survey[4] of eight markets found an average of 9.5 distrib-

TABLE 4.2
GROWTH OF SIX LARGE DAIRIES BY MERGERS BEFORE 1948

| Dairy | Percent Growth Due to Mergers up to 1948 |
|---|---|
| The Borden Co. | 75.4 |
| National Dairy Products Corp. | 64.4 |
| Beatrice Foods Co. | 62.6 |
| Carnation Co. | 13.6 |
| Fairmont Foods Co. | 7.9 |
| Pet Milk Co. | 5.4 |

Source: Worksheets used by J. Fred Weston, *The Role of Mergers in the Growth of Large Firms* (Berkeley: University of California Press, 1953).

---

[4] Data on number of distributors per market and their market share were compiled from twenty-four newspaper brand preference surveys.

utors delivering to homes, 8.2 delivering to retail stores, and 11.3 distributors in total (Table 4.3). A direct relationship has been shown between population and the number of milk distributors in a market.[5]

*Size.* The accumulative market share of the first through the sixth largest distributors in each market was tabulated from the surveys mentioned above. (Table 4.4). The average of the largest distributor's share on retail and wholesale routes for 24 markets was 34.0 percent. The accumulative share of the four largest distributors averaged 75.6 percent. This compares with 72.8 percent found in another study.[6] Concentration ratios on retail and wholesale routes are about the same.

*Organization.* Fluid milk distributors in most markets are organized into one or more trade associations to exchange ideas and solve mutual problems. In some markets, they also operate a bottle exchange to which access may be necessary for profitable operation. Some of the mutual problems handled by distributor associations are labor and producer contracts, relations with both private and public groups, unfair methods of competition, and pricing practices.[7] Several dealer associations have been involved in antitrust suits for their part in alleged price maneuvering.

*Product Differentiation.* It is to the seller's advantage to convince the public that his product is superior to his competitor's even though it may not be. Fluid milk distributors try to differentiate

TABLE 4.3

AVERAGE AND RANGE IN THE NUMBER OF FLUID MILK DISTRIBUTORS IN TWENTY-FOUR UNITED STATES MARKETS

| Type of Route | No. of Markets in Study | Av. No. of Distributors Per Market | Lowest No. of Distributors Per Market | Highest No. of Distributors Per Market |
|---|---|---|---|---|
| Retail (home delivery) | 8 | 9.5 | 5 | 17 |
| Wholesale | 8 | 8.2 | 6 | 11 |
| Retail and Wholesale Combined | 24 | 11.3 | 5 | 22 |

Source: Tabulation of 24 newspaper brand preference surveys.

---

[5] William H. Alexander, "Market Concentration in the Fluid Milk Distribution Industry," *Louisiana Rural Economist,* La. State Univ., Vol. XXIV, No. 1 (Feb. 1962).

[6] *Ibid.*

[7] The fact that distributors bargain as a group with labor unions and producers has led one antitrust official to say that price fixing to some extent is inevitable in the industry. He was of the opinion that distributors are not likely to concede to either group until they have reached an understanding that all will raise their prices to cover their increased costs.

TABLE 4.4

AVERAGE ACCUMULATIVE MARKET SHARE FOR THE FIRST THROUGH THE
SIXTH LARGEST FLUID MILK DISTRIBUTORS ON RETAIL AND WHOLESALE ROUTES,
BOTH SEPARATELY AND COMBINED

| Type of Route | No. of Markets | Average Market Share of | | | | | |
|---|---|---|---|---|---|---|---|
| | | Largest dist. | Two largest dist. | Three largest dist. | Four largest dist. | Five largest dist. | Six largest dist. |
| Retail | 8 | 30.0 | 49.7 | 65.0 | 74.2 | 81.9 | 86.7 |
| Wholesale | 8 | 32.4 | 55.9 | 70.3 | 81.0 | 88.2 | 92.4 |
| Retail and Wholesale Combined | 24 | 34.0 | 54.2 | 67.0 | 75.6 | 81.4 | 85.8 |

Source: Tabulation of 24 newspaper brand preference surveys.

their product, but find it difficult because of local, state, and federal regulations. These regulations specify minimum sanitary requirements for the production, processing, and distribution of the product, and set minimum composition requirements, as well as limit the type of containers in which it can be sold. As the cost of exceeding these requirements is significant, distributors wishing to compete for the same market are forced to offer nearly the same product. They go to great lengths, however, to make their product appear different.

Fluid milk distributors use three general methods of differentiating themselves to wholesalers and the public. They are product promotion, development of goodwill, and price and nonprice inducements. Distributors promote their products by advertising, store demonstrations, clean trucks, and courteous drivers. They build goodwill by such methods as participating in civic affairs and sponsoring scholarships and athletic teams. Their price and nonprice inducements include coupons, discounts, storage boxes, store equipment, loans, and prizes. Direct product promotion and the establishment of goodwill are designed more for a long-run program of attracting consumers, while price and nonprice inducements are used more in a short-run program of building up new accounts.

*Entry.* Entry into a fluid milk market can be limited in four principal ways. These include local health ordinances, federal and state milk marketing orders, established relationships with existing buyers, and economies of scale in processing and distribution.

Local health ordinances have been used to limit the area of production and processing to within a few miles of the city[8] and a New York rule has stated that new distributors cannot enter a

---

[8] *Dean Milk Co. v. City of Madison*, 340 U.S. 349 (1951).

market without showing that the market is not already being adequately served.[9]

Federal and state fluid milk marketing orders limit entry to some extent. In most instances distributors cannot sell in order markets unless they pay producers on the basis of how their milk is used. This may make it difficult to compete in markets not under an order and will add to the accounting load. Some state orders limit the area of production and the number of processors.[10]

The fact that retailers and consumers are usually already being adequately served by established distributors often makes it difficult for a new distributor to enter the market. The cost of entry in these cases can become a real barrier. This may involve buying out existing routes, persuading buyers that the entrant's product is better than existing brands, offering the buyer a price or nonprice inducement, and/or hiring an existing distributor to distribute the entrant's products on his routes. All of these methods of entry are expensive. The cost of a business has run ten dollars or more per point (one quart). Building up retail routes is slow and tedious as retail customers are generally loyal to their route men and will not switch unless dissatisfied. Wholesale customers are usually well supplied and only unusual inducements will wean them away. Selling through established vendors is probably the easiest way to break into a market, but then profits must be shared with the vendor. It is not unusual for the supplier to buy the vendor out after a period of time but this too is expensive. Entry is made easier when a distributor has satisfactorily served a chain store in another territory. The chain may actually encourage the distributor to enter the new market through its stores if the relationship has been particularly satisfactory to the store.[11]

A fourth barrier to entry is the tendency toward decreasing costs for the large, established firms in the industry. These firms often have a cost advantage in both processing and distribution which makes it difficult for a new firm to compete.

*Excess Capacity and Cost Relationships.* The amount of excess plant capacity and the shape of the firm's cost curves are elements of market structure in that they affect the way firms behave. Firms are encouraged to add volume until their marginal costs equal their marginal revenues. If the average cost curves for dairy plants tend to be downward until practical capacity is reached, firms gain from

[9] Leland Spencer and S. Kent Christensen, *Milk Control Programs of the Northeastern States*, Part II, Northeast Regional Publication 23, Cornell Univ. Agr. Exp. Sta. (Ithaca, 1955), p. 90.

[10] *Ibid.*, pp. 90–92.

[11] See, for example, the spread of Adams' Dairy through A & P, Kroger, and Safeway stores in Kansas and Missouri. U.S. Congress, House, *Hearings, Price Discrimination in Dairy Products*, Part I, 85th Cong., 1st Sess., 1957–58.

increased volume not only from selling additional milk but also from being able to process their entire output at a lower unit cost. Dairies may have falling average unit costs on the distribution side as well. The combination of decreasing processing and distribution costs attainable from serving large-volume customers causes distributors to compete vigorously for the large-volume accounts.

Several studies have shown that rather substantial economies in processing and distribution are attainable from increased output. For example, using a model plant analysis, Conner, Webster, and Owens found that processing cost per quart dropped from 5.17 cents in a 1,200-quart (quart packages) capacity plant to 2.03 cents in a 20,000-quart capacity plant when both are operated at full capacity.[12] The decrease in per quart cost resulting from moving from 50 percent to 100 percent capacity in the two plants was 3.68 cents and 0.87 cents, respectively.

On the distribution side Cook, Halvorson, and Robinson found that the costs of serving wholesale customers in Milwaukee dropped from 4.51 cents per quart when the average volume delivered per store was 30.0 units to 2.88 cents per quart when the average volume delivered per store increased to 841 labor quarts.[13] It thus becomes readily apparent that the potential reduction in unit costs from added volume can be quite significant particularly at the lower output levels. Using the model plant processing cost data determined by Conner, Webster, and Owens, and the distribution cost data obtained by Cook, Halvorson, and Robinson, it can be shown that a distributor operating the Conner, Webster, and Owens 20,000-quart capacity plant at about one-half capacity and selling to customers who took an average of 50 quarts per day could process and distribute an additional 10,000 quarts at 2.62 cents per quart less than the cost of processing and distributing the first 10,000 quarts and maintain the same total profit for the firm, providing the new customers averaged 840 quarts per delivery. This might be feasible on a large, new chain store account.

### Characteristics of Buyers

The two broad classifications of buyers of fluid milk are wholesale and retail home delivery. The principal wholesale accounts are grocery stores and institutions. Competition for these outlets is decidedly more vigorous than for home delivery. While there is a

---

[12] M. S. Conner, Fred C. Webster, and T. R. Owens, *An Economic Analysis of Model Plants for Pasteurizing and Bottling Milk*, Va. Agr. Exp. Sta., Bul. 484, Virginia Polytechnic Institute (Blacksburg, 1957), p. 28.

[13] Hugh L. Cook, Harlow W. Halvorson, and R. Wayne Robinson, *Costs and Efficiency of Wholesale Milk Distribution in Milwaukee*, Res. Bul. 196, Agr. Exp. Sta., Univ. of Wis. (Madison, 1956), p. 28.

great deal of rivalry for the latter, the importance of any one customer is much less.

*Number and Size (wholesale).* The number of wholesale buyers of fluid milk in a market is almost directly proportionate to the population. The size of the wholesale buyer ranges from the small store doing less than $75,000 annual volume to The Great Atlantic and Pacific Tea Company with annual sales of over $5 billion.

On the basis of aggregate data for the United States, it is estimated that there are an average of 155 retail grocery stores per 100,000 population and that 11 of these stores, or 7 percent, are chains.[14]

Concentration in grocery retailing is surprisingly high considering the relatively large number of individual grocery stores found. This is because the bulk of the business is usually done by a few large concerns. One study found that in 133 cities in 1958 the largest retailer averaged 25.4 percent of retail grocery sales, the two largest retailers had 42.2 percent, and the four largest had 58.3 percent of sales.[15]

*Organizations (wholesale).* Grocers in most markets have organized into trade organizations much like the milk distributor associations. One of their tasks has been the regulation of trade practices which not infrequently involves milk distributors. Two examples will suffice. Independent grocers in Madison, Wisconsin, were successful in getting the state to order the local distributors not to offer more favorable discounts to their chain store competitors except on the basis of volume.[16] A Corpus Christi grocers' organization formed a committee to investigate alleged discriminatory price practices of dairies there. The committee heard a lot of talk of rebates but found no one who would say he had received one.[17]

*Entry (wholesale).* Obstacles to entry do not appear to be a strategic factor affecting competition in the grocery business. Most areas of the country seem to be well covered with grocery chains and independents willing to build new stores where it appears profitable to do so. As the number of small stores and superettes is declining, it would also appear that the problem of entering a market by buying one of them would not be too great. Help in financing the transactions can sometimes be obtained from ice cream and fluid milk distributors and grocery wholesalers.

---

[14] A chain is an organization with eleven or more stores.

[15] Computed from *Distribution of Food Store Sales in 133 Cities* (Supermarket News, 1958) and found in Willard F. Mueller and Leon Garoian, *Changes in the Market Structure of Grocery Retailing* (Madison: Univ. of Wis. Press, 1961) p. 35.

[16] The court record, *In the Matter of Trade Practices of The Great Atlantic and Pacific Tea Company, et al.* (Madison, Wis.), hearing commenced Feb. 15, 1954.

[17] U.S. Congress, House, *Hearings, Price Discrimination in Dairy Products, op. cit.,* p. 150.

*Differentiation (wholesale).* The fluid milk business is a buyers' market; therefore, it may seem strange that buyers would want to differentiate themselves. They do it for price and nonprice considerations. Grocers can offer the following types of agreements with milk suppliers: (1) to exclude all other suppliers from the store, (2) to be the number-one supplier,[18] (3) to be a secondary supplier, (4) to serve more than one store in a chain system, and (5) to bottle private label milk for one or more stores in a chain. Some of the above agreements, of course, could be combined making them even more attractive. The most attractive arrangement would be a full line exclusive agreement with the dairy's own label in all stores of a chain. The different agreements with suppliers might be considered as various forms of vertical integration.

*Home Delivery.* The structure of retail home delivery customers is almost atomistic. Their numbers vary with the size of market and the percent of the market buying home delivery. The latter figure is usually within the 30 to 50 percent range (see Table 4.5).

Retail customers range in size from the one-quart stop to the customers taking as much as a small store. Other than size, retail customers cannot be distinguished except perhaps on convenience of location, e.g., a small third floor apartment compared with a suburban home. Location is not generally considered important enough for bargaining purposes, but size is.

Bargaining strength results from the economies of serving the larger volume customers. Bergfeld and Holdworth, management engineers, found that the average cost of serving a customer in four New York markets was about sixteen cents per delivery.[19] Because

TABLE 4.5

PERCENT OF FLUID MILK SALES ON RETAIL ROUTES FOR SELECTED CITIES, UNITED STATES, 1954

| Market | Percent Sales on Retail Routes |
|---|---|
| California | 32.2 |
| Minneapolis–St. Paul | 43.2 |
| New York Marketing Area | 24.3 |
| Rochester, New York | 44.8 |
| St. Louis | 42.6 |

Source: Helen V. Smith and Louis F. Herrmann, *Changing Patterns in Fluid Milk Distribution* (Washington: Marketing Research Report No. 135, U.S.D.A., August 1956) pp. 10–17.

---

[18] Most grocers carry several brands of milk but one is usually featured above the others by being placed first in the case and by being given the largest space. The number-one supplier generally supplies a full line of other dairy products while secondary suppliers often do not.

[19] S. Kent Christensen and John R. Moore, *Quantity Discount Pricing on Retail Milk Routes in New York State,* A.E. 985, N.Y. State College of Agr. (Ithaca, 1955).

the marginal cost of delivering a quart of milk is nearly zero after the first quart, the average delivery cost per quart for a four-quart customer is only about four cents compared with sixteen cents for the one-quart customer. The range for bargaining is therefore at least two cents per quart if it is assumed that the dairy breaks even on a two-quart customer. The price to the customer will depend on the following factors: (1) the customer's bargaining ability, (2) whether or not there are any implicit or explicit agreements among distributors not to compete, (3) the differential between the store and route price, (4) the margin to the distributor on milk sold through stores, and (5) the share of store business the distributor handles. Dealers in several markets have adopted quantity discount plans to reflect the economies of serving the larger customers. This has served to reduce haggling on the routes and the raiding of customers.[20]

## COMPETITIVE BEHAVIOR IN THE FLUID MILK INDUSTRY

The economic model that seems to best describe competitive behavior in the dairy industry is joint-profit maximization.[21] Joint-profit maximization in its pure form is the setting of prices by a group of sellers at a level that maximizes their joint profits, a level that tends to be near the price that would be established by a single seller (a monopolist). The basic tendency toward joint-profit maximization is indicated by the prevalence of both price fixing and price leadership in the fluid milk industry.

### Price Fixing

Price fixing is an overt agreement to set the price at a specified level. It is not uncommon. French and Jarrett reported that 43 percent of the distributors they interviewed (the management of 275 Indiana fluid milk plants that changed hands between 1946 and 1955) "freely admitted they got together with other plants to set prices."[22] In spite of the difficulties of proving price fixing (plaintiffs must prove overt agreement as the same pricing pattern could result from price leadership), the U.S. Department of Justice has gotten more than an acquittal on charges of price fixing in at

---

[20] *Ibid.*

[21] For a thorough treatment of the theory of joint-profit maximization, see William Fellner, *Competition Among the Few* (New York: Alfred A. Knopf, Inc., 1949).

[22] Charles E. French and William A. Jarrett, "Lessons Learned From 275 Dairy Ownership Changes," paper read before the Milk Indus. Foundation Ann. Conv., Chicago, Ill., Dec. 1958, p. 7.

least eight markets[23] and the state of Wisconsin has done as well on charges of price fixing in two markets.[24]

## Price Leadership

Price leadership, the pattern of following the price of some identified leader, is probably even more common than price fixing in the fluid milk business. French and Jarrett reported that approximately two-thirds of the distributors covered in their survey depended on other companies to set the price.[25] The fact that all distributors within a market usually change prices simultaneously indicates that some form of price leadership (or fixing) is going on and testimony at hearings before congressional investigating committees is full of references to a pattern of price leadership.

There seem to be two basic types of price leaders in the dairy industry—dominant firm and barometric firm. In general, it appears that the former is usually the largest seller in the market and has the power to coerce rivals into following his pricing pattern. The latter seems usually to be a large, well-managed firm which sets a price favorable to the majority of the sellers or at least the major ones.

Price leadership is rational behavior in the fluid milk industry in that the price followers are forced to go down with the leader when he drops his price if they are to maintain their volume. They have little incentive not to increase their price with the leader because the leader will simply drop his price again if they do not follow. They also stand to gain from increased revenue if they follow the price when it rises, if aggregate sales remain substantially the same.

Contrary to what might be expected, price leaders have little trouble in keeping the trade informed of impending price changes. It is done by phone, mail, at meetings, through routemen, and in

---

[23] *U.S. v. Anderson Dairy, Inc., et al., Trade Reg. Rep.* (New York: Commerce Clearing House, Inc.), par. 68, 284; *U.S. v. Associated Nevada Dairyman, et al., Trade Reg. Rep.,* par. 68, 172; *U.S. v. Beatrice Creamery, et al., The Federal Anti-Trust Laws With Summary Cases Instituted by the United States 1890–1951* (New York: Commerce Clearing House, Inc.) 1952, case 589; *U.S. v. The Borden Co., et al., Trade Reg. Rep.,* par. 25, 341; *U.S. v. Milk for Health, Inc., et al., Federal Anti-Trust Laws With Summary of Cases Instituted by the United States 1890–1951,* case 927; *U.S. v. Northland Milk and Ice Cream Co., et al., Trade Reg. Rep.,* par. 66, 069; *U.S. v. Sheffield Farms Co., et al.,* 43 F. Sup. 1; *U.S. v. Universal Milk Bottle Service, Inc., et al.,* 188 F. 2d 959.

[24] *State of Wisconsin v. Golden Guernsey Dairy Coop., et al.* Several Milwaukee dairies were found to have had identical prices after a meeting of milk distributors in a downtown hotel. In the matter of Racine Milk Distributors, several distributors in Racine were found to have offered practically identical bids for school milk contracts.

[25] French and Jarrett, *op. cit.,* p. 7.

extreme cases, through newspaper advertisements. It is much more important to the price leader that his competitors be informed of a price increase, however, than a price drop, though they may be consulted on each. One dairy official related that he belonged to the distributors' association so that he could keep informed on impending price changes or other market developments. Another distributor said that he could always count on a phone call when the price was going up but not when it was going down.[26] This particular distributor was not in good standing with his competitors.

### Joint-Profit Maximization Limited

Though joint-profit maximization is a basic tendency in the fluid milk industry, it is usually not fully realized because the structural characteristics of most markets are less than optimum for its achievement. The most important market structure variables limiting its realization are number and size of sellers, product differentiation, barriers to entry, and lack of accurate market information.

*Number and Size of Sellers.* The number of distributors in most markets is too large and their size variation too great for a high degree of joint-profit maximization without coercive controls. A large number of distributors (8 to 15 in most markets) is not conducive to good communications among firms, thus frustrating joint-profit maximization, while the large number and size variation of firms lessens the interdependence of price among them, particularly the prices of the smaller firms. The latter situation tends to frustrate joint-profit maximization because it encourages price cutting by the smaller firms since retaliation against them, though sure in time, is not alway immediate.

*Product Differentiation.* The differences between the products and services of competing distributors tend to frustrate joint-profit maximization as they force them to set a price relationship between many types of products (and attached services) that seldom suits them all. Thus there is likely to be constant pressure for their alteration.[27] Some of the price relationships that have to be determined include the difference between paper and glass containers, homogenized and regular milk, two-quart and gallon jug, home delivery and wholesale delivery, advertised and unadvertised brands, and brands with and without nonprice attachments. The decision is not infrequently made on the basis of coercive power

---

[26] These two statements were made in personal interviews with the author.

[27] The author is aware that not every distributor uses the same price list. There is, however, usually very little difference among the prices of major items.

but price relationships so determined are under constant pressure to be changed.

*Entry.* The prospect of outside entry is a constant threat to joint-profit maximization where barriers have not been erected against entry. For this reason, the trend toward outer-market distribution in paper packages is probably the strongest deterrent to joint-profit maximization in the fluid milk industry. In spite of attempts to keep them out, even to the extent of maintaining a low margin, outside distributors have been entering markets at a rapid pace in many areas because (1) the entering distributor may have lower costs than the established firms, especially if he does not handle too many by-products and has an efficient plant, (2) the wholesale quantity discount schedule in the market may not reflect the savings that are possible from serving the larger volume customers, and (3) some dairies may enter a market at marginal costs to get the business, hoping to raise prices and show a profit after they become established.[28] It should be noted that once distributors have entered a new market and become established they not infrequently adopt the prevailing pricing pattern and act as one of the "in" group.

*Character and Means of Market Information.* Full joint-profit maximization requires 100 percent participation by sellers. Where such participation is in doubt, individual sellers are often reluctant to leave their price structure vulnerable to the competitive thrusts of their rivals. Doubt of full participation is not unreasonable because of the ease and prevalence of secret and discriminatory pricing.

The most common secret price inducements used by fluid milk distributors are discounts off the list price, rebates after the bill is paid, and so-called advertising allowances. All are often given in a discriminatory manner. They seem to be more frequently offered to large new customers than to smaller and loyal ones and, not surprisingly, seem to increase with the profit margin. It appears that when distributors start seeing their profits pile up, particularly under the present high tax structure, they try expanding business as it may prove more profitable in the long run. Under these conditions, larger distributors in particular may seek a price at the competitive level (one yielding normal profits) so that competition will be based more largely on quality, service, and brand promotion—areas in which they are often more effective.

---

[28] Operating producers' cooperatives, selling their milk under an individual handler's pool, have a fourth reason they might expand into new markets. They can profitably do so at a loss on additional class I sales as long as the added volume brings more than its highest alternative price, usually the manufacturing price.

### Coercion

Though certain market characteristics tend to limit full joint-profit maximization, various means are used to try to come close to it by enforcing an "acceptable" pattern of competitive behavior. This is done through moral suasion and coercion from competing distributors. It can take several forms. Some of the following methods have been employed.

**Bottle Exchanges.** In some cases, distributors have been denied access to local bottle exchanges for failing to conform to accepted market practices.[29]

**Milk Producers' Associations.** Milk producers' associations have discriminated in price against price cutters and, in at least one case, refused to supply a distributor who had proposed using a quantity discount plan.[30]

**Labor Unions.** Labor unions have refused to deliver to stores selling "below cost" and to competitors' customers.[31]

**Pressure from Creditors.** Some distributors have complained of pressure from their creditors allegedly brought on by their competitors.[32]

**Price Wars.** A price war (deliberate pricing below cost) is probably the most common method of coercing competitors into line. It is also the main cause of the relatively unstable prices found in many local fluid milk markets.

Most price wars result from the efforts of distributors to increase their competitive advantage by altering the market price structure in their favor. Others are started by general price cuts made by distributors to enter or expand within a market, retailers cutting prices and then demanding wholesale prices to make the cuts profitable, and strong product promotion.

No two price wars are exactly alike. They vary as to their length and depth and as to how they are terminated. In general, the deeper a price war goes, the shorter it lasts. One distributor stated that the deeper ones often cost less than the ones that do not go as far below cost because distributors are more acutely aware of how much the former type is costing them.

One of the reasons price wars often last as long as they do is

---

[29] See 188 F. 2d 959 and D. H. Kellogg, *History of Twin Ports Cooperative Dairy Association* (Duluth Superior, by the author, 1944), pp. 52–56.

[30] *Superior Dairy, Inc. v. Stark County Milk Producers Association, Trade Reg. Rep.* (New York: Commerce Clearing House, Inc.), par. 62, 920.

[31] See *U.S. v. Beatrice Creamery Co., et al., The Federal Anti-Trust Laws With Summary Cases Instituted by the United States 1890–1951* (New York: Commerce Clearing House, Inc.), 1952, case 589.

[32] The writer's conversation with a Wisconsin distributor who reported his creditors tried to pressure him through his bank. Also see distributor testimony U.S. Congress, House, *Hearings, Price Discrimination in Dairy Products*, Part I, *op. cit.*, p. 11.

that no distributor wants to be the first to give up. Each wants to show his competitors that he can take it as long as they can, thus demonstrating that that type of discipline is not effective with him.

Price wars may end abruptly or take several weeks or months. When the distributor(s) to be disciplined "mends his ways," prices may go up in a few days. Where other distributors tire first, various ones may try to get the price back up by "testing" the market. One will announce a price increase. If the rest follow, a second increase will be announced. If others do not follow, the price may drop to the old level or even lower until the market is "ready" for the increase. It seems apparent that some price wars end by general agreement. There is no other way to explain the large increases prices take at the end of some price wars.

Attempts to alter the market price structure may be initiated by both established and entering distributors. If either side is decidedly strong economically the war may last only a short period. But where competitors are evenly matched it may drag out for months. The following are some examples of price wars that started when prices were altered by the introduction of a new container and by a change in the price of an old one.

*New Container (gallon jug).* The sale of milk in gallon jugs in a market usually starts in milk depots or small groceries and spreads to other stores as the jugs become popular. In some cases, there are some sizable economies in their processing and distribution. Their popularity depends largely on their price. Gallon jugs seem able to hold their own at differentials of about ten cents per gallon below the price of a gallon in two-quart containers. Often gallon jugs will be in a market a year or longer before other distributors start to feel their effects and do something about them. The first act of the nongallon jug operators is usually to threaten the jug operators with a price war to get the price up. If this does not work, nongallon jug operators may either go into the gallon jug business themselves or actually try to force the gallon jug price up with a price war.[33]

*Advertised vs. Unadvertised Brands.* A prime example of a serious price war caused by a dominant distributor or distributors trying to eliminate an established price differential took place in New York City in 1949 and 1950. Unadvertised milk there had generally sold for one cent less per quart than the advertised brands. Because this was hurting the sales of branded milk, the branded milk distributors announced price cuts of one and a half to two and a half cents a quart for different types of milk and services. In a short time, prices

---

[33] For an interesting description of price wars started over gallon jugs in two Texas markets see U.S. Congress, House, *Hearings, Price Discrimination in Dairy Products,* Part I, *op. cit.*

on some items had dropped five cents per quart. The issue was not settled for ten months. By that time, the unadvertised brand differential was eliminated in the chain stores and the differential between store and retail route prices was increased. As might be expected on the basis of cost, the price war also resulted in the reduction of the differential between glass- and paper-packaged milk and regular and homogenized milk.[34]

*Paper Packages vs. Glass Bottles, Regular vs. Homogenized.* Affidavits from milk distributors in northern Michigan alleged that a price war started when a national concern located in Green Bay, Wisconsin, came into that area with milk in paper packages.[35] Prior to their entry, glass bottles sold for one cent less than milk in paper packages and nonhomogenized milk sold for one cent less than homogenized milk. The affidavits stated that a representative of the national concern called the local milk distributors together telling them his firm was in the area to stay and that they intended to have paper-packaged milk selling for the same price as glass-packaged milk. The national concern's representative is reported to have further stated that if the local distributors did not raise their price on their glass-bottled milk, his firm would drop the price of their homogenized paper-packaged milk to the price of the market's glass-packaged nonhomogenized milk. The local distributors stood to lose their differential on paper-packaged and homogenized milk. Wise or not, they refused to change their price structure. The national concern is reported to have made its threat good. The local dairies claimed this put their prices below cost and accordingly reduced the price to their producers—an occurrence not uncommon in nonorder markets. The national concern pleaded guilty to a federal indictment in this matter and was fined $25,000.[36]

*Retail vs. Wholesale Prices.* The differential between retail and wholesale routes has also been the cause of some price wars. In each market some distributors are generally important on retail routes and others on wholesale routes. Outside distributors are usually in the second group. Each group has an interest in the retail-wholesale spread as it affects the amount of milk that will be sold by either method. Naturally, stores encourage a wide spread in their favor. Testimony at a hearing indicates that a dairy in the Kansas City area, for example, may have precipitated several price wars by insisting on a four-cent differential on half-gallon con-

[34] Leland Spencer, "The Price War in the New York Milk Market" and "Recent Developments Concerning Prices and Distribution Spreads in the New York Milk Market," talks presented at Farm and Home Week, Cornell Univ., Ithaca, N.Y., 1950 and 1951.

[35] U.S. Congress, House, *Hearings, Price Discrimination in Dairy Products,* Part II, *op. cit.,* pp. 314–22.

[36] *U.S. v. Fairmont Foods of Wisconsin,* Cr. 3634 (W.D. Mich., 1958).

tainers of milk between retail routes and stores in markets it had entered. The distributors serving retail customers in these markets naturally looked upon this with disfavor. The entering dairy appeared willing to maintain the differential down to a very low price. The established distributors realized this and were forced to take it because in many cases they were small rural operators without sufficient funds to put up a good fight. The entering dairy appeared to have a practice of holding the price considerably below cost until every one in the market fell in line. Then it raised the price again.[37] This practice applied to differentials on dairy by-products as well.[38]

*Entry of New Distributors.* Price wars sometimes start when a distributor tries to enter a market on the basis of price or by buying his way in with gifts and loans. Established distributors may try to neutralize the entering distributor's effect by putting the price below cost. Unless the entering distributor has financial reserve, he will find it difficult to maintain these practices. The store receiving the lower price may help precipitate a price war as well if the store tries to use a lower price to undersell its competitors.[39]

*Retailers Cutting Prices.* From interviews with distributors it appears that price wars frequently result from the retailers' practice of passing savings acquired through discounts (often on private label milk) on to their customers or selling at a loss. Competing distributors are forced to lower their prices to permit their wholesale customers to meet the price with their customary markup.

*Strong Product Promotion.* Overzealous product promotion can bring on a price war in some cases, especially when the product is given away. The practice of two-for-one pricing by a prominent dairy in Kansas and Missouri on weekends and at store openings has apparently been behind more than one price war there. In one area, it brought the price from forty-five to thirty-seven cents per half gallon.[40] A distributor's attempt to give away limited amounts of cottage cheese ended with everyone giving it away in wholesale quantities in one market in 1955.[41]

---

[37] U.S. Congress, House, *Hearings, Price Discrimination in Dairy Products,* Part II, *op. cit.,* p. 208.

[38] *Ibid.,* p. 260.

[39] For an example of this see U.S. Congress, House, *Hearings, Price Discrimination in Dairy Products,* Part I, *op. cit.,* p. 190. In this case an outside distributor tried twice, unsuccessfully, to enter the Kansas City market with a 13 percent discount to stores. In retaliation, the established distributors lowered their price and neutralized his advance.

[40] U.S. Congress, House, *Hearings, Price Discrimination in Dairy Products,* Part II, *op. cit.,* p. 207.

[41] Raymond G. Watson, "Price Wars Are Folly," *American Milk Review* (July 1957), p. 88.

### Some Policy Alternatives

Price fluctuations in fluid milk markets, it has been pointed out, stem mainly from market structure characteristics. The tendency of pricing extremes has been detrimental to producers, distributors, and consumers. Attacks on the problem can take two approaches: (1) altering market structure and (2) enforcing or preventing certain types of conduct. The former would have a greater effect in leveling off high prices while the latter would probably prove more beneficial in keeping them from going too low.

It appears that several types of structural changes could be made in certain markets to limit joint-profit maximization. These include measures that would maintain or increase the number of distributors, reduce the size of the largest three or four distributors, and differentiate the product to a greater extent. These changes could be partially achieved by the removal of certain barriers to entry, placing restrictions on the number and type of mergers, and encouraging the growth of small business. There seems to be little in the way of public policy measures that would increase product differentiation.

The principal artificial barriers to entry have been local health ordinances, federal and state milk control laws, and some exclusive buyer-seller relationships. Local restrictive health ordinances could be removed by the wider adoption of the United States Public Health Service ordinance and code and reciprocal inspection agreements among markets. There is no apparent method of altering federal and state milk marketing orders to make entry easier without reducing their effectiveness in facilitating orderly marketing, except in the case of state orders or rules which specifically limit the number that can operate within a market. Little can, or probably should, be done about the barrier resulting from established relationships between distributors and retailers except where the relationship is maintained by a discriminatory price, an exclusive dealing arrangement, or unduly large nonprice inducements. In these cases, appropriate preventive legislation could be passed and enforced.

Mergers that tend to create a monopoly are presently prohibited by Section 7 of the Clayton Act. A new federal law which would require premerger notification has been proposed. Its passage and the active enforcement of the two acts would seem to go a long way toward preventing some of the less desirable mergers in the dairy industry.

More might be done by the government to encourage the growth of small business as a means of maintaining a favorable structural environment in American industry. Two possible measures include a more favorable tax structure and greater financial aid for small business. These measures would help the smaller firms to withstand the competitive pressures of their larger competitors.

Most of the public policy measures taken to insure "fair" but competitive prices in the dairy industry have been aimed directly at sellers' conduct. The most intensive of these has been the regulation of distributor prices. Also important are measures that prohibit such unfair trade practices as price discrimination, sales below cost, use of certain nonprice inducements, and collusive price fixing.

Milk control laws that set minimum and sometimes maximum retail and wholesale prices were initiated by the federal government and several states in the early part of the depression largely to prevent destructive competition which had created hardships for producers and distributors alike.[42] Since then, some states and the federal government have dropped the program, but twenty states retain it in some form.[43] There are fair-minded men both in favor of and opposed to this type of legislation. Bressler and Clarke have written that resale price maintenance laws can be "positive instruments in encouraging the development of efficiency and so improving some aspects of welfare."[44] On the other hand, Spencer and Christensen have written that "resale price fixing is difficult to administer, and tends to prevent or delay changes in the pricing and distribution of milk that would be desirable and in the public interest." They added that the difficulty of administering the program caused its abandonment in New York State in 1937.[45] And even Bressler and Clarke admit that "resale price control can and has caused serious distortions in market structure as evidenced by the development of the 'captive creameries' and 'captive supermarkets' in California."[46]

Such undesirable conduct as collusive price fixing and the use of unfair trade practices are presently regulated to some extent by both federal and state statutes. Collusive price fixing is regulated by the state and federal antitrust laws where interstate commerce is involved while unfair trade practices are regulated by two federal statutes—the Clayton Act and Federal Trade Commission Act—and several laws, the number and type of which vary among states. According to one study, forty-two states regulate the trade practices

---

[42] Spencer and Christensen, op. cit., pp. 8–12.

[43] "Role of Governments in Pricing Fluid Milk in the United States," *The Dairy Situation,* U.S.D.A. (Washington, May 1965), p. 37.

[44] R. G. Bressler, Jr., and D. A. Clarke, Jr., "Resale Milk Price Control—Outmoded and Antisocial?" *Journal of Farm Economics,* Vol. XXXVII (May 1955), p. 291.

[45] Spencer and Christensen, op. cit., p. 116.

[46] Bressler and Clarke, op. cit., p. 291.

involved in merchandising dairy products to some degree.[47] Twenty-one of the states have unfair trade practice regulations specifically designed for the dairy industry while the other twenty-one states' unfair trade practice regulations covered several industries. All states with milk control commissions also had unfair trade practice laws.

Unfortunately, legislation regulating collusive price fixing has not been too effective on either the state or federal level. Both state and federal regulatory agencies find it nearly impossible to win convictions on circumstantial evidence (usually the only evidence available) because the same results can come from price leadership which is generally acceptable to the courts. Neither can these agencies begin to handle all the cases where price fixing occurs (at least in the sense where price fixing is the discussion of price by distributors) because, as one federal antitrust official put it and as is borne out in the testimony obtained by the House Select Committee on Small Business, "price fixing to some extent occurs in nearly every market of consequence and controlling it completely would be like trying to roll back the tide." The effectiveness of price fixing, however, is not always complete, owing mainly to the dissimilar interests of the firms involved.

Laws regulating unfair trade practices in the dairy industry, like those regulating collusive price fixing, have not been wholly effective. Again this seems largely due to the difficulty of obtaining proof of a violation and the relatively meager resources allocated for this purpose. Price discrimination and sales below cost are usually legal where done in good faith to meet competition. It is nearly impossible to prove they are not in good faith because retaliation is usually immediate and investigation slow. A sales-below-cost statute is also difficult to enforce because of the problem of separating joint costs. The offering of nonprice inducements is difficult to detect because of the many ways they can be given. Also enforcement of the laws prohibiting nonprice inducements has been discouraged by the attack on the laws by the larger dairy interests and, in several cases, they are being found unconstitutional.[48] The dairies attacking the law charged that it deprives them of the right to offer nonprice inducements without showing that these practices were harmful.

It appears that none of the present programs to limit price fixing or unfair trade practices in the fluid milk industry are en-

---

[47] T. A. Wilson and E. F. Baumer, *Trade Practice Regulations With Special Reference to the Dairy Industry*, Res. Bul. 816, Ohio Agr. Exp. Sta. (Wooster, 1958).

[48] *Fairmont Foods v. Bergum*, 81 N.W. (2) 639 (1957); *State of Kansas v. Fleming Co.* (C.C.H.) 59 Trade Cases 75, 375, Kans., May 16, 1959; *Fairmont Creamery Company v. Minnesota*, 274, U.S. 1, Apr. 1, 1957.

tirely satisfactory. But new approaches are possible. Spencer and Christensen have offered an interesting solution to the problem of price cutting in particular.[49] They suggested the formation of a milk control agency to hold public hearings for discussion of factors related to retail prices of milk and to announce findings and recommendations. The hearings could include discussions of store differentials and quantity discounts as well, where they were important. The milk control board would suggest a price for the most popular package sold. Any distributor charging prices substantially less than this price or having prices on other packages at comparably reduced rates would have to justify that practice to the state agency.

Wilson and Baumer recently offered some suggestions for the regulation of unfair trade practices. They stress the use of economic principles in setting up the regulations, adequate funds for their enforcement, and the localization of regulatory agents so that they would be in touch with the industry much as the federal order market administration.[50] Neither writer seems particularly concerned with the problems of price fixing or overly generous profit margins resulting from a "live and let live" policy of price leadership.

Some suggestions for protecting fluid milk distributors from unfair conduct have come from the House Select Committee on Small Business.[51] They recommend that Congress should enact legislation which would

1. Strengthen the antitrust laws by providing that the "good faith" defense of Subsection (b) of Section 2 of the Clayton Antitrust Act shall be a complete defense to a charge of unlawful price discrimination "unless the effect of the discrimination may be substantially to lessen competition or tend to create a monopoly."
2. Amend the Clayton Act so as to supplement existing laws against unlawful restraints and monopolies by providing that violations of Section 3 of the Robinson-Patman Act shall constitute violations of the antitrust laws.
3. Amend Section 11 of the Clayton Act to provide for the more expeditious enforcement of cease-and-desist orders issued thereunder, and for other purposes.

It appears to the writer that both the structure and conduct of

---

[49] Spencer and Christensen, *op. cit.*, Part I.
[50] Wilson and Baumer, *op. cit.*, pp. 41–42.
[51] U.S. Congress, House, *Hearings, Price Discrimination in Dairy Products,* Part I, *op. cit.*, p. 49.

the fluid milk industry are in need of improvement. The question is how it should be done. It would seem that helpful measures requiring the least government action would be the passage of the premerger notification law and the above bills outlined by the House Select Committee on Small Business. However, no plan short of rigid price control is going to protect the efficient distributor from occasional discriminatory and coercive pricing practices, and not even this will protect the consumer from schemes to hold prices above competitive levels where the regulatory agency becomes too closely associated with the regulated organization.

# 5

# THE ICE CREAM INDUSTRY[1]

### HUGH L. COOK

ICE CREAM returns more to producers per hundredweight than any other dairy product except bottled milk and cream. Ice cream was once highly profitable to dealers and, as such, often helped pay for the less profitable bottled milk distribution. But for the last few years, market conditions have brought a financial squeeze on ice cream manufacturers that has resulted in agitation for milk control laws and FTC investigations. Within recent years, there have been significant changes in competitive conduct. This roughly parallels the shift to supermarket outlets, the development of private labels, and strategic technological innovations such as the half-gallon package.

A whole new list of pricing practices has evolved, which may or may not be cost justified. The principal impact of these on competition has come since the early 1950's. As smaller firms have disappeared and the ice cream business has become concentrated in fewer firms, overt price competition on the regular brands has become less but other forms of competition, often hidden, have increased and have become widespread. Therefore, competition, when viewed as the entire bundle of competitive practices, has substantially increased.

Conditions of competition in this industry are similar to those in many other food distribution industries—particularly fluid milk, bread, various soft drinks, and, to a lesser extent, frozen and canned foods. The social consequences of this kind of competition may be broad.

In this study, the "ice cream industry" is considered the group of firms that manufacture ice cream for consumption off the premises. Diversified dairy manufacturers regard ice cream as being

---

[1] The material in this chapter is adapted from a study by Hugh L. Cook, *Consequences of Structural Change in the Ice Cream Industry,* Wis. Res. Bul. 236 (Madison, June 1962). Hugh Cook is Professor of Agricultural Economics, University of Wisconsin.

as near to a separate and distinct industry as any other in the dairy business, often with separate facilities for manufacture and distribution, separate salesmen and pricing policies.

## HISTORY

### Changes in Per Capita Consumption Rates

Factors affecting consumer demand, though external to the structure of the market, are partly responsible for market behavior. Per capita consumption of total frozen dairy products has increased almost every year for the last quarter century in the United States as a whole, though shifts have taken place in the relative importance of particular frozen products.[2] On an average, each person consumed 2.44 gallons of frozen products per year in 1939, 4.02 gallons by 1949, and 5.33 gallons by 1959. Since 1949, however, per capita consumption of ice cream alone has changed little, standing at around 3.5 to 3.8 gallons per capita. During this period, ice milk consumption has increased nearly fourfold, sherbet has more than doubled, and mellorine entered the market and occupies a position of some prominence in the few states where it is legal.

The development of ice milk stands such as Dairy Queen has affected competitive conditions in the ice cream business only indirectly. National per capita consumption of ice cream (exclusive of ice milk, mellorine, or ices) is now as great as it has ever been, except for about three years immediately after World War II. By the turn of the 1950's, the ice cream industry was shifting rapidly from drugstore sales to grocery store sales in quantity containers for consumption off the premises. Ice cream stands took over part of the market for ice cream and ice cream drinks for consumption on the premises because they were built as drive-ins with convenient parking facilities. Parking space gained importance as the number of cars increased rapidly during postwar years. However, ice milk stands have never developed an appreciable volume of take-home sales. They do not compete directly with the manufacturers of ice cream for packaged ice cream accounts at wholesale nor do they compete with grocery stores at retail. Wisconsin ice cream manufacturers feel that Dairy Queen and other counter operations have had very little effect on their business. The preceding facts lead us to conclude that changes in the demand for ice cream have not been responsible for the recent problems in the ice cream industry.

---

[2] Frozen dairy products include ice cream, ice milk, sherbet, and mellorine. The latter is the same as ice cream except that vegetable fat has been used to replace all or part of the milk fat which is in ice cream.

### Innovations That Reshaped Local Demand

In seeking an explanation of the recent changes in competition in the ice cream industry, dealers were asked what innovations—technological and other—had "enlarged and improved" it. Dealers named some innovations in the technology of manufacturing and delivery. These are discussed under the heading, "Effect of Technological Change on Barriers to Entry." Other innovations referred to essentially reshaped the nature of demand for a manufacturer's ice cream at the local level. Among such innovations, home freezers and freezer compartments were named most frequently and were followed closely by improved cabinets and cold boxes in retail stores, improved packages, and related developments. Many dealers connected these with shortages of World War II which "shook up" the essentially local character of ice cream marketing arrangements.

*Supermarket Merchandising.* The trend to supermarket merchandising was accelerated at the same time, and supermarket management was alert to sense the profit opportunities of ice cream as a good markup item. Container people responded with a variety of attractive, convenient, and cheap packages in sizes ranging up to a gallon. Ice cream cabinets were greatly improved, offering better availability of product to customer, better lighting and visibility of contents, and automatic defrosting devices.

Along with the sharp trend toward supermarket sales, the housewife grew increasingly food-price conscious. As food chains increased their bargaining power with ice cream dealers, they were able to get lower prices from them and sell for lower prices to consumers. Each of these developments favored the growth of quantity sales of ice cream to households.

*Packages.* The growth of factory-filled quantity containers in the ice cream industry is graphically reflected in the sales by size of containers from 1951–1960. Bulk sales declined from 48.0 to 20.0 percent during that period. Pints declined from 25.0 to 14.0 percent. Half gallons increased from 7.0 to 46.0 percent.

*The Specialized Dairy Store.* Another innovation, the specialized dairy store, has affected market structure. Though many of these were firmly established before World War II, this new form of store has been greatly extended since the late 1940's. Usually these are owned or supplied, under some form of agreement, by a single-unit firm that is struggling for a greater share of the take-home sales in the face of competition by multi-unit dairies for the supermarket business. They are operated at cut-rate prices on packaged milk and ice cream. Typically, these stores handle other groceries as well as dairy products at higher prices than those charged by supermarkets, but they compete servicewise by staying open longer hours.

The dairy store could be viewed as a form of competitive behavior—a device employed usually by a medium-sized dairy to compete against private label deals between large dairies and chain stores. Thus vertical integration appears here as well as in the manufacturing operations of plants, and in private labeling arrangements of food chains.

## CHANGES IN THE MARKET STRUCTURE OF ICE CREAM MANUFACTURING

Economic theory suggests that industrial performance is determined by certain structural characteristics. The ones usually described in studies are (1) numbers and relative sizes of firms, (2) market concentration, (3) extent of vertical integration, (4) nature and extent of product differentiation, and (5) barriers to entry.

This section describes essentially the usual ones. Numbers of exits and entries (turnover) are also shown. Data on mergers are included for their effect on concentration. Extent of vertical integration is chiefly the nonownership type associated with the private label. The peculiarities of product differentiation are discussed along with competitive behavior later in this chapter. The effects of technological change on the barriers to entry are described.

### Number and Relative Sizes of Firms

*National Markets.* U.S. census data show no important changes in concentration ratios for the last three census years (Table 5.1). Industry numbers declined about 8 percent from 1947–1958, while sales increased about 27 percent. The market for ice cream is not

TABLE 5.1

CONCENTRATION RATIOS FOR FOUR, EIGHT, AND TWENTY LARGEST SHIPPERS OF ICE CREAM AND ICES, UNITED STATES, 1947, 1954, AND 1958

| | | | Concentration Ratio: Percent of Value of Shipments Accounted For by | | |
|---|---|---|---|---|---|
| Year | Number of Companies | Value of Industry Shipments | Four largest companies | Eight largest companies | Twenty largest companies |
| | *(number)* | *(thous. dols.)* | | *(percent)* | |
| 1958 | 1,171 | 777,716 | 38 | 48 | 59 |
| 1954 | 1,375 | 727,433 | 36 | 45 | 57 |
| 1947 | 1,273 | 611,755 | 40 | 48 | 57 |

Source: *Concentration Ratios In Manufacturing Industry*, U.S. Congress, Subcommittee on Antitrust and Monopoly, 87th Congress, 2nd Session (1958), p. 11.

TABLE 5.2

CONCENTRATION RATIOS FOR FOUR, EIGHT, AND TWENTY LARGEST MANUFACTURERS
OF ICE CREAM, WISCONSIN, 1948 AND 1958

| | | | Concentration Ratio: Percent of Sales Gallonage Accounted For by | | |
| Year | Number of Companies | Gallonage Produced* | Four largest companies | Eight largest companies | Twenty largest companies |
|---|---|---|---|---|---|
| | *(number)* | *(000 gal.)* | | *(percent)* | |
| 1958 | 158 | 21,512 | 42.3† | 52.5 | 75.3 |
| 1948 | 200 | 16,639 | 32.0 | 42.5 | 60.4 |

Source: Data for 1958 from field survey and licensing records, Wisconsin
State Department of Agriculture. Data for 1948 from Manufactured Dairy
Products reports, Federal-State Crop and Livestock Reporting Service, filed in
the Archives of the Wisconsin State Historical Society.
    * Ice cream only.
    † Only 34.6 percent of sales in Wisconsin were accounted for by the top 4; these sold 2
million gallons outside Wisconsin.

national, however, but is local or, at most, regional. Concentration
on the national level is of minor importance to this analysis.
*The Wisconsin Market.* In Wisconsin, sales became considerably
more concentrated between 1948 and 1958. The four largest ice
cream manufacturers accounted for 32.0 percent of total sales in
1948; by 1958, they accounted for 42.3 percent (Table 5.2). The
comparable figures for the eight largest were 42.5 percent and 52.5
percent, and for the twenty largest, 60.4 percent and 75.8 percent.
Nearly all the decline in numbers since 1941 occurred after 1951,
probably reflecting the impact of the private label discussed later.

Table 5.3 shows the size distribution of the ice cream firms
operating in Wisconsin in 1958 based on gallonage and sales volume. Seventeen (13 percent) of these distribute over 400,000 gallons each per year, totaling nearly three-fourths of Wisconsin's ice
cream sales. Seventy-seven firms (57 percent) distributed less than
100,000 gallons each per year.

TABLE 5.3

SIZE DISTRIBUTION OF WISCONSIN FIRMS MANUFACTURING ICE CREAM FOR
WHOLESALE DISTRIBUTION, BASED ON ANNUAL GALLONAGE SOLD IN WISCONSIN, 1958

| Thousands of Gallons | Number of Firms |
|---|---|
| 1,500 and over | 3 |
| 1,000 – 1,499 | 3 |
| 500 –  999 | 8 |
| 400 –  499 | 3 |
| 300 –  399 | 9 |
| 200 –  299 | 6 |
| 100 –  199 | 16 |
| 50 –   99 | 24 |
| Under 50 | 53 |
| Total | 125 |

The degree of diversification associated with size is significant. All the multi-unit concerns manufacture diversified dairy products. Two are diversified among ice cream and other fluid milk products, and 10 are diversified among ice cream, other fluid products, and manufactured products. Furthermore, among the single-unit firms (corporate or proprietary), the ones with the greatest average ice cream sales are diversified.

The significance of this is that diversification and conglomeration may give firms additional market power, all other things being equal.[3] Two advantages are: (1) firms can recover temporary losses in competing for markets in one line from other lines that are profitable and (2) brand names established with consumers on one line have a value when they appear on a new line. In this connection, multi-unit corporations are usually in other lines of business as well as dairy products (conglomerate firms).

There were four national multi-unit concerns with ice cream factories in Wisconsin: National Dairy Products, Borden, Beatrice Foods, and Fairmont. These accounted for 30.5 percent of total gallonage manufactured. By 1960, each of these firms had total national sales exceeding $100 million. Their average ice cream production in Wisconsin was 1,835,750 gallons. In addition, these firms distributed fluid milk and made other manufactured dairy products.

There were three regional and state multi-unit firms and five multi-unit cooperative dairies, each group accounting for 11 percent of the gallonage. The former firms averaged 862,000 gallons of ice cream each, and the latter, 525,000.

In addition, there were 48 single-plant corporations making ice cream accounting for 19 percent of the gallonage; 20 of these manufactured only ice cream, whereas the other 28 made other dairy products as well.

Individual proprietorships still constituted the largest number of ice cream firms in the state. The 75 such firms had an average production of only about 55,000 gallons, and 43 of these sold only ice cream. They accounted for only 17 percent of the gallonage.

The final group of firms making ice cream were those manufacturing solely for retail sale. These accounted for the balance of the gallonage. Four were food stores; only one, A & P, had an operation of any significance. One of the others was licensed to manufacture ice cream but apparently did not do so in 1958.

*Local Markets.* We also may conceive of local markets, such as

---

[3] Corwin Edwards, "Conglomerate Bigness as a Source of Power," *Business Concentration and Price Policy,* Nat. Bur. of Econ. Res. (Princeton Univ. Press, 1955). It is recognized that George Stigler and some others do not agree with this point of view.

those in a city, where the products of all the sellers are viewed by consumers as closer substitutes than they are in a larger geographic area. If we assume that a city is the relevant market in which competition occurs, we may obtain an estimate of the number and size distribution of rivals in particular cities. We have made such estimates for Wisconsin's largest city, Milwaukee, which had about 29 percent of the entire population in Wisconsin in 1960.

According to the annual "Consumer Analysis" in the *Milwaukee Journal,* in 1960, 76.1 percent of the consumers purchased ice cream from four ice cream manufacturers, and 90.1 percent from eight ice cream manufacturers (Table 5.4). These estimates overstate actual sales concentration by about 4 percent because they are weighted in favor of the most widely used brands.

These data further suggest that the share of the Milwaukee market supplied by the largest manufacturers declined between 1948 and the mid-1950's and has since started to increase again.

Also these data overstate the impact of this market concentration in the Milwaukee market because they take into account only those firms which actually are selling in this market. In many cases, the number of potential competitors is a more relevant structural variable than the number actually making deliveries in the market.

TABLE 5.4

PERCENTAGE OF GREATER MILWAUKEE CONSUMERS USING* BRANDS MANUFACTURED
BY THE EIGHT LARGEST MILWAUKEE ICE CREAM DISTRIBUTORS, 1948 TO 1960

| Year | Four Largest Firms | Eight Largest Firms |
|------|--------------------|---------------------|
| 1960 | 76.1 | 90.1 |
| 1959 | 73.8 | 88.6 |
| 1957 | 72.7 | 87.7 |
| 1956 | 72.3 | 88.0 |
| 1955 | 70.7 | 86.0 |
| 1954 | 72.7 | 87.3 |
| 1953 | 69.5 | 82.6 |
| 1952 | 73.6 | 87.9 |
| 1950 | 79.5 | 89.8 |
| 1948 | 83.2 | 93.9 |

Source: *Milwaukee Journal,* "Consumer Analysis" (various editions). Greater Milwaukee includes Milwaukee County plus a border area 4 miles wide on the west and north. This area had a population of 1,126,289 in 1960.

* These estimates are based on responses to the question, Do you buy ice cream and, if yes, what brand? Another question asked in 1960 was, Have you bought ice cream in the last 7 days and, if yes, what brand? Responses to the first question tend to overstate the frequency of purchase of familiar brands because consumers buying several brands mention only one. The last question tends to be more accurate because it is based on actual experience. Based on responses to the last question about 4 percent fewer Milwaukee consumers preferred the top four brands than was indicated by responses to the first question.

The four multi-plant national firms are potential entrants into any market in Wisconsin. The next largest dozen or so in size are potential entrants in sections of the state ranging up to 150 miles in diameter from their points of production. However, most of the small plants in the competitive fringe do not plan to make deliveries outside the town where their plants are located. There are nearly five times as many companies operating trucks for distances over 75 miles as there were in the mid-1930's according to a truck analysis by the International Association of Ice Cream Manufacturers.[4]

### Turnover (exit and entry)

Though the number of plants manufacturing ice cream has decreased over the past 10 years, such data fail to describe the nature of turnover. In 1949, there were 219 Wisconsin dairy plants licensed to manufacture ice cream; in 1958, there were 166 plants. This net decrease of 53 represents a drop of approximately 24 percent in number of plants. A more detailed analysis shows that 106 plants went out of the business of producing ice cream, while 53 new manufacturers of ice cream entered the field in this 10-year period. Of the 53 new manufacturers of ice cream listed, 21 were in the dairy industry in 1948. These had made an addition to the product line either by internal expansion or by acquisition of a going concern.

Of all the ice cream firms that went out of business during the period 1940–1960, 32 percent were sold to a previously existing dairy firm (merger or consolidation), and 20 percent were sold to a new dairy firm. A little less than one-half (48 percent) were closed and dismantled, which means that nearly half exited with no market for the business as such.[5]

### Merger

During this 10-year interval, 1949–1959, 60 separate mergers occurred among ice cream manufacturers and other dairy firms. In some cases, the acquired firms retained their firm name and trademark, so no change was made in the number of plants licensed to manufacture ice cream. The 60 mergers involving ice cream firms indicate that at least one-quarter of the dairy firms in operation in 1949 have merged.

"Merger" may be defined as the acquisition of one firm by another, or any reorganization of two or more companies into a

---

[4] *Trucking and Delivery Analysis, 1956,* Intl. Assn. of Ice Cream Manufacturers, Spec. Bul. 100 (Apr. 1958).

[5] Jerome Hammond and Hugh L. Cook, *Financial and Market Causes for Wisconsin Dairy Plant Mergers,* Wis. Exp. Sta. Bul. 249 (Madison, 1964).

new firm. The motive for merger on the part of the acquiring firm is one or a combination of the following:[6]

1. To get the sales outlets in old territory or in a new market. This is usually the most important motive.
2. To get the personnel with the know-how, especially where the firm has never been in the ice cream business.
3. Occasionally to get the ice cream manufacturing facilities.

Buying into a market or buying customers is often cheaper than the competitive practices necessary to come in by other means. Sometimes mergers to get customers have been viewed by the FTC or the Justice Department as undesirable compared to the competition that would have been required to break into the market. Those agencies may object to the effect the merger may have by increasing concentration, with its frequent result of less competitive market structure.

These results, however, are not always the case. W. F. Mueller has acknowledged,

> Mergers among small firms may actually stimulate rather than stifle competition. The Supreme Court pointed out this fact in its important *Brown Shoe* decision when it said, 'Congress recognized the stimulation to competition that might flow from particular mergers. When concern as to the Act's breadth was expressed, supporters of the amendments indicated that it would not impede, for example, the merger between two small companies to enable the combination to compete more effectively with larger corporations dominating the relevant market, nor between a corporation which is financially healthy and a failing one which no longer can be a vital competitive factor in the market.'[7]

It is doubtful if merger has been a primary cause of the increased concentration among the larger firms in the Wisconsin industry because acquisitions were made by dairy firms of all sizes except the very small. Of the 60 firms acquired by ice cream concerns during the period 1949–1959 only one-third were acquired by firms in the top four, about one-fourth by firms in the top eight, and about half by the firms in the top 20. Only nine of the top 20 were among the acquiring firms, generally the larger ones.

---

[6] *Ibid.*

[7] *Brown Shoe v. United States*, 379 U.S. 290, 319 (1962), quoted from Willard F. Mueller, "The Current Merger Movement and Public Policy," paper given before Faculty Seminar, College of Bus. Admin., Univ. of Fla., May 16, 1963. Mueller is Res. Dir., Bur. of Econ., FTC.

## Effect of Technological Change on Barriers to Entry

The barriers to entry as a structural variable will be discussed in various parts of this chapter. All effects of technological change on the height of barriers have not been in the same direction. However, what Bain called the "minimum optimal scale" of the plant or firm has increased in recent years.

Technological innovation may occur either in the ice cream manufacturing plant or in transportation or refrigeration on the routes. Important technological innovations include a host of changes in design of equipment, greatly increasing the range in capacity at which the newer equipment may be economically operated. Presumably, this applies to freezers, packaging equipment, hardening room equipment, and load-out equipment. Improvements of this kind may help explain the tremendous proportion of capacity that is unused (see section on performance).

In the late prewar years, the larger ice cream dealers were shifting to mechanically refrigerated trucks which they called a "cheaper, cleaner operation," but the full impact of this new technology was not felt until the late 1940's. Also maximum truck capacity has increased from 600 to 1,200 gallons within a few years, with trucks operating at about the same cost per mile.

The effect of technological developments on costs depends on whether the firm made concomitant changes in its method of operating, and whether increases in volume were experienced. Some 76 percent of the dealers (mostly small local firms) felt sure that their costs had increased as a result of technology.

Most dealers were directly conscious of the developments named here and under the section on demand. No doubt other developments were contributing, however. Such innovations include paper packaging of fluid milk (which extends the brand names of dealers into larger geographic areas), ever-improving roads, reciprocity in inspection, and other things of a general social character.[8] By and large, all these developments were reducing the barriers to entry for those with capital to adapt changes in their business. Apparently the minimum optimal scale of firms to survive in the markets where there is growth opportunity (chain store and supermarket outlets) has increased in recent years. This point, which is explored later in the chapter, suggests that the scale barrier is higher than a few years ago, even though other barriers may be less in some markets.

---

[8] Hugh L. Cook, *Paper Packaged Milk in Wisconsin: Its Part in Expanding Distribution Areas*, Wis. Res. Bul. 179 (Madison, 1953). The same trends were evident throughout the North Central region, and most of the United States.

## CHANGES IN MARKET STRUCTURE OF ICE CREAM BUYERS
### Changes in Outlets

The most striking change in sales outlets for ice cream dealers over the last 20 years has been the general shift to retail store sales. For the United States as a whole, this is shown by data from surveys by the International Ice Cream Dealers Association (Figure 5.1). Store sales increased from 11.4 percent of the total in 1938, to 47.1 percent in 1956, with most of the change occurring during the past decade. Wisconsin estimates obtained by surveying 88 ice cream dealers show trends roughly similar to the national industry. Most of this increased volume was business formerly handled by drugstores, restaurants, and confectionery stores. In effect, this means a shift from consumption on the premises to home consumption.

### Market Structure of Ice Cream Outlets

Traditionally, the market structure of ice cream manufacturers has been characterized by large numbers of small retail outlets.

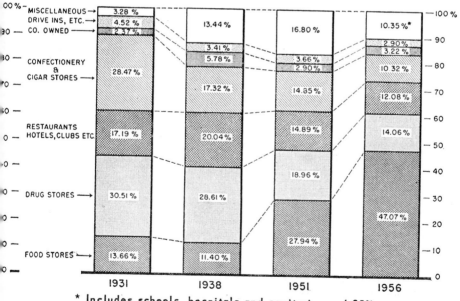

* Includes schools, hospitals and sanitariums--4.35%.

FIG. 5.1—Ice cream gallonage by outlets—percentage of total sales in the United States. (Courtesy, **Dealer Analysis and Other Products Sold,** Internatl. Assn. of Ice Cream Manufacturers, Spec. Bul. 99, Sept. 1957.)

The most important type of outlet during the 1930's was the drug-store. They sold nearly 30 percent of all ice cream in 1938. Drug-store retailing traditionally has been a field of small, independent businesses.

The second most important outlet until recent years was restaurant and hotel trade which, in 1938, accounted for 20 percent of all sales. This was followed by confectionery and cigar stores which accounted for 17.3 percent of all sales. These two fields also consisted primarily of single-unit firms.

The increasing shift of ice cream sales to food stores has significantly changed the structure of the market in which ice cream dealers sell. *Food retailing is considerably more concentrated than the other industries to which ice cream dealers traditionally have sold most of their output.* Nationally, the percentage of sales by grocery chains with over 10 stores increased from 34.4 percent in 1948 to 42.6 percent in 1958.[9] Moreover, the independent segment of grocery retailing is increasingly organized into cooperative and voluntary chains. By 1958, 73 percent of all independent retailers belonged to voluntary or cooperative chains, compared to only 46 percent in 1940.

Of course, the preceding comparisons show only the concentration of grocery business at the national level. Market concentration is considerably greater in regional and local markets. Whereas there are only three chains with sales as great as 2 percent of total United States' sales, the typical large chain does about 10 percent of the total business in the regions in which it operates. Thus, even chains which are small nationally are relatively important in their operating areas.

Local market concentration is even more pronounced. According to the Federal Trade Commission study, the four largest chains and/or cooperative and voluntary chains averaged about 63 percent of the grocery business in 13 cities studied.[10] Analyses from "Consumer Analysis" of the *Milwaukee Journal* show corresponding results. Thus the continuing shift to store sales of ice cream has accompanied the increasing concentration of the retail grocery industry.

### Vertical Integration by Retailers

Not only has the grocery portion of the ice cream market become more concentrated, but an increasing number of retailers have actually integrated into ice cream manufacturing. Prior to 1950,

---

[9] Willard F. Mueller and Leon Garoian, *Changes in the Market Structure of Grocery Retailing* (Madison: Univ. of Wis. Press, 1961).

[10] Federal Trade Commission, *Economic Inquiry Into Food Marketing*, (Jan. 1960), p. 248.

none of the country's grocery chains operated their own ice cream manufacturing plants. Since then, however, three chains have begun manufacturing part of their own ice cream requirements and, by 1957, operated a total of 16 ice cream plants.[11] At least one other large chain has entered this field since 1957.

The successful entrance by ice cream manufacturing chains results in the loss of potential markets by ice cream manufacturers.

## Retailer Labeling of Ice Cream

As already noted, some chains have integrated into the ice cream industry by manufacturing their own product. Other chains have developed their own brand name but buy the ice cream from other manufacturers. Chains selling ice cream under their own label, in effect, have partially entered the ice cream industry because they are now performing a merchandising function (branding) previously performed by the ice cream manufacturers. This may be viewed as partial integration from which these chains achieve many of the advantages of complete integration.

Retailer branding of grocery items has become increasingly common among chain stores. By 1958 all large chains and about 80 percent of all chains with less than 100 stores had their own brands of some products.[12] About 57 percent of all supermarkets owned by retailers with from 1 to 99 stores carried their own brand of ice cream.

In 1960 about 13 percent of Milwaukee consumers purchased retailer-labeled ice cream more often than other types. If the brands of drugstore and ice cream shops are included, in 1960, over 20 percent of Milwaukee consumers purchased primarily retailer-labeled ice cream. This compares with 4.3 percent in 1948 when apparently the only two brands of retailer-labeled ice cream in Milwaukee came from a drug chain and from A & P (which had just begun to manufacture for its own label). It began manufacturing for its Milwaukee stores in 1946 and gradually expanded throughout the state.

*Motive for Retailer Labels of Ice Cream.* The basic economic motive underlying the development of retailer brands is that they increase a retailer's profits. To understand why retailer labeling may result in higher profits, it is necessary to analyze exactly what is involved when a retailer develops its own brands.

Retailers buying from firms with market power built on successful product differentiation have an incentive to develop their own brands for such products in order to enjoy greater freedom in

---

[11] Mueller and Garoian, *op. cit.*
[12] Mueller and Garoian, *op. cit.*

their retail merchandising policies and to enjoy profits similar to those of the profitable manufacturers. These private labels help the retailer to build a "consumer franchise"; they help tie the consumer to the store.

Once chains have developed a line of differentiated products, they are in a position to place their brand on practically any additional product with no additional advertising expense. This places them in an extremely favorable position vis-à-vis their suppliers. They are in the unique position of being able to integrate into many lines of manufacturing because they can overcome the product differentiation barrier to entry, which Bain calls probably the most formidable barrier to entry confronting other prospective entrants. But chains need not actually manufacture their own products to take advantage of their product differentiation. By coordinating closely the manufacturer's and chain's operations through a form of nonownership integration, various manufacturing and marketing economies may be achieved which at least permit the chain to pay a supplier with a little-known brand name a better price than he could obtain elsewhere.

Of course, food chains are able to buy some requirements even from firms which have developed their own brands. The reasons big suppliers may be willing to sell some of their output under retailer labels at prices below that sold under their own brands include the following:

1.  To lower their own average costs of production.
2.  To forestall entry by chain stores into ice cream manufacturing.
3.  To keep other ice cream dealers from increasing capacity in order to supply the ever-expanding private label accounts. Excess capacity in the industry could lower profit margins for all manufacturers.
4.  As a strategy to obtain shelf space for their own brands.

These motives help to explain why large manufacturers may enter the retailer label business on a large scale, while at the same time maintaining and even attempting to expand sales under their own brands. Actually, in Wisconsin, most private label ice cream is supplied by the largest manufacturers with the best-known brand names.

The sort of bilateral oligopoly resulting from concentration among dealers on the one hand and newly developing concentration among buyers on the other may be producing some of the price and output results that would be expected theoretically from atomistic competition. An important effect of private labeling is that the value of ice cream manufacturers' brand names has fallen.

## COMPETITIVE BEHAVIOR

There is little about the structure of the ice cream manufacturing industry to suggest the sort of competition that has prevailed in the industry for the last decade or so. Some of the changes in structure suggest a trend toward increasing competition. However, some structural characteristics suggest that the industry would tend to follow a policy of limited joint-profit maximization. Indeed the industry does keep the listed prices of regular (advertised) brands stable over long time periods and comfortably above average costs. There is a minimum of overt price competition with regular brands. However, other structural elements and particularly the structure of buyers impede or frustrate the basic tendency. The analysis by John Moore in his chapter on fluid milk is relevant here, except that the private label has had less impact on behavior in fluid milk than in the ice cream industry. Despite methods to enforce joint-profit maximization, the price situation seldom satisfies all competing dealers. The result is a constant pressure for alteration of price relationships among frozen products (and attached services). Competitive behavior takes the form of product competition and many hidden forms of price and nonprice competition.

These are outlined and described briefly to illustrate the complexity of the problem facing the dealer in trying to compete and of public agencies in their efforts to regulate competition. With awareness that the categories cannot be mutually exclusive, the forms of competition may be grouped as follows:

I. Product competition
  A. The regular brand
    1. Price competition
      (a) Overt (nondiscriminatory)
      (b) Hidden (discriminatory)
    2. Implicit-price competition
    3. Nonprice competition
  B. The private label
    The same subclassifications as above
  C. The competing brand
    The same subclassifications as above
II. New forms of business organization
  A. Subdealers
  B. Dairy stores
  C. Mergers

The basic notion is that several groups of competitive practices are carried on within the framework of product competition (with attached services). The private label and the competing brand are classed as product competition with price consequences. The firm therefore competes against rivals with a regular brand product, a private label product, and a competing brand product. The regular brand has been advertised over a period of years, and the consumer has been familiarized with its characteristics as well as possible. The term private label is used here to refer to the retail food store brand which in Wisconsin is manufactured by ice cream dealers except for the A & P private label, the first private label to appear in the state. Private labels are usually packed in half gallons of the cheapest flavor and cheapest package. They usually contain the minimum butterfat and maximum overrun. Not only are all economies reflected in price, but the price difference is even greater; most of the dealers interviewed freely admitted that the price difference between this and their regular brand could not be cost justified. The competing brand is furnished by dealers to small independent stores to help them compete with the supermarkets' private label prices. It is made to specifications similar to the private label, but wholesale prices are not as low. Competing brand prices ranged around 25 cents per gallon below the dealer's regular brand whereas private labels were as much as 45 cents cheaper. Regulatory agencies thus far have tended to view the regular brand, private label, and competing brands as separate products, although there is evidence that the FTC suspects that private labels may be a form of price discrimination and may call on the industry for cost justification.[13]

Several variations of price, quality, or service may occur within a product line for competitive purposes. These variations may take the form of price competition, implicit-price competition, and nonprice competition. Price competition may be overt or hidden, but implicit-price and nonprice forms of competition are here viewed as hidden. Price competition is conceptualized as including any change in prices of a frozen product for purposes of getting a new account or holding an old one. Changes in listed prices or listed price discounts may be viewed as overt price competition. "Off list pricing" in some cases may be viewed as "hidden" price competition. Implicit-price competition is a term used for all competitive practices with readily computed values. Nonprice competition includes all practices the value of which cannot be readily computed.

Overt price competition with a particular product occurs less frequently than product (or service) competition and hidden price

---

[13] Since publication of the research from which this material was taken, competitive practices have changed in Wisconsin due to more rigorous enforcement of the law on price discrimination and unfair trade practices. However, what is said here still describes competition in much of the nation.

competition. Overt price competition would include price wars, price reductions "to meet competition," any open revisions of discount schedules, and any cost-justified price reductions for "dock," "drop," or "tail gate" delivery.

In general, the concept of overt price competition is here used when the practice is nondiscriminatory and takes the form of price or discount adjustments. The classification does not depend on whether the practice is legal. For example, dropping price to meet competition for a particular outlet is legal, even though there is no cost justification. When this price reduction is not extended to other outlets of the same size and service requirements, it is usually hidden and discriminatory.

A major form of hidden price competition is price discrimination among areas and among purchasers. Others have been the sales of milk and other dairy products at unreasonably low prices—in some cases alleged to be below cost.

The most important of the implicit-price factors which affect the cost of ice cream to retail handlers and the cost of sales to dealers is the practice of furnishing ice cream cabinets. Other factors are free cabinet repair service, various advertising allowances, loans to retailers, etc.

Nonprice factors include some unfair and some fair. The unfair include free signs that make little or no reference to products of the supplying dealer, and pseudoadvertising allowances. Many of the fair nonprice factors, which could be viewed as product competition, are just as expensive to the entrepreneur and as wasteful from a social point of view as unfair practices. For example, some dealers stock over 100 separate items—numerous flavors and package sizes and types. Frequent change of flavors often becomes the focal point of advertising and promotion. These step up the cost to the dealer and perhaps to the public. On the other hand, much of the product service results in good merchandising such as practices to keep stocks attractive and in top condition.

New forms of business organization are sometimes adopted primarily to get new sales accounts and, when that is the motivation, these may be viewed as forms of competitive behavior. Mergers, dairy stores, and subdealers may be used for this purpose. Mergers and dairy stores already have been discussed. Both of these have been the subject of court actions. A relatively unexplored area from the viewpoint of court action is the business practice of arranging for subdealers or vendors to take over the functions of sales and delivery. This change in organization of the firm has occurred chiefly in recent years. A recent study of milk subdealers in Pennsylvania reported that over half of the subdealers had begun operating since 1950 and four-fifths had begun since 1941. Some of these handle ice cream,[14] although most subdealers handle only fluid milk. Nearly all were proprietorships. Nearly all purchased products from only one processor, with the processor's label. The arrangements by which the processing company assures that its product will be handled exclusively or be sufficiently promoted by these subdealers are not always expressed in legal documents. In the Pennsylvania study, nearly two-thirds of the contracts between subdealer and processor were verbal.

The reasons usually given for this new practice by milk and ice cream dealers are (1) that a particular owner-operator of a wholesale route may perform this function more cheaply than the manufacturer can perform it with union labor and (2) that smaller units can handle distribution more efficiently than very large ones. Both of these suggest that subdealers can justify lower prices in their distribution areas than the manufacturing dealer could justify on routes operated by his own employees. An additional competitive advantage could exist in some instances. Ice cream may be sold at the dock to subdealers (carefully chosen). These subdealers may resell as they see fit without the original company having the same legal responsibility for the terms of resale that it would have if the product were distributed by the company's regular employees.

### Relationship Between Structure and Conduct

This section focuses on particular market situations including the sizes of buyers and sellers in each, the nature of integration, product (and service) differentiation, and the barriers to entry and exit.

Judging the effect of these structural variables on competition depends on the definition of the markets. If the market is viewed as state-wide, in a general sense, the data on concentration and numbers suggest a moderately concentrated oligopoly with a differentiated product, moderately difficult entry, and a large competitive fringe. Bain suggests that for high concentration the top eight firms handle two-thirds or three-fourths of the total sales. In ice cream, the largest eight handle only 52.3 percent of total sales in Wisconsin. With moderate concentration, there is a probability that collusion among sellers will be ineffective so that prices will be lower and outputs larger than when seller concentration is very high.

Wisconsin consists of several kinds of markets with differing kinds of competitors and of outlets in each, with varied price-output policies, and with other variations depending on competitors and

---

[14] D. C. Arms and W. T. Butz, "Subdealers in the Milk Industry. . . ," *Farm Economics,* Penn. State Univ. (May 1960), and "Statistical Summary of Subdealer Study," mimeo., by same authors.

outlets. For example, the national and regional chain store retailers may be viewed as a market. In view of the data on trend-to-store sales of ice cream and particularly the trend-to-chain-store sales, it may be argued that opportunities for growth as an ice cream dealer are largely in this market. In this market are competing chiefly the large multi-unit dairies, perhaps primarily because their brands have the greatest value to the chains, but also because chain store managers feel these dairies can assure the necessary volume and can furnish the central billing and other standardized services sought by chain store management.

Two people can arrange a deal on private labels and discounts for many stores. Conceivably, this could make it easier to keep the deals secret. With the market defined in this way, a sort of bilateral oligopoly could be defined. Perhaps the Galbraith concept of countervailing power would constitute a more flexible analytical framework. In any case, the chain stores can force dealers to give them low prices on their private label under threat that the chains will integrate into manufacturing their own ice cream or go to another dealer, and they agree to handle the regular brand of a large manufacturer as part of the deal. The private label amounts to nonownership integration by chain stores into manufacturing.

The large multi-unit concerns are frustrated in joint-profit maximization by the threat that large single-unit concerns with valuable brand names (for a considerable radius from their plants) may underbid their private label prices. They, therefore, may set their profit margins at a level to forestall entry of these firms. In this market, entry may be described as blocked because none but the multi-plant (or multi-unit) dealers appears able to get into this market. (Often, however, the best-known local brand may receive a small amount of cabinet space.) Perhaps for this market, the most relevant concentration variable would be the proportion of total national or regional chain store sales from Wisconsin retail stores that is accounted for by the top four or eight Wisconsin dairies. No such data were obtained in this study, but the figure is sure to be high.

For some purposes, the city or village may be viewed as the relevant market and the chain stores may be excluded from the market concept. In theory, the cross-elasticity of demand separates markets. Most regular customers of chain stores would not be induced to shift to smaller, independent retail stores or drugstores by changes in ice cream prices and vice versa (at least in the short run). Those who now patronize small stores do so because of convenient location and extra services such as credit, telephone orders, home deliveries, or because of personal relationships. The cross-elasticity of demand among the markets so described would therefore be low.

In addition, the dealers who supply large outlets may not be in the market for the small accounts. This again is an elasticity ratio, not on demand, but on the supply side. The ratio between costs of supplying the outlet (product plus services) and revenue that may be expected from it, as compared with alternatives, sets a limit on whether other dealers are in this market. Expressed another way, the price received per gallon, less the cost of services to small accounts, multiplied by the volume, is usually lower than would be received from chain store accounts.

With the relevant market defined as the city or village, there is a competitive fringe which may be viewed as monopolistically competitive. This fringe includes a relatively large number of small ice cream manufacturers (either specialized or making and handling ice cream in addition to fluid products) selling differentiated products or services. Locational differentiation arises because many consumers are relatively immobile. An element of ignorance as to the measurable difference in composition and quality of ice cream contributes to this differentiation. Personal relationships and extra services play a part, as does the prejudice against "foreign" chain stores and dealers who come in from outside the local community. Large dealers may expend their major efforts on the large accounts. As a result, they neglect many small retailers, drugstores, and restaurants who find they can get more personalized service from small, local ice cream dealers. These factors, plus others unique to particular areas, provide the demand conditions conducive to monopolistic competition.

On the other hand, to enter the ice cream business on a small, local basis requires a low ratio of capital to labor and relatively low levels of technical and administrative skill, so long as the entrant does not aim for the large, more profitable accounts and contents himself with batch freezers and low levels of technology in general. Even so, the *barriers to entry* probably furnish a smaller part of the explanation for the many small firms in the business than the *barriers to exit.* Apparently many of the small firms were manufacturing ice cream prior to the shift toward retailer labeling and other factors associated with changing structure of outlets. The height of the barriers to exit is a major reason they are now there.

Given these entry and exit conditions, any suggestions of high profits would bring additional dealers into the picture. Either larger dealers would come in from outside to supply the outlets, the customers would shift to supermarkets, or some small, local dealer who is unable to leave the business might sell for whatever he could get above out-of-pocket costs. The result may well be what the Chamberlinian model suggests—that none of the dealers in the monopolistically competitive fringe are making excess profits, but that their marketing margins are larger than if differentiation were less.

One way to conceive of these markets is that the large multi-unit firms compete among themselves on a state-wide basis for the larger accounts, especially of chain stores, and that entry to this market is blockaded. The fringe firms compete among themselves for the smaller accounts in their highly localized market, with moderately difficult entry.

However, the price-output policies of neither group is what would be expected from the above circumstances. In Wisconsin, a score or so large firms handle between 300,000 and 1,000,000 gallons of ice cream annually. These have several sales branches or subdealers which blanket a substantial section of the state. They compete with multi-unit concerns for any chain store account within their section of the state and for all independent supermarket accounts in local markets. Though they are unable to get the state-wide accounts of chains, they do get a small amount of space in one or more units of a large chain and also get the accounts of the supermarkets that have sales volumes comparable to that of individual chain stores in a particular area. These supermarkets make the same price appeals to customers as chain stores.

It, therefore, appears likely that the individual markets of the state are interrelated into one general state-wide market by the operations of these large single-plant firms. The multi-plant firms tend to set "entry forestalling" prices at levels low enough to keep chain stores from integrating into manufacturing and to keep sectional chain stores and supermarkets from shifting to single-plant firms. They compete further with the variety of expensive nonprice and implicit-price devices as pointed out above.

The competitive fringe finds that large plants (multi- or single-plant firms) will enter competition for any of their small accounts at the first suggestion of high profits. They therefore step up the personalized services and hold down actual prices to forestall entry of these larger firms to the market which consists of small accounts. These large single-plant firms may therefore serve as barometric price leaders for both larger and smaller firms in the state.

### Influence of Public Regulation on Conduct

Public regulation may place restraints on certain types of behavior with a given structure. Sometimes the effects feed back on structure by having a differential impact on firms of various sizes and also on firms differing as to the range of marketing functions covered (differing degrees of vertical integration).

Public regulation of particular importance to the ice cream business takes the form of (1) minimum standards and definitions for ingredients and labeling, (2) minimum sanitation and purity standards, and (3) regulation of competitive behavior. These various regulations may be imposed at federal, state, or municipal levels. Federal standards on ingredients provide a minimum specification for ice cream moved intrastate. No federal sanitation standards for ice cream are enforced by law except those applying generally to foods. Federal regulation applies to competitive behavior under the Sherman Act, Federal Trade Commission Act, and Clayton Act, especially as amended by the Robinson-Patman Act. Wisconsin state regulations deal with all three types of regulation—definitions, standards, and competitive practices. Municipal regulations apply only to the quality of ingredients; the local health ordinance may require ice cream to be made from Grade A milk ingredients as, for example, the almost unique requirement of Chicago that ice cream be made from Grade A inspected ingredients.

The practical importance of these product standards and inspection requirements is in terms of the ease with which ice cream or ingredients may move among markets, the costs to firms of overcoming the frictions to such movement, the restraints on quality competition, and the effect each of the foregoing may have on growth of firms. Sometimes product standards may limit the extent to which a firm may compete through product differentiation.

Regulation of competitive practices could be viewed as barriers to entry into a particular market, and as such, these would relate to a structural variable. To illustrate: where a local market is in the general trade area of a large multi-unit concern, a firm might seek entry by giving discounts greater than it gives within surrounding territory, and greater than small local manufacturers can give. Unfair trade practice laws, however, under some conditions, would prevent the large firm from entering the market by this device.

The impact of such laws could restrain growth of the large concern, and the surviving small local firms might be larger, thus tending to change the structure of the industry by decreasing concentration ratios. However, the effectiveness of these laws is frequently questioned, as, for example, in the report of the House Select Committee on small business problems in the dairy industry.

## PERFORMANCE OF THE INDUSTRY

Now what are the consequences of this competitive behavior? For data bearing on this, the author had access to corporate income tax records for ice cream dealers for an 11-year period beginning with 1947. Field surveys were made of 88 of Wisconsin's 158 ice cream dealers. Findings from these and other sources show the consequences of this competitive behavior.

## Profit Declines

The 11-year series of ratios (from state income tax returns) show that profits of Wisconsin corporate ice cream firms have declined to the point where they are little more than one-fifth of the 1947–49 average. Percentagewise, the decline has been about the same for large firms as for smaller ones, though the absolute profit ratios of the large firms were greater by 1958 than for the smaller ones because they began at a higher level (Table 5.5). This measurement was the ratio of net income before taxes to net worth. Over the same period, profit ratios for combination milk and ice cream dealers fell to 81 percent of their 1947–49 average (Table 5.6). Thus, it appears that they have been affected less than specialized ice cream concerns. However, it may be noted that the smallest group of combination firms has actually been in the red for the last three years of the period, whereas the smallest specialized ice cream firms were still making a little money.

## Changes External to the Structure

The decline in profits is believed to be chiefly for reasons associated with the market structures of the ice cream industry and that of its outlets. None of the changes external to the structure of these markets furnishes much of the explanation for such drastic decline in profits in ice cream manufacturing. Judging only from general changes in external factors, profits would be expected to remain at least as high as average 1947–49 levels. Market prices for purchased inputs in manufacturing and delivery have steadily increased during the 11-year period, but when the principal cost components, labor, milk solids, and packaging materials are weighted into an index based on the 1947–49 period, the increase has been only about 30 percent. General demand levels have improved steadily. Consumer disposable income has increased during the period, being 74 percent greater in 1958 than during the base period. The retail prices for competing consumer foods have increased less than disposable incomes (20 percent compared to 74 percent for disposable incomes in the aggregate). The general level of wholesale prices has increased slightly less than retail food prices in most years. The consumption of ice cream has increased nearly every year since 1949, notwithstanding substitute products.

## Comparisons With Other Industries

Comparisons of the earnings in ice cream manufacturing with earnings of other food manufacturing concerns and with earnings of food chains provide a rough indication of changes in the relative profitability of these industries during the period studied. The largest specialized corporate ice cream firms in Wisconsin showed

## TABLE 5.5
### Net Income as a Percent of Net Worth, Corporate Ice Cream Dealers, Wisconsin, 1947–58*

| Size Group† | 1947 | 1948 | 1949 | 1950 | 1951 | 1952 | 1953 | 1954 | 1955 | 1956 | 1957 | 1958 |
|---|---|---|---|---|---|---|---|---|---|---|---|---|
| Gross Sales | | | | | | | | | | | | |
| Less than $500,000 | 18.12 | 17.52 | 18.92 | 8.10 | 8.26 | 8.82 | 8.74 | 8.49 | 10.37 | 6.99 | 3.57 | 4.41 |
| $500,000 and above | 23.56 | 19.03 | 24.26 | 13.85 | 12.83 | 18.08 | 18.17 | 9.99 | 11.64 | 6.99 | 4.97 | 4.95 |
| All firms | 21.73 | 18.47 | 22.32 | 11.86 | 11.27 | 14.95 | 15.08 | 9.50 | 11.21 | 6.99 | 4.42 | 4.71 |

* Net income before provision for income taxes.
† Classified according to sales volume in the year 1957. The smaller and the larger groups are composed of 13 and 4 dealers who manufacture ice cream exclusively.

## TABLE 5.6
### Net Income as a Percent of Net Worth, Corporate Milk and Ice Cream Dealers, Wisconsin, 1947–58*

| Size Group† | 1947 | 1948 | 1949 | 1950 | 1951 | 1952 | 1953 | 1954 | 1955 | 1956 | 1957 | 1958 |
|---|---|---|---|---|---|---|---|---|---|---|---|---|
| **Gross Sales** | | | | | | | | | | | | |
| Less than $500,000 | 11.88 | 6.60 | 8.67 | −1.45 | .17 | 2.13 | 7.92 | −.77 | −1.30 | −1.66 | −1.49 | −3.02 |
| $500,000 to $1,499,999 | 19.21 | 16.74 | 20.53 | 14.48 | 8.80 | 8.29 | 15.72 | 9.67 | 10.50 | 8.15 | 6.46 | 7.09 |
| $1,500,000 and above | 18.56 | 15.79 | 21.33 | 16.47 | 11.77 | 12.62 | 15.17 | 13.46 | 17.42 | 16.25 | 13.94 | 16.95 |
| All firms | 18.27 | 15.37 | 20.40 | 15.18 | 10.68 | 11.32 | 14.76 | 12.10 | 15.39 | 14.27 | 12.12 | 14.64 |
| National firms over $3,000,000‡ | 35.51 | 29.92 | 32.19 | 23.24 | 17.48 | 18.81 | 22.41 | 18.85 | 24.61 | 20.48 | 19.56 | 21.38 |
| All firms over $3,000,000‡ | 19.73 | 16.81 | 22.48 | 17.51 | 12.94 | 14.07 | 16.01 | 13.90 | 18.24 | 17.17 | 14.77 | 17.19 |

* Net income before provision for income taxes.
† Classified according to sales volume in the year 1957. Refers to all sales, not ice cream only. The three size groups contain respectively 13, 12, and 15 firms at the maximum. The number of firms varied somewhat from year to year, but in each year included all the corporate firms who manufactured ice cream, except those that manufactured exclusively for sale at retail. Borden's Wisconsin milk and cream data included only for years 1947–51 and 1957–58.
‡ There are four national firms over $3 million and 10 firms including the national firms over $3 million.

earnings a little higher than 50 food processing companies during the 1947–49 period, but earnings have been lower every year except one since then. During the latter half of the 1950's, these earnings averaged no more than one-third of the earnings for the food processing firms. Retail food chains earn more on net worth than food processing concerns, and their earnings have trended upward during the late 1950's. Trends for the combination firms have been in the same direction, but not so extreme as for specialized ice cream.

### Advertising Expenditures

Advertising expenditures have been increased both by specialized ice cream concerns and by combination milk and ice cream firms. These probably were increased to keep up the value of the regular brand in competition with the private label in food stores. About 2.3 percent of sales now goes for advertising in the ice cream business. The author estimates that at least as much is spent on hidden competitive devices. For ice cream, when the advertising expenditures are added together with expenditures on hidden competitive devices, they total about 5 percent, which is twice as great as average profits expressed as a percent of sales. This is expensive to the businessman, and it is doubtful whether consumers get benefits comparable with this level of expenditure.

### Excess Capacity

Excess capacity in the ice cream industry is an indicator both of performance and of competitive behavior. Only about 38 percent of total capacity was in actual use. This is unusually low for an industry in which neither supplies of raw materials nor demand is highly seasonal. Capacity in use varied from only 11 percent in the small size groups to 49 percent in the largest size group.

So far as the smaller firms are concerned, the excess capacity probably results from the competitive behavior of the ice cream industry which in turn, so it may be argued, is a consequence of structure. For the larger firms, the excess capacity may be a function of the peculiar technology whereby the total unit costs are less with newly installed equipment operated considerably below capacity than it was with older equipment when operated at capacity.

### Growth Rates

Growth rates, as measured by annual sales for those that have been in business since 1948, have declined in the last six years as compared with the previous six years in all but the largest size bracket of firms.

## CONCLUSION

The author has concluded that ice cream firms with about 300,000 gallons annual capacity are of sufficient size to manufacture efficiently, to service all outlets but the national food chains to their satisfaction, and to develop brand names with consumer appeal over a trade area of several counties in size. This suggests the optimum minimal size to service outlets which promise growth for the ice cream firm.

Slightly more than 10 percent of the Wisconsin firms are in this size bracket. About 13 percent of the firms in the industry, accounting for perhaps three-fourths of total wholesale ice cream sales, appear to be larger than this size which is necessary for efficiency, and concentration in the industry is rapidly increasing. On the other hand, perhaps two-thirds of the ice cream manufacturers are too small for efficiency and experience great difficulty in growing because of competitive practices. Where size is greater than necessary for efficiency, any increase in size may be chiefly of benefit to the firm instead of to the economy as a whole.

The evidence appears clear that ice cream distributors have reached a point where their competitive practices are no longer serving their purpose. The industry is worse off on an average, and no size group is better off profitwise. The public, though it temporarily gets lower cost products, may suffer in the long run from destruction of competition. Presumably, many of these practices were introduced originally because they were thought less difficult to control than the simpler and more overt forms of price competition.

The author believes that most of the dairy industry, including some of the largest firms, might welcome more public control of the hidden forms of competition. For example, after the Wisconsin law on unfair trade practices in the dairy industry (Section 100.201) was sustained in the Wisconsin Supreme Court, the industry almost eagerly discontinued the practice of giving free ice cream cabinets and milk cabinets. Yet none could have done so before without loss of accounts. They, of course, may be less eager to move on eliminating some of the less expensive promotional devices and on eliminating discriminatory pricing.

# 6

# THE VEGETABLE
# PROCESSING INDUSTRY[1]

## PETER G. HELMBERGER

### AND

## SIDNEY HOOS

THE VEGETABLE PROCESSING INDUSTRY exhibits numerous characteristics which make a study of its industrial organization of considerable value to those economists or faculty interested in the performance of the markets for farm products. Whereas vegetable proces·
sors sell their products in a market that is essentially national in
scope, the raw crops are obtained in local markets where the
number of processor-buyers may be quite limited. In this respect,
the vegetable processing industry is not dissimilar to other food
processing industries and provides a good opportunity to study the
significance of concentration in local farm markets. Partly as a reflection of the high concentration in processor procurement of raw
product, vegetable growers have to an increasing extent turned
toward cooperative bargaining as a means of counterbalancing
what seems to them to be the substantial market power of processor-
buyers. This raises the little-explored question of the effectiveness
of cooperative bargaining associations in gaining market power for
members. Another interesting facet of the vegetable processing
business concerns the extent to which processors have integrated
vertically through contractual relationships with growers. The
vegetable processing industry has a long history in integration
through contracts, and this has provided many insights into the
reasons for this type of integration and its consequences for efficiency in marketing.

Before taking up these and related matters in more detail, it

[1] Adapted from Peter Helmberger and Sidney Hoos, *Cooperative Bargaining in Agriculture: Grower-Processor Markets for Fruits and Vegetables* (Berkeley: Univ. of Calif. Press, 1965). Peter G. Helmberger is Associate Professor of Agricultural Economics, University of Wisconsin; Sidney Hoos is Professor of Agricultural Economics, University of California.

is useful to note some of the important benchmarks in the history of the vegetable processing industry. This will serve as a backdrop for subsequent discussion of the nature and extent of competition both in the sale of final products and in the procurement of raw crops.

## INDUSTRIAL ORIGINS AND GROWTH

Necessity is the mother of invention, so it is said; and in the case of the canning process, it was the problem of logistics confronting nations at war that provided the spark leading to invention. Near the end of the eighteenth century, a prize of 12,000 francs was offered by the French Government to anyone developing a method for successfully preserving food. The prize was won in 1809 by Nicholas Appert who developed the idea of preserving food in sealed glass containers.[2] War was the unlovely mother of the canning process, but the need for an inexpensive method of preserving the palatability and nutritive value of foods provided the potential for a commercial market.

A steady stream of technological progress following Appert's early efforts made the potential a reality. The introduction of tin cans, their machine manufacture, and pressure cooking are early examples of important inventions contributing to low cost. Technological improvement has continued to the present day and on a broad front, including improved plant varieties, the use of pesticides, increased mechanization of crop harvesting and preparation, and continuous cookers. Perhaps the most dramatic development in vegetable processing since World War II has been the growth in the production of frozen vegetables. Freeze-dehydration, now commercially feasible, is another step forward; and food preservation by irradiation is expected to receive clearance soon by the Food and Drug Administration. These latter two techniques of preservation may well revolutionize the industry.

The vegetable processing industry got its start in the United States in the 1820's and began to grow very rapidly after 1860. At the present time, processed vegetables account for just under 50 percent of the per capita civilian consumption of vegetables in the United States (computed on the basis of fresh weight equivalent).[3] The proportion of total vegetable consumption accounted for by the processed form has been increasing steadily, however. In 1937, processed vegetables accounted for 32.4 percent of per capita consumption of vegetables; the corresponding percentage in 1961 was 48.9. As of 1961, canned vegetables made up about 41.1 percent of

[2] *The Canned Food Reference Manual,* 3rd ed. (New York: American Can Co., 1947).

[3] *Vegetable Situation,* U.S.D.A., E.R.S. (Washington, Oct. 1962), pp. 25–30.

per capita consumption with frozen vegetables accounting for the remaining 7.8 percent. The share of the consumption accounted for by frozen vegetables has increased in every year since 1949. The trends in consumption patterns have not been the same for all vegetable products, of course. Per capita consumption of some canned items such as green peas and spinach has been declining in recent years—probably because of the increased availability and attractiveness of their frozen counterparts. Per capita consumption trends for canned tomatoes and tomato products and snap beans on the other hand have been tending upward, as have the trends for frozen vegetables generally.

According to data prepared by the Bureau of the Census, the value of processed vegetable shipments of food processors in the United States in 1958 was $903 million. Shipments of canned vegetables amounted to $673 million or 74 percent of the total with frozen vegetables accounting for the remaining 26 percent. These figures refer by and large to the standard processed vegetables; such items as catsup and other tomato sauces, baby foods, soups, canned mushrooms, pickles and sauces, and other specialty items are excluded. The standard processed vegetables are of primary interest in this chapter.

Processed vegetables account for a modest proportion of the total value of shipments of the food and kindred products industry, at least in comparison with such products as meat and fluid milk. At the farm level, the production of vegetables for processing apparently is not a major source of United States farm income. Total vegetable production for both the processing and fresh outlets generally accounts for about 5 percent of cash receipts from total farm marketings.

## THE MARKETING CHANNEL FOR PROCESSED VEGETABLES

In assessing the nature and extent of competition in the processed vegetable industry, it is helpful to begin by briefly describing the entire marketing channel for processed vegetables. This will help place the more detailed discussion of the various segments of the channel in proper perspective.

Vegetables for processing are grown in many areas of the nation. Although some processors grow substantial proportions of their own raw product requirements, most production takes place on numerous and relatively small farms where vegetable production may often be considered a sideline cash crop operation. The farm production of vegetables for processing is highly seasonal, as is true of most agricultural crops. Vegetables mature at different dates but usually during the summer and early fall months and must be harvested and processed in a short length of time because of their perishable nature. Thus, the actual processing of vegetables is also a highly seasonal operation.

The processing industry is resource oriented so that plants are scattered throughout production areas, with plant concentrations closely correlated with areas of high crop density. In order to minimize procurement-processing costs, plants obtain supplies of vegetables from local areas, oftentimes obtaining their total supplies within a radius of 30 miles from plant locations. Contractual relationships between growers and processors determined prior to planting dates are common in all areas. In this manner, growers are assured of a sales outlet and processors of the availability of raw products.

The technology of processing differs depending on the vegetable in question and the type of processing involved. Prior to cooking or freezing, vegetables must be cleaned and waste material such as husks and stems removed. Fans, flotation methods, and specialized machines are used in performing these functions. Once readied for processing, vegetables for canning generally must pass through a filling operation where the raw product is placed in cans which are then sealed. The sealed cans are then conveyed to continuous cookers or retorts of various types for cooking. After the cooking process, the cans are cooled and conveyed to a labeling and boxing operation before being transported to storage. In the case of freezing, the vegetables are first blanched but may be packaged either prior to or after the freezing operation. Of course frozen vegetables require refrigerated storage.

Although each product poses its own special processing problems, the similarity of operations to be performed makes single-product plants rare. Numerous production setups can be used for a wide variety of products, and there are incentives for spreading the costs of the machines used in these setups over many products. The canning of lima beans, for example, entails the same production setups used in the canning of green peas except that lima beans pass through a different sizing operation and the large beans are soaked in water prior to cooking.

Size of vegetable processors varies from the small single-plant firm canning or freezing a few products closely related in processing to the large national processor with plants in most major production areas packing a wide variety of fruits, vegetables, seafoods, and specialty items. Processors, particularly the smaller ones, rely heavily on brokers in locating customers and negotiating sales. National processors may sell through brokers in some areas but mostly maintain their own distributive organizations with warehouses located in various regions so as to provide quick service and a full line of processed fruits and vegetables to customers.

Beyond the processor level, processed vegetables flow into the broad and complex marketing channel for food. Institutional buyers and other food manufacturing companies are processor customers, but the dominant outlet is the grocery retailer who might buy direct (as in the case of the large food chain), or indirect, through traditional or other type wholesalers.

Two links in the marketing channel for processed vegetables of primary interest here are the market for the final product in which processors participate as sellers and the markets for raw crops in which processors are buyers. The final product market is essentially national in scope as evidenced by interregional competition and the product flows from any one major production area to most parts of the nation.[4] Raw crops, on the other hand, are purchased in literally hundreds of local markets scattered hither and yon throughout major production areas.

## COMPETITION IN THE SALE OF PROCESSED VEGETABLES

In assessing competition in the processed vegetable market, major attention is focused on the structural characteristics of the processing industry. Concentration, product differentiation, and barriers to entry will be examined in turn. Thereafter, attention will be shifted to the structural characteristics of the retail-wholesale buying side of the market.

### The Number and Size Distribution of Processor-Sellers

Available evidence suggests that concentration in the vegetable processing industry is fairly low (see Table 6.1). The largest four canners accounted for 30 percent of the total value of shipments of canned vegetables in 1958. The next four accounted for 8 percent, or an average of 2 percent apiece. This leaves a substantial fringe of small firms, each doing less than 1 percent of the vegetable canning business, that in total account for more than half the total industry output. While the identities of the major vegetable canners have been concealed in the source of the data given in Table 6.1, it is known that, as of 1960, the five largest corporations in the canned fruits, vegetables, and seafoods industry on the basis of sales—and excluding the Campbell Soup Company—were California Packing Corporation; H. J. Heinz Company; Hunt Foods and Industries, Incorporated; Libby, McNeill and Libby; and Stokely-Van Camp, Incorporated, in that order.[5] These companies and Green Giant are major processors of vegetables.

---

[4] For evidence on this point, see *Transportation and Distribution of Products by Canned Fruits and Vegetables Industry: 1954*, U.S. Bureau of the Census (Washington, 1957), 45 pp.

[5] *Mergers and Superconcentration: Acquisitions of 500 Largest Industrial and 50 Largest Merchandising Firms*, U.S. Congress, House, Select Committee on Small Business, 87th Cong. (Nov. 8, 1962), 272 pp.

TABLE 6.1

PERCENTAGE OF VALUE OF VEGETABLE SHIPMENTS ACCOUNTED FOR BY THE
LARGEST COMPANIES, U.S., 1958

| Percent of Value of Shipments Accounted For by | Canned Vegetables | Frozen Vegetables |
|---|---|---|
| | (percent) | |
| 4 Largest Companies | 30 | 45 |
| 8 Largest Companies | 38 | 59 |
| 20 Largest Companies | 49 | 76 |
| 50 Largest Companies | 63 | 93 |

Source: *Concentration Ratios in Manufacturing Industry: 1958*, U.S. Congress, Senate, Subcommittee on Antitrust and Monopoly of the Committee of the Judiciary, prepared by the Bureau of the Census, 87th Cong., 2d Sess., Part I (1962), pp. 108 and 109.

Concentration is substantially higher in frozen vegetables where the four largest producers accounted for 45 percent of the total business. It should be noted, however, that the frozen vegetable industry is a relatively young one and concentration appears to be declining. In addition, canned vegetables are good substitutes for frozen vegetables and, with the primary exceptions of Libby and Stokely-Van Camp, the largest national freezers are not also among the largest canners. The largest freezers of vegetables other than the two already mentioned include General Foods (Birds Eye), Seabrook Farms, Slayton Canning Corporation, and Lamb Weston, Incorporated.

The four largest, eight largest, and 20 largest vegetable freezers accounted for 52 percent, 63 percent, and 78 percent, respectively, of total industry shipments in 1954. Comparison of these figures with the corresponding figures for 1958 in Table 6.1 suggests that a substantial decrease in concentration has taken place in the short span of four years. Comparable data for the canned vegetable industry are not available, but data for the entire canned fruit and vegetable industry suggest fairly stable concentration ratios for the entire postwar period. There has, however, been a substantial decline in the number of firms—the mortality being highest among the small, single-plant companies.

While concentration ratios are generally higher in individual product lines than the ratios for the overall industry would suggest, there are reasons for discounting their economic significance.[6] They include the presence of many good substitutes for any one processed

---

[6] *Economic Inquiry Into Food Marketing: Part II, The Frozen Fruit, Juice, and Vegetable Industry*, U.S. Fed. Trade Comm. (Washington, 1962), p. 44; and *Concentration Ratios in Manufacturing Industry: 1958*, U.S. Congress, Senate, Subcommittee on Antitrust and Monopoly of the Committee of the Judiciary, prepared by the Bureau of the Census, 87th Cong., 2nd Sess., Part II (1962), p. 486.

vegetable and keen interproduct competition. Perhaps the more compelling reason, however, concerns the manner in which barriers to entry decline as one moves from broad to successively narrower industries. This facet of the industry's structure will be explored more fully at a later point in the discussion of barriers to entry.

## Product Differentiation

Product differentiation supported through advertising, product quality variation, and other promotional schemes is of interest here because of the possible protection which such might afford the individual processor from the competitive pressure of other established processors and potential entrants. In sizing up product differentiation as a dimension of structure, care must be taken to distinguish between the nationally advertised brands and what may be referred to as the "minor brands," including canner labels that are not advertised nationally and the private labels owned by retailers and wholesalers. While a precise estimate is not possible, it appears that the national brands likely account for no more than 50 percent of total sales of processed vegetables.

In the case of the minor brand market, product differentiation provides the processor with essentially no protection from the rigors of competition. There are a great many relatively small sellers in this segment of the market, and the buyers are big and informed. The large distributor buyers, about whom more will be said later, contract to have their labels placed on products packed according to specifications. Samples of processed products are inspected, and a few large buyers maintain their own laboratories for close quality control. Substantial quality differences are reflected in price.

Nationally advertised brands command price premiums and likely give the national processors some advantages over others. Presently available data do not allow close examination of these advantages, but there are reasons for downgrading the importance of national brands as a sustainable source of market power. First, small as well as large processors are able to put up a high-quality pack, and private labels on fancy grade products, as opposed to standard or extra standard grades, are very common. Second, the products as consumer goods are relatively nontechnical in nature and are purchased and consumed frequently so that comparisons can be easily made. In fact, there appears to be some evidence that private labels are offering increasing competition to the big brand names. Finally, the higher prices received by national processors are at least partially offset by advertising and promotional expenses. For example, according to a Federal Trade Commission study, the five leaders of the packer brand sales of frozen fruits, juices, and vegetables incurred over $1 million apiece in advertising in 1959. On the basis of comparisons between profit rates and the extent of advertising, the report concludes that the "advertising burden for the third to fifth packer label leaders apparently did not generate a sufficient total revenue to permit these firms to earn a very high rate of profit. . . . This indicates that even relatively large firms found it difficult to make advertising-created product differentiation pay for itself."[7]

In conclusion, product differentiation is essentially without economic significance in the minor brand segment of the market for processed vegetables. National brands, on the other hand, likely give the largest processors some modest advantages over their smaller competitors, but the resulting market power for any one company can be expected to be narrowly constrained by competition from other national brand and minor brand producers.

## Barriers to Entry in the Vegetable Processing Industry

Barriers to entry refer to the advantages, in terms of the factors that determine profits, which established sellers (or buyers) have over the most favored potential entrants. The only two potentially important sources of barriers to entry in the processed vegetable industry are product differentiation and economies of scale. The implications of product differentiation for entry conditions may be treated with dispatch in light of the foregoing discussion. Retaining our distinction between the national and minor brand segments of the market, product differentiation does not bestow important advantages on established sellers in the private label and minor brand business over and above potential entrants. The national brand segment is another story, however. Here product differentiation does result in barriers to entry in that the potential entrant would likely need to spend several million dollars for a number of years to establish a brand name with sufficient consumer allegiance to secure price premiums. Aside from the question whether there exists a substantial incentive for entry, there are numerous giant food processing corporations in the food and kindred products industry—the leading dairy product companies might be mentioned as examples—that loom large and conspicuous as potential entrants with considerable financial resources.

In evaluating economies of scale as a potential barrier to entry, two quite different issues arise. One refers to the addition to total industry output that would result from the entry of a new firm of

---

[7] *Economic Inquiry Into Food Marketing, op. cit.,* p. 109.

minimum optimum scale. The other refers to the impact of such entry on the level of production of the raw crop in the local production areas. A barrier resulting from economies of scale would be said to exist if entry of an efficient-sized firm tended to lower prices of the finished products and/or to increase prices of the raw crops in local processor-grower markets. Our discussion of the impacts of entry on raw crop prices will be deferred until a later point.

Scale economies as a barrier to entry may be analyzed by first estimating minimum optimum size of firm and then comparing the resulting firm size to size of the total industry. Stigler suggests, in what he calls the survivor technique, that the optimum size of firm can be determined as follows:

> Classify the firms in an industry by size, and calculate the share of industry output coming from each class over time. If the share of a given class falls, it is relatively inefficient, and in general more inefficient the more rapidly the share falls. An efficient size of firm, on this argument, is one that meets any and all problems the entrepreneur actually faces: strained labor relations, rapid innovation, government regulation, unstable foreign markets, and what not.[8]

The survivor technique is not without some notable shortcomings, but there seems to be no happy alternative for assessing optimum firm size in an industry where most companies are multiproduct companies and many are multi-plant. Using the "Source Book of Statistics of Income" for his data for the years 1948 and 1951 and measuring size of firm by the value of its total assets, Stigler estimates that the optimum company size in the canned fruits, vegetables, and seafoods industry has total assets equal to $6,536,000. Analysis of the dates for 1948 through 1957 suggests, however, that optimum size might be closer to $17 million.[9] Even a firm of this size accounted for a mere .7 percent of total industry receipts in 1957, and there undoubtedly exists some opportunity for entry of smaller companies. Indications are that economies of scale at the level of the firm are very modest when viewed as a potential barrier to entry.

The above evidence relating to a broad grouping of rather heterogeneous firms can be supplemented by some results of a study of the Wisconsin canning industry. Using physical production data, Rens classified all vegetable canners according to their combined Wisconsin production of green peas, sweet corn, and snap

---

[8] George J. Stigler, "The Economies of Scale," *Journal of Law and Economics*, Vol. I (Oct. 1958), pp. 54–71.

[9] Helmberger and Hoos, *op. cit.*

beans.[10]   The  size  class  producing  from  200  to  300  thousand
standard  cases  (24  size  303  cans)  annually  maintained  a  roughly
constant  share  of  total  Wisconsin  production  over  the  period  1954
to  1960.  This  was  a  good  period  for  using  survivor  analysis  since
many  firms  were  leaving  the  industry  because  of  low  profits.  Two
hundred  and  fifty  thousand  cases  amounts  to  a  bare  .25  percent  of
the  U.S.  annual  pack  of  green  peas,  sweet  corn,  and  snap  beans.

Bearing  in  mind  that  we  have  yet  to  judge  the  consequences  of
entry  on  raw  product  prices,  the  following  overall  conclusions  are
tentatively  proposed.  Barriers  to  entry  in  the  production  of
processed  vegetables  appear  to  be  unimportant  in  the  sense  that
persistent  and  pervasive  excess  profits  could  be  expected  to  attract
additional  resources  to  the  industry  and  would  continue  to  do  so
until  excess  profits  disappeared.  Product  differentiation  and,  to  a
lesser  extent,  scale  economies  probably  give  national  processors
some  modest  net  advantage  over  other  established  sellers  and
would-be  entrants,  and  we  would  expect  their  profit  accounts  to
reflect  these  advantages.

It  is  convenient  at  this  juncture  to  tie  a  loose  end  left  from  the
discussion  of  concentration.  Considering  entry  into  a  very  narrowly
defined  industry  such  as  canned  green  peas,  it  must  be  realized  that
there  exist  many  canning  plants  that  could  can  peas  with  nominal
investment  in  new  machinery  and  equipment.  This  is  not  at  all
atypical.  Depending  on  the  plant  in  question,  much  of  the  existing
productive  capacity  can  be  used  for  a  wide  variety  of  products.
Conveyor  systems,  retorts,  fillers  and  cappers,  labeling  equipment,
and  cooling  systems  are  all  concrete  examples  of  machines  and
production  setups  that  are  used  for  a  wide  variety  of  products.
Moreover,  many  processing  companies  have  well-established  organizations  that  can  deal  effectively  with  the  technological  and
marketing  problems  that  arise  in  the  vegetable  processing  business,
with  considerable  expertness  already  developed  and  at  hand  for
dealing  with  the  problems  of  adding  a  new  product.  Trade  channels  already  have  been  established.  In  some  instances,  brand  names
have  been  developed  for  selected  products  that  could  be  easily  used
in  expanding  product  lines.  For  these  reasons  it  cannot  be  supposed  that  established  sellers  in  any  one  narrow  commodity  line
have  significant  advantages  over  the  *most  favored*  potential  entrants
already  in  the  processing  business.  It  is  on  these  grounds  that  we
attach  little  significance  to  concentration  in  single  commodity  lines,
even  though  concentration  measured  in  this  way  is  generally  higher

---

[10] Lawrence  Rens,  "The  Wisconsin  Processed  Vegetable  Industry,"  unpublished  Ph.D.  thesis,  Dept.  of  Agr.  Econ.,  Univ.  of  Wis.  (Madison,  1963),  202  pp.

than the levels discussed earlier for the entire vegetable processing industry. In the absence of barriers to entry, the potentially higher levels of concentration cannot support significant monopolistic tendencies.

### Structural Change in the Retail-Wholesale Food Business

Performance of a market reflects the competitive nature of the buying side of the market as well as the selling side. In the present instance, this means attention must be given to the retail-wholesale food business. The retail-wholesale food industry has been the object of much recent research, and we may here avail ourselves of the major findings, noting very briefly their implications for the performance of the national processed fruit and vegetable market.[11]

The outstanding structural change taking place in food distribution is the rise of bigness, both absolute bigness and bigness relative to the total distribution system. The institution that is primarily responsible for precipitating these changes is the food chain whose growth and success has had a profound effect on the nature of food distribution and has forced other types of retailers and traditional wholesalers to alter their methods of operation. According to the Federal Trade Commission, the share of the total U.S. food store sales accounted for by chains with 11 or more stores increased from 29 to 38 percent between 1948 and 1958. This increase in the chains' share of the total business has been largely at the expense of the single-unit company with annual sales of around $50,000 or less. Largely to cope with the increasing competition of the chain, other type retailers and wholesalers have formed new economic organizations to secure greater efficiencies. The retailer-owned cooperative food wholesalers and wholesaler-sponsored voluntary retail groups have been the outgrowths of these efforts, and their emergence has also contributed to bigness in the food marketing channel.

The rise of bigness in the retail-wholesale food business should not be taken to mean necessarily that concentration in procurement of processed vegetables is alarming or will become so in the near future. The four largest chains accounted for 19.7 percent of total food store sales in 1958. The next four largest accounted for less than 1.4 apiece. Of course, there are many buyers besides the large chains. The Federal Trade Commission, in a study previously cited, reports that of the total sales of 270 freezers of fruits, vegetables, and juices, 24 percent went directly to the 10 largest chains, 38 percent to 675 wholesale distributors before further distribution,

---

[11] See, for example, *Economic Inquiry Into Food Marketing: Part I, Concentration and Integration in Retailing*, U.S. Fed. Trade Comm. (Washington, 1960), 338 pp.

with the remaining 38 percent channeled directly to the remaining retailers, manufacturers and processors, and others. It can be concluded that the vegetable processor who is reasonably diligent in establishing his sales channel will, potentially, have hundreds of alternative buyer outlets for his production. With the many small chains, the voluntary wholesale groups, other type wholesalers, and the institutional trade participating in the national market, concentration cannot be viewed so high as to support a charge of substantial monopsonistic tendencies.

There are allegations, however, that the largest buyers—because of their absolute size, control over shelf space, and use of private labels—are undermining the market power position of national processors.[12] National processors complain that private labels are encroaching on their segment of the market, and there is evidence to support this view. The former president of Libby, McNeill and Libby, commenting on the use of chain labels, is quoted as saying "this obviously has increased the pressure on the advertised brands, necessitating larger expenditures to hold their share of the consumer's business.[13] It is also alleged that processors are granting special terms to big buyers to maintain sales outlets, and as a consequence are practicing price discrimination. Certainly Robinson-Patman investigations in the processed fruit and vegetable industry have not been uncommon in recent years. Whether these allegations and complaints are actually based on abuses of market power by the big buyers or represent the healthful signs of firms experiencing the pain of intense competition is a question that is both important and, as yet, unanswered.

If one were to conclude that the vegetable processing industry is highly competitive merely on the basis of its industrial structure, that conclusion would surely not be abandoned because of the structure of the retail-wholesale buying industry. Quite the contrary, on the hypothesis of countervailing power, a perusal of recent trends in the food distribution system reinforces the belief that competition among vegetable processors in the sale of the finished product is indeed vigorous.

## STRUCTURAL CHARACTERISTICS OF PROCESSOR-GROWER MARKETS

As previously noted, processors obtain their raw crop requirements in local processor-grower markets. Levels of concentration in

---

[12] *Hearings, Small Business Problems in Food Distribution*, U.S. Congress, House, Subcommittee No. 5 of the Select Committee on Small Business, 86th Cong., 1st Sess., 1960, Pursuant to H. Res. 51, Vol. I, Part II, p. 565.

[13] Williard F. Mueller and Leon Garoian, *Changes in the Market Structure of Grocery Retailing* (Madison: Univ. of Wis. Press, 1961), p. 156.

procurement in local markets have convinced many growers of the need for countervailing power to protect their interests. It will be shown subsequently, however, that the significance of the high levels of concentration can be very easily exaggerated.

### Concentration in Procurement

Complete documentation of the nature of concentration in procurement in local processor-grower markets is virtually impossible because of the lack of good data and the conceptual problems associated with market measurement. Available researches show fairly conclusively, however, that the levels of concentration in local markets are, in any man's language, fairly high. A few of the existing case studies are here cited as illustrative of a larger body of literature.[14]

A study of tomato processing in California shows that of the total tomato acreage purchased in northern California by 40 canners in 1956, the five largest purchased 40 percent (averaging 8 percent per firm). The 10 largest purchased nearly 60 percent, and the 15 largest purchased nearly 75 percent.[15] A fringe of 25 small processors accounted for the remaining 25 percent. The authors reported much higher levels of concentration in spatial segments of the market, but these segments were judged too small for purposes of analysis of competition.

A 1963 survey of all canners of green peas and sweet corn in Wisconsin revealed a substantial variation in the levels of concentration in various counties.[16] Concentration appeared to be only moderately high in Dodge County. Fifteen canners there reported

---

[14] In addition to the two studies discussed below, see Bennett A. Dominick, Jr., *The Fruit and Vegetable Processing Industry in New York State*, Cornell Univ. Agr. Exp. Sta. A. E. 714 (Ithaca, 1949), 25 pp.; Henry A. Green and David J. Burns, *Procurement Practices of New Jersey Processors of Asparagus and Tomatoes: An Economic Appraisal*, N.J. Agr. Exp. Sta. A. E. 234 (New Brunswick, 1959), 36 pp.; Vernon W. Ruttan and James F. Ritchey, *The Marketing of Indiana Canned Tomatoes and Tomato Products*, Purdue Univ. Agr. Exp. Sta. Res. Mimeo. ID-24 (Lafayette, 1958), 52 pp.; R. G. Kline and M. E. Cravens, *Grower-Processor Agreements in the Sweet Corn for Processing Industry*, Ohio Agr. Exp. Sta. Res. Bul. 806, North Central Reg. Publ. 85 (Wooster, 1958), 47 pp.; Herbert P. Stutts, *Some Marketing Aspects of the Food Processing Industry in Maryland, Delaware and New Jersey*, Md. Agr. Exp. Sta. Misc. Publ. 329, Contribution 2945 (College Park, 1958), 19 pp.; and Basil Coley, "Structure and Performance of the Pennsylvania Fruit and Vegetable Processing Industry," unpublished Master's thesis, Dept. of Agr. Econ. and Rural Soc., Penn. State Univ. (State College, 1962).

[15] Norman R. Collins, Willard F. Mueller, and Eleanor M. Birch, *Grower-Processor Integration: A Study of Vertical Integration Between Growers and Processors of Tomatoes in California*, Calif. Agr. Exp. Sta. Bul. 768 (Berkeley, 1959), pp. 18–21.

[16] This survey is part of a research project on the Wisconsin vegetable canning industry currently in progress. The project will hereafter be referred to as the Wisconsin canning industry study.

buying green peas and 13 reported buying sweet corn. There were several buyers of each crop in contiguous counties, leading one to suppose that a vegetable grower in the Dodge County area would have many alternative buyer outlets for his production. As one would expect, concentration increases sharply in areas of low product density. In many of these counties there exists but one buyer.

The data in Table 6.2 shed further light on concentration in Wisconsin processor-grower markets. Companies accounting for not less than 20 percent of total production in their respective procurement areas procured in total 21 percent of the Wisconsin production of green peas and a little over 46 percent of the state's production of sweet corn. Concentration appeared somewhat higher in sweet corn, where just under 15 percent of Wisconsin output was procured by companies purchasing over 60 percent of the production in their respective procurement areas. Interestingly, it was not the national canners' operations that led to the highest levels of concentration since these companies tend to operate in the major production areas where several other companies compete for the raw crops.

In brief, one can expect to find moderately high concentration in the major production areas where there may be several dominant buyers and a fringe of smaller competitors. In these markets,

TABLE 6.2

FREQUENCY DISTRIBUTION OF WISCONSIN CANNERS OF GREEN PEAS AND SWEET CORN ACCORDING TO MARKET SHARE AND PERCENTAGE OF TOTAL WISCONSIN PRODUCTION ACCOUNTED FOR BY GROUPS OF FIRMS CLASSIFIED ACCORDING TO SIZE OF MARKET SHARES, WISCONSIN, 1960*

| | Green Peas | | Sweet Corn | |
|---|---|---|---|---|
| Market Share | Number of canners | Percentage of Wisconsin production | Number of canners | Percentage of Wisconsin production |
| (percent) | (number) | (percent) | (number) | (percent) |
| 0 – 10 | 16 | 15.9 | 12 | 18.3 |
| 11 – 20 | 11 | 41.0 | 7 | 28.4 |
| 21 – 30 | 3 | 14.5 | 3 | 29.7 |
| 31 – 60 | 4 | 3.6 | 2 | 1.9 |
| 61 and over | 3 | 2.9 | 7 | 14.8 |
| Totals | 37 | 77.9† | 31 | 93.1† |

Source: Based on a survey of Wisconsin canners conducted by the senior author and data supplied by the Wisconsin Canners Association.

* A company's procurement area is defined as those counties in which the crop in question, either green peas or sweet corn, is normally obtained. Market share is computed as the percentage of production in each company's procurement area procured by that company.

† Totals do not add to 100 percent for a variety of reasons. Information on procurement areas was not collected for some companies. Company inputs of green peas (sweet corn) for products other than straight canned peas (sweet corn) were excluded from the analysis for want of appropriate data. Total production in Wisconsin and in the procurement areas, however, reflect such inputs.

recognized interdependency exists and processors admit as much. In the fringe or marginal areas of production, concentration becomes very great with many instances where there is but one processor-buyer in the market. As it turns out, however, the consequences of concentration in procurement cannot be fully understood without examination of the nature of the supply response at the farm level.

## Supply Functions for Vegetables Used in Processing

Perhaps the simplest way to see that the elasticity of supply at the farm level is a relevant dimension of market structure is to suppose that supply is perfectly elastic. In this case, average resource cost equals marginal resource cost and concentration among buyers is without significance in long-run equilibrium. Greater elasticity in the supply function tends to decrease the difference between average and marginal resource cost and facilitates independent conduct among buyers because input variation on the part of any one buyer will tend to have a correspondingly smaller impact on price paid. In brief, there is a very definite relationship between a buyer's share of the market, supply elasticity, and the impact on price of some percentage change in that buyer's level of input.

To specify precisely what this relationship is, we adopt the following notation: Let $Q$ represent the total production in a local market and $X$ the amount purchased by a processor so that the ratio of $X$ to $Q$ equals the processor's share, $S$, of the market output. Let $E$ represent the elasticity of supply and $P$ the price of the raw product. Now we suppose that the market is in an equilibrium of some sort and that our hypothetical processor is contemplating a change—an increase—in his level of purchases and wonders how this change will affect market price on the assumption that his competitors want to continue buying as much as previously. Let $c \cdot X$ represent the proportionate change in $X$ that is contemplated, where $c$ is the factor of proportionality. Using an arc-elasticity formula, the fact that the increase in $Q$ is given by $(Q_1 + c \cdot S \cdot Q_1) - Q_1$ implies the following relationship:

$$\frac{P_2 - P_1}{\frac{P_2 + P_1}{2}} = \frac{2cS}{E\,(2 + cS)} \tag{1}$$

where $P_2$ equals the price prevailing after the change is made. With this formula, we can specify the percentage change in price resulting from the processor's contemplated proportionate change in output, once values for $E$ and $S$ are known. Table 6.3 summarizes various situations that might arise, given that $c = .10$ so that the contemplated increase equals 10 percent of the firm's input.

If anyone doubts the relevance of supply elasticities to the present discussion, equation (1) ought to convince him otherwise. Consider, for example, two firms contemplating a 10 percent increase in input. If $E = 3$, a firm accounting for 60 percent of the total purchases would cause a smaller increase in price than would a firm accounting for only 20 percent of the total purchases in a situation where $E = 1$! Obviously, an analysis of competition in local processor-grower markets cannot go forward unless definite commitments are made regarding supply elasticities.

It is here argued that the vegetable production industries tend to be constant-cost industries so that long-run supply functions are extremely elastic. About the only potentially important reason for supposing increasing costs in the long run concerns rising farm input prices, especially rents. The production of vegetables for processing is in the aggregate a relatively minor farm enterprise, however, and is usually a sideline operation from the viewpoint of a single farmer. In relatively few counties will the acreage of a vegetable crop amount to as much as 10 percent of total cropland harvested. Aside from intensification on a given acreage, new areas can be brought into production and in the marginal areas vegetable crops account for minute proportions of cropland harvested. In a word, there seem few good reasons why input prices should rise very much as a result of expanded vegetable production.

The above hypothesis concerning supply elasticities can be checked through statistical analysis. U.S.-planted acreage for each of four major vegetable crops was expressed as a linear function of prices received by growers and other explanatory variables. Parameter estimates derived using regression analysis on time series data are summarized in Table 6.4. Only in the case of sweet corn was estimated price elasticity less than 1.

These estimates can be supplemented by some early results of the Wisconsin canning industry study referred to earlier. Planted

TABLE 6.3

PERCENTAGE CHANGE IN PRICE ASSOCIATED WITH VARIOUS VALUES
OF E AND S ASSUMING THAT c EQUALS .1

|   | S | | | |
|---|---|---|---|---|
| E | .60 | .40 | .20 | .10 |
|   | (percentage change in price) | | | |
| 1 | 5.8 | 3.9 | 2.0 | 1.0 |
| 2 | 2.9 | 2.0 | 1.0 | 0.5 |
| 3 | 1.9 | 1.3 | 0.7 | 0.3 |
| 5 | 1.2 | 0.8 | 0.4 | 0.2 |

TABLE 6.4

VEGETABLES UTILIZED IN PROCESSING: REGRESSION COEFFICIENTS AND
AUXILIARY CONSTANTS WITH PLANTED ACREAGE AS THE DEPENDENT VARIABLE,
U.S., 1947–1962

| Crop | Constant Term | Net Regression Coefficients*<br>(figures in parenthese are t ratios) | | | $R^2$ | Price Elasticity |
| | | $X_2$ | $X_3$ | $X_4$ | | |
|---|---|---|---|---|---|---|
| Snap Beans | 28,867 | 1376.29<br>(1.57) | −520.44<br>(.60) | 9179.31<br>(5.73) | .80 | 1.04 |
| Sweet Corn | 101,700 | 20,718<br>(2.53) | −589.88<br>(.29) | . . .† | .52 | .92 |
| Tomatoes | 424,720 | 13,015<br>(3.18) | −3,157.44<br>(2.19) | −10,482<br>(4.68) | .74 | 1.10 |
| Green Peas | −133,800 | 7018.30<br>(1.58) | −478.03<br>(.27) | . . .† | .21 | 1.42 |

Source: *Vegetables for Processing Acreage Production, Value by States, 1949–55, Revised Estimates,* U.S.D.A., Agricultural Marketing Service, Statistical Publication No. 210 (Washington, 1957); *Vegetables for Processing Acreage Production, Value by States, 1954–59, Revised Estimates,* U.S.D.A., Statistical Bul. No. 299 (Washington, 1961); *Vegetables-Processing, 1962 Annual Summary: Acreage, Production and Value of Principal Commercial Crops by States, With Comparisons,* U.S.D.A. (Washington, 1962); *Agricultural Prices,* U.S.D.A., Statistical Reporting Service (May 15, 1962).
    * $X_2$ = Average price received by growers of the indicated vegetable crop, United States. $X_3$ = Index of prices received by United States farmers for all crops, lagged one year (1957–59 = 100). In the case of snap beans, $X_4$ = 0 for years 1947–54 with a trend starting in 1955, the year that the mechanical harvesting of snap beans started on a fairly large scale. In the case of tomatoes, $X_4$ is a linear trend variable inserted to reflect sharply rising yields.
    † There was no $X_4$ in this regression.

acreage of green peas utilized in processing in Wisconsin was expressed as a linear function of prices received by Wisconsin growers for peas, $X_2$, and a one-year lagged index of prices received by Wisconsin farmers (1910–1914 = 100), $X_3$. Using time series data for the years 1947–1962 yields the following results where the numbers in parentheses are $t$ ratios:
$$X_1 = 51.83 + 9.232X_2 - 1.799X_3; R^2 = .37$$
$$\phantom{X_1 = 51.83 +} (3.61) \phantom{X_2 -} (.55)$$
Price elasticity computed at the means equaled 2.3. Economic and statistical analyses of sweet corn production in Wisconsin suggested that field corn is the most important crop alternative. Planted sweet corn acreage was therefore expressed as a linear function of prices received by growers for sweet corn, $X_2$, and a lagged price of field corn, $X_3$. The analysis of the postwar period was stymied by the high correlation between the two independent variables. Using the data for 1931–1941 resulted in the following estimates:

$$X_1 = 51.83 + 9.232X_2 - 1.799X_3; R^2 = .37$$
$$\phantom{X_1 = 51.83 +} (2.20) \phantom{X_2 -} (.07)$$

The price elasticity computed at the means equaled 3.3. Using a lagged index of prices received by Wisconsin farmers rather than lagged field corn price yielded an estimate of price elasticity of 3.9, but the $t$ ratio for the $X_2$ coefficient fell to 1.9. Andrews estimated that the elasticity of the supply function for sweet corn is about 3.5 in Minnesota, 2.5 in Wisconsin, and between 3.5 and 3.8 in Illinois.[17] These estimates were derived using linear programming techniques and relying in part on responses of farmers in a farm survey.

The estimated price elasticities based on time series data are judged to be less, perhaps considerably less, than true long-run supply elasticities. It cannot be supposed that growers form their expectations of long-run price merely on the basis of price in any single season, particularly in view of the price variability that exists. Even if farmers were convinced that the profitability of producing vegetables for processing had risen relative to other alternative crops, considerable time would be required to adjust the organization of farm enterprises to the new situation. Finally, entry into production by new producers would depend on their ability to obtain contracts with processors; there have existed instances where price has been in excess of that required to bring forth sufficient production for the processing outlet and where potential producers have been denied contracts. In conclusion, we prefer to interpret the computed elasticities discussed above as meaningful evidence supporting the hypothesis that the long-run supply functions for processing vegetables are highly elastic. Using Andrews' estimates and those derived in the Wisconsin canning industry study as benchmarks, long-run supply elasticities for processing vegetable crops are judged unlikely to be less than 3.0 in major areas and much higher in marginal areas.

The implications of the above analysis of supply are twofold. First, elastic supply response tends to encourage independent market conduct in procurement even where concentration might be quite high. Suppose, for example, that a buyer's share of the market is 50 percent and that supply elasticity equals 3.0. If the buyer increases input by 5 percent, price would rise by roughly .5 percent, given input levels for all other firms. Under these circumstances, there would be little incentive for collusive agreements to restrict total input, and departures from such agreements on the part of one's rivals would be very hard to detect.

Second, elastic supply response tends to lower barriers to entry in that entry of new plant capacity need not be associated with substantial price hikes. The point is that a potential entrant has considerable latitude in locating new plants, ranging all the way from

---

[17] Richard A. Andrews, *A Study of the Sweet Corn Industry in the Midwest Farm Economy*, Minn. Agr. Exp. Sta. Tech. Bul. 232, North Central Reg. Publ. 95 (St. Paul, 1959), 116 pp.

areas of high product density where entry might raise crop prices significantly, at least in the short run, to areas where there may be no other processor. Of course, one can infer from the existence of production patterns that some areas have a comparative advantage over others. As product density in such areas increases, price will tend to rise, not because of a single entrant but because of the procurement needs of a succession of entrants. As price rises, potential production areas formerly not profitable become so. It cannot be supposed, however, that the location of a single plant in a local market serves as the basis for gaining excess profit through monopsonistic exploitation, for if excess profit is in fact observed, further entry can be expected to occur. On this argument, little significance should be attached to the higher levels of concentration found in the minor production areas with low product density. The apparent monopsonistic structure in such areas *is the result* of economic conditions that do not support highly profitable operations.

### Grower-owned Cooperative Processors

Because of their nonprofit character, grower-owned cooperative processors can be expected to contribute to effective competition depending on the extent of their operations. Farm cooperatives have been playing an increasingly important role in the fruit processing industry but have yet to assume a substantial position in vegetables nationally. Peaches, pears, oranges, Concord grapes, and red tart cherries are examples of fruits processed on a fairly wide scale by farm cooperatives. Frozen sweet corn and canned tomato products, since the entry of California Canners and Growers, Incorporated, in the late 1950's, are examples of vegetables where cooperative processing likely contributes in a meaningful way to the effectiveness of competition in certain processor-grower markets.

### Concentration Among Sellers of Raw Vegetable Crops

The market structures of the selling industries in processor-grower markets are atomistic in the absence of cooperative bargaining associations. The growers of processing vegetables are numerous and, with few exceptions, relatively small. Quality differences are established by grading standards and procedures rather than through persuasive advertising and brand names. Barriers to entry into the production of processing crops are negligible.

Perhaps the largest growers of processing vegetables can be found among those processors who produce some of their own raw product requirements. Just as growers have in certain areas integrated forward into processing, processors have integrated backward into raw product production. No systematic data are available at this time on the extent to which processors have integrated backward into production. There are known examples such as asparagus and peas in Illinois where processors produce more than 50 percent of their own raw product requirements.[18] In Wisconsin, nearly a quarter of the snap bean canners produce all of their own snap bean requirements. These examples are exceptions to the rule, however, in that independent farmers produce the bulk of vegetable crops for processing.

### Cooperative Bargaining Associations

Because of the levels of concentration in procurement and certain characteristics of processor-procurement policies, vegetable growers have shown an increasing interest in cooperative bargaining associations as a means of counterbalancing the supposed market power of processors.[19] Cooperative bargaining in vegetables dates back to the early efforts to organize Utah growers shortly after World War I. These efforts resulted in the Utah State Canning Crops Association which is one of the leading bargaining associations today. Only two vegetable bargaining associations had been organized by 1940 and one of these had been discontinued by that date.

By 1960, however, the number of associations representing vegetable growers had increased to 24. These associations are found in nearly all major production areas, but many of them have merely been organized and have not yet commenced negotiating contract terms with processors. The American Farm Bureau Federation (AFBF) has also become quite active in cooperative bargaining in fruit and vegetable markets. The American Agricultural Marketing Association incorporated in 1960 (an affiliate of AFBF) was created to assist state farm bureaus in organizing state and regional bargaining associations and to coordinate their bargaining efforts and assist in data collection and analysis. As of March, 1962, 18 state-wide marketing cooperatives, each consisting of various crop divisions (depending on the state), had been organized as members of the American Agricultural Marketing Association.

The apparent drift toward cooperative bargaining in processing vegetables, as well as in other farm sectors, raises the question of growers' objectives and the effectiveness of the institutional vehicles

---

[18] R. A. Kelly, *The Vegetable Canning Industry in Illinois,* Ill. Agr. Exp. Sta. Bul. 612 (Urbana, 1957), 44 pp.
[19] Helmberger and Hoos, *op. cit.*

created to attain them. In order to understand the economic consequences of cooperative bargaining, it is necessary to know something of their institutional and economic nature.

Crucial to the bargaining association is the membership agreement through which the grower appoints the association as his exclusive sales agent for a specified period of time, usually no longer than two years. Through signing membership agreements, growers integrate horizontally their selling operations in quest of market power. There are certain legal remedies available to the association in the event of a breach of the membership contract that serve to strengthen further the association's control. When a sufficiently large number of growers in the market have been signed up, the association asserts itself to processors in search of recognition of its right to bargain for members. While there are numerous objectives sought by growers through their joint effort, it is reasonably clear that their primary aim is to enhance net returns.

Regarding the potential effects of cooperative bargaining associations, it is essential to realize that a voluntary association of farmers in an otherwise atomistic industry is *not* an appropriate vehicle for increasing price by limiting supplies, for example, through product dumping or output quotas. Price theory and industrial experience agree that a pattern of market conduct which limits supplies below the competitive level is highly collusive in nature and must be supported by either a few large firms who recognize their interdependence and are willing to do something about it or by industry-wide government programs. This means that the maximum long-run potential increase in price that could be secured for association members can be measured by the difference between the purely competitive price and the price which would prevail in the absence of bargaining. The potential role of a bargaining association is essentially that of a catalyst that acts to accentuate the intrinsically competitive relations among processors at the same time ridding their procurement policies of any monopsony elements that may be present. In this manner, the market outcome may be pushed toward that associated with a highly competitive equilibrium. Of course, if processors are highly competitive to begin with, there is little that can be done by way of price enhancement for growers. There are other useful functions that bargaining associations can perform, however, which can conveniently be taken up after our discussion of the integrating arrangements between processors and growers.

## PROCUREMENT POLICIES OF VEGETABLE PROCESSORS

The procurement policies of vegetable processors are influenced by market structure and such factors as technology, uncertainty,

and imperfect knowledge. These latter environmental characteristics are important in attempting to understand the vertically integrating relationships that have been used in processor-grower
markets for a very long time.

### Processor-Grower Integration

Written contracts between processors and growers are common
in all production areas. They are usually agreed upon in advance
of planting dates. Important contract terms include a price structure reflecting quality differences, acreage to be planted by the
grower, cost of seed, grading procedures and standards, provisions
for settling disputes, control over planting and harvesting dates, in-
sect control methods to be used, deductions for waste, and service
and equipment charges. The exact provisions vary from one crop
to another and between geographic areas. Some contract terms
merely relieve growers of certain production costs, but the total
effect is to bind the parties to certain courses of action in advance
and delegate decision-making authority from one party to another.

Why have such relationships between processors and growers
evolved and what are their consequences for market performance?
The answers to these questions are apposite to the possible implications of vertical integration in other farm sectors.

The need for supplementing the market mechanism with
integrating relationships stems from technological and market
conditions that create special problems in coordinating crop production with the processing operation. Vegetable crops must be
harvested and promptly processed at a certain stage of crop matura-
tion in order to forestall serious quality deterioration. Growers
may not have the technical know-how required to produce vegetables with the desired product attributes. To obtain the desired
finished product, special crop varieties and cultural methods must
be used. Except in areas near large centers of population, growers
generally have no fresh market outlets for vegetables. Processors,
on the other hand, must look to local areas for supplies. In addition, the plans for production must be made well in advance of the
harvesting and processing period and at a time when processors
could not know the intentions of growers and vice versa in the absence of forward contracting.

The problems of coordination could be left to buying and
selling transactions at the time the crop is to be harvested but a
moment's reflection will reveal the difficulties inherent in that approach. Leaving planting and harvesting dates to the independent
judgment of growers—without advanced scheduling—might easily
give rise to an unwanted variability of total supplies among seasons
and of supplies delivered to processing plants within any given

season. The price differentials that a processor pays because of quality differences may be an incomplete signal of raw product attributes desired. Without forward contracting, growers would be uncertain of market outlets for their production on the one hand, and processors would be less certain of expected supplies on the other. Through vertical integrating relationships, production of vegetable crops can be closely coordinated with the processing operation and uncertainty reduced for all parties concerned. The result is a more efficient and economical method of marketing than would prevail in the absence of such relationships.

### Market Conduct in Procurement

Concentration in procurement is occasionally viewed with some alarm, and grower suspicions are not allayed by observing that processors normally confront them with contract terms on a take-it-or-leave-it basis. Yet, the implications of high levels of concentration can easily be exaggerated, as has been noted, and the mere absence of pure price-taking behavior means little.

Empirical research on the market conduct of processors in the determination of their procurement policies suggests barometric price leadership of a competitive variety as a plausible form of pricing behavior, and the plausibility of this suggestion is increased by a study of market structure.[20] In the words of Jesse Markham, a barometric price leader of a competitive sort "appears to do little more than set prices that would eventually be set by forces of competition." In this type of price leadership, the price leader is more or less the victim of competition; an announced price by a would-be leader is not intended to achieve price discipline among other firms but rather to reflect or anticipate an inevitable development.

### PROFITS IN THE VEGETABLE PROCESSING INDUSTRY

The structural characteristics of the vegetable processing industry suggest vigorous competition both in the procurement of the raw crops and in the sale of the finished products. There is the further suggestion that brand names and large-scale promotional programs act as a source of some market power for the national processors but that such power is fairly narrowly constrained by market forces. These conclusions are tentative, of course, and it is desirable to check their consistency with the available profit data.

The U.S. Department of Agriculture regularly publishes data on net profits after taxes expressed as a percentage of stockholders'

---

[20] See, for example, Norman R. Collins, Willard F. Mueller, Eleanor M. Birch, *op. cit.*, pp. 54–60; and Peter Helmberger, "Cooperative Bargaining in Agriculture," unpublished Ph.D. thesis, Dept. of Agr. Econ., Univ. of Calif. (Berkeley, 1961), pp. 216–23.

equity for five leading canning companies and for 50 leading food processing companies in various agricultural processing industries including baking, grain mill products, meat packing, and dairy products.[21] The rate of return on investment was higher for the leading canners than for the 50 companies combined in only one year in the period 1950 to 1960. Excluding that year, 1950, the leading companies in the various food lines with the exception of meat packing always showed profit rates above those for the canners.

Profit after taxes expressed as a percentage of net worth for the leading corporations with assets equal to $50 million or more and for all corporations combined in the canned fruits, vegetables, and seafoods industry (includes freezers) is shown in Table 6.5. The choice of the time period, 1956 through 1959, is dictated by the availability of data. Obviously these data reflect the profitability of processing products other than vegetables, but it should be noted that many companies—including the largest ones—process a great many food products in addition to vegetables; data available at this time do not allow estimation of industry-wide profit ratios for processed vegetables alone. Net profit expressed as a percentage of net worth ranged from a low of 2.0 in 1957 to a high of 6.9 in 1959. The corresponding percentage for the leading corporations was higher in every year. Notice, however, that in two years the leading corporations fared better than all corporations combined by not more than .3 percent. The conclusion is that the largest corporations do only slightly better profitwise than the industry average.

TABLE 6.5

NET PROFIT AFTER TAXES EXPRESSED AS A PERCENTAGE OF NET WORTH FOR ALL CORPORATIONS COMBINED AND FOR CORPORATIONS WITH ASSETS NOT LESS THAN $50 MILLION, CANNING FRUITS, VEGETABLES, AND SEAFOODS INDUSTRY, U.S., 1956–1959*

| Year | Leading Corporations | All Corporations |
|------|----------------------|------------------|
| | (percent return on investment) | |
| 1956 | 7.7 | 6.0 |
| 1957 | 2.3 | 2.0 |
| 1958 | 7.3 | 6.5 |
| 1959 | 7.1 | 6.9 |

Source: *Source Book of Statistics of Income,* U.S. Treasury Department, Internal Revenue Service.

* The Campbell Soup Company is excluded. There were seven corporations with assets not less than $50 million in 1956, eight in 1957, six in 1958, and eight in 1959.

[21] *Marketing and Transportation Situation,* U.S.D.A., E.R.S., MTS–146 (Washington, 1962), p. 16.

The above data relating to the rather broad canning and freezing industry can be supplemented by profit data on vegetable canners in Wisconsin. Excluding the national canners, the 10 largest Wisconsin vegetable canners in 1959 were identified using total production of canned peas, sweet corn, and snap beans as the measure of size. The operations of these canners are centered almost exclusively around vegetable processing. Over the five-year period 1955 through 1959, their profits before U.S. and state corporate income taxes were deducted averaged 5.2 percent of net worth. This represents a fairly low rate of return on investment. The rate of return would have been even lower if the smaller companies, particularly the egressors, had been included in the sample.

The available profit data are by no means completely satisfactory in assessing the nature of competition in vegetable processing. Aside from the vexing problems arising out of multiple product operations and industry classifications that are too broad for our purposes, accounting profits are subject to numerous well-known limitations in ascertaining the extent of "economic profits." In spite of these limitations, however, the data—such as they are—are quite consistent with inferences based on a study of structure. There is no evidence of pervasive and substantial excess profits in the vegetable processing industry. The largest companies may be enjoying elements of excess profits but such excesses tend to be lower than those of leading corporations in other food processing industries and would appear to be on the whole rather modest.

## SUMMARY AND CONCLUSIONS

Evaluating the extent and consequences of competition is an enormously complex research problem in which theory is only of partial help and good empirical evidence often hard to come by. Under such circumstances, the most the researcher can do is assemble the available data in mosaic fashion according to the outline provided by price theory, using judgment to bridge the gaps, and taking care that the parts add up to a consistent and meaningful whole.

When this is done in the present instance, the following general picture emerges. Competition in the vegetable processing industry is keen and effective with associated benefits accruing to both vegetable growers and consumers. Growers generally do not appear to be exploited by processors as evidenced by the lean marketing margins and low profit rates obtained by processors. Consumers, on the other hand, benefit from high-quality products, wide selection, and prices that closely reflect the costs that must be incurred in supplying the market.

The view that bargaining associations are effective in enhancing growers' long-run net returns by counterbalancing the market power of processors seems largely unfounded as a general case, although special situations may exist. Perhaps too much emphasis has been given to the high levels of concentration in local processor-grower markets, which can be very misleading if the problem is not probed more deeply. This should not be taken to mean that cooperative bargaining associations have no useful role in processor-grower markets. Bargaining associations can seek to strengthen the mutuality and uniformity of contracts used by processors in procurement, thereby further protecting the interests of growers and reducing discrimination among them. Services may be provided to members similar to those provided by trade associations. In marketing order programs, there is a need for legitimized leadership that can speak with authority for the interests of farmers; bargaining associations are well suited to this purpose. It may well be that bargaining associations will play an increasingly important role in agriculture as vertically integrating relationships of the type found in vegetable processor-grower markets become more commonplace in other farm sectors.

# 7

# THE APPLE
# PROCESSING INDUSTRY

## HOMER C. EVANS[1]

THE OBJECTIVE of this chapter is to determine the nature and the amount of competition among apple processors. The primary effects of competition are registered through price. Price is the focal point of our allocating mechanism; that is, it directs production and consumption and distributes incomes. In order to evaluate competition in the apple processing industry, it is helpful to examine the historical production and utilization of apples in the United States.

### APPLE PRODUCTION

Production of apples has been reported in every state, but commercial production is limited to about 35 states. According to the 1950 Census of Agriculture, only 1 percent of the total national apple production was in the 13 states where commercial production was not reported. In 1934, the U.S. Department of Agriculture's Crop Reporting Services began reporting production and utilization of apples for commercial areas and since 1938 has confined its estimates to commercial areas in the 35 states. Observations will be confined to the period of 1934 to 1962.

Figure 7.1 shows the distribution of apple trees in the United States in 1954. The bulk of the commercial production is concentrated in a few areas. Washington State is the most important, accounting for slightly less than one-fourth of the commercial crop in recent years. The Appalachian area (Pennsylvania, Maryland, West Virginia, and Virginia) is second, producing approximately one-fifth of the crop. New York State is in third place, accounting for slightly less than the Appalachian area. Michigan and California

[1] Professor and Chairman of the Department of Economics and Rural Sociology, West Virginia University.

FIG. 7.1—Apple trees of all ages in the United States in 1954. One dot represents 20,000 trees, county unit basis. (Courtesy, U.S. Dept. of Commerce, Bur. of the Census.)

produce smaller, but important, quantities. The remainder, about one-fourth of the crop, is scattered over several states, mostly east of the Mississippi River. In summary, about two-thirds of the national crop comes from an area extending out from the Appalachian area for a distance of about 500 miles, mostly to the north and west (Figure 7.1).

Average annual commercial production in the United States from 1934 to 1962 was 114,093,000 bushels (Table 7.1).

## Apple Utilization

Sales to the processors total a large proportion of the crop. The average annual sales to processors from 1934 to 1962 were 31,585,000 bushels, or slightly over 25 percent of the crop. In the last five years, processor sales accounted for one-third of all sales.

Variety and price are important factors in determining the utilization of the apple crop. Although there appears to be a rather high degree of substitution among varieties of apples, some varieties are better suited for some uses than others. Red Delicious, McIntosh, and Winesap are generally preferred for fresh use, and Gravenstein, Greening, York, and Baldwin are preferred for processing. Stayman, Rome Beauty, Golden Delicious, and Grimes Golden are considered desirable by either fresh or processing outlets. Although there is a rather wide distribution of each variety,

TABLE 7.1

APPLES—PRODUCTION, FARM DISPOSITION, AND UTILIZATION OF THE
COMMERCIAL CROP, UNITED STATES, 1934–1962

| | | | Farm Disposition | | Utilization of Sale | |
|---|---|---|---|---|---|---|
| Year | Total Production | Production Having Value | Farm household use | Sold | Fresh sales | Processed sales |
| | | | *(thousand bushels)* | | | |
| 1934 | 106,005 | 104,757 | 7,499 | 97,258 | 73,790 | 23,468 |
| 1935 | 140,398 | 131,843 | 9,440 | 122,403 | 91,349 | 31,054 |
| 1936 | 98,025 | 97,295 | 6,364 | 90,931 | 68,994 | 21,937 |
| 1937 | 153,169 | 141,035 | 9,123 | 131,912 | 98,123 | 33,879 |
| 1938 | 105,718 | 101,850 | 6,367 | 95,483 | 75,546 | 19,937 |
| 1939 | 139,247 | 124,729 | 7,565 | 117,164 | 83,839 | 33,325 |
| 1940 | 111,436 | 106,811 | 6,673 | 100,138 | 78,195 | 21,943 |
| 1941 | 122,217 | 119,642 | 6,680 | 112,962 | 79,629 | 33,333 |
| 1942 | 126,707 | 118,368 | 6,404 | 111,964 | 77,853 | 34,111 |
| 1943 | 87,310 | 87,310 | 4,851 | 82,459 | 58,103 | 24,356 |
| 1944 | 121,266 | 119,225 | 6,113 | 113,112 | 77,808 | 35,304 |
| 1945 | 66,686 | 66,686 | 2,906 | 63,780 | 47,264 | 16,516 |
| 1946 | 118,901 | 118,394 | 5,406 | 112,988 | 75,658 | 37,330 |
| 1947 | 112,892 | 108,422 | 4,846 | 103,576 | 77,207 | 26,369 |
| 1948 | 89,330 | 88,497 | 4,155 | 84,342 | 64,887 | 19,455 |
| 1949 | 134,309 | 122,077 | 4,777 | 117,300 | 80,082 | 37,218 |
| 1950 | 123,769 | 119,974 | 4,437 | 115,537 | 75,184 | 40,353 |
| 1951 | 111,799 | 101,723 | 4,374 | 97,349 | 69,153 | 28,196 |
| 1952 | 94,085 | 94,085 | 3,580 | 90,505 | 65,587 | 24,918 |
| 1953 | 95,778 | 95,778 | 3,143 | 92,635 | 65,023 | 27,612 |
| 1954 | 111,878 | 111,578 | 3,189 | 108,389 | 69,277 | 39,112 |
| 1955 | 106,263 | 103,394 | 2,628 | 100,766 | 67,836 | 32,930 |
| 1956 | 101,315 | 101,295 | 2,726 | 98,569 | 63,408 | 35,161 |
| 1957 | 119,258 | 117,492 | 2,665 | 114,827 | 78,553 | 36,274 |
| 1958 | 127,485 | 125,179 | 2,540 | 122,639 | 82,297 | 40,342 |
| 1959 | 126,847 | 125,240 | 2,365 | 122,875 | 79,872 | 43,003 |
| 1960 | 108,515 | 108,415 | 2,160 | 106,255 | 70,164 | 36,091 |
| 1961 | 126,565 | 126,138 | 2,202 | 122,936 | 77,533 | 45,403 |
| 1962 | 125,425 | 125,350 | 2,116 | 123,234 | 76,564 | 46,670 |

Source: *Fruits (Noncitrus)—Production, Farm Disposition, Value and Utilization of Sales*, U.S.D.A., issued as follows: 1889–1944, May 1948; 1944–1949, October 1952; 1950–51, July 1952; 1951–1952, July 1953; 1952–1953, July 1954; 1953–1954, July 1955.

the Appalachian area and New York State produce a high proportion of the processing and dual-purpose varieties.

Even though processors prefer certain varieties for processing, some like to use a blend of many varieties in making applesauce. Due to yearly variations in variety production, blending enables processors to produce a more uniform product than would be possible with only one or two varieties. Although some varieties are preferred for processing and others for the fresh market, all are used by both outlets. Price is important in determining whether apples will go to the fresh or to the processor outlet.

## The Production of Apple Slices and Sauce

Applesauce and slices account for a considerable part of all apples processed and have increased in importance over the past years. In the Appalachian area, applesauce and slices are more important than they are over the United States as a whole. Sauce and slices are important to apple processors in the Appalachian area, and this area also is a major source of supply for the nation. Table 7.2 gives the total pack of sauce in the United States and the percentage packed in the various areas. The Appalachian area supplies slightly less than one-half of the supply, followed by New York and California.

Table 7.3 gives the total pack of sliced apples in the United States and the percentage packed in the various areas and states. Again the Appalachian area is a major source of supply, producing

TABLE 7.2

Applesauce—Total Pack United States and Percentage Distribution by States or Groups of States, 1934–1962

| Year | U.S. (thousand cases) | Md., Pa., Va., W. Va. | N.Y. | Calif. | Others |
|------|------|------|------|------|------|
| 1934 | 1,829 | . . . | . . . | . . . | . . . |
| 1935 | 1,887 | . . . | . . . | . . . | . . . |
| 1936 | 2,353 | 48.9 | 49.7 | . . . | 1.4 |
| 1937 | 3,161 | 58.7 | 40.0 | . . . | 1.3 |
| 1938 | 1,526 | 44.7 | 54.7 | . . . | 0.6 |
| 1939 | 3,056 | 46.1 | 53.5 | . . . | 0.4 |
| 1940 | 2,634 | 62.1 | 36.9 | . . . | 1.0 |
| 1941 | 4,182 | 52.0 | 45.3 | . . . | 2.7 |
| 1942 | 4,590 | 59.7 | 37.0 | . . . | 3.3 |
| 1943 | 2,225 | 44.7 | 48.5 | . . . | 6.8 |
| 1944 | 4,301 | 64.3 | 28.3 | . . . | 7.4 |
| 1945 | 1,984 | 66.6 | . . .* | . . . | 33.4 |
| 1946 | 8,239 | 57.3 | 27.5 | . . . | 15.2 |
| 1947 | 6,083 | 56.0 | 36.8 | . . . | 7.2 |
| 1948 | 4,851 | 60.2 | 31.6 | 6.3 | 1.9 |
| 1949 | 8,611 | 54.4 | 30.7 | 8.3 | 6.6 |
| 1950 | 12,541 | 53.4 | 31.8 | 7.3 | 7.5 |
| 1951 | 8,982 | 46.8 | 38.0 | 10.2 | 5.0 |
| 1952 | 8,914 | 46.7 | 32.1 | 15.8 | 5.4 |
| 1953 | 11,204 | 48.1 | 31.2 | 14.9 | 5.8 |
| 1954 | 15,294 | 48.2 | 32.8 | 14.0 | 5.0 |
| 1955 | 13,477 | 47.8 | 30.9 | 15.6 | 5.7 |
| 1956 | 15,339 | 47.1 | 32.2 | 13.6 | 7.1 |
| 1957 | 14,006 | 43.6 | 30.5 | 17.8 | 8.1 |
| 1958 | 16,003 | 45.8 | 29.0 | 15.8 | 9.4 |
| 1959 | 17,240 | 48.7 | 27.5 | 14.4 | 9.4 |
| 1960 | 17,571 | 46.4 | 26.2 | 15.3 | 12.1 |
| 1961 | 19,663 | 39.0 | 31.9 | 13.4 | 15.7 |
| 1962 | 20,399 | 42.5 | 31.9 | 13.6 | 12.0 |

Source: National Canners Association data.
* Included in other states.

TABLE 7.3

Sliced Apples—Total Pack United States and Percentage Distribution
by States or Groups of States, 1934–1962

| Year | U.S. (thousand cases) | Md., Pa., Va., W. Va. | N.Y. | Wash., Oreg. | Others |
|------|------|------|------|------|------|
| 1934 | 2,584 | . . . | . . . | . . . | . . . |
| 1935 | 2,331 | . . . | . . . | . . . | . . . |
| 1936 | 2,620 | 34.2 | 4.1 | 59.1 | 2.6 |
| 1937 | 2,672 | 53.5 | 9.7 | 35.1 | 1.7 |
| 1938 | 1,750 | 49.7 | 11.6 | 37.1 | 1.6 |
| 1939 | 2,840 | 48.9 | 14.2 | 36.2 | 0.7 |
| 1940 | 2,249 | 52.8 | 13.7 | 32.5 | 1.0 |
| 1941 | 4,348 | 51.4 | 13.0 | 31.0 | 4.6 |
| 1942 | 4,164 | 61.4 | 15.6 | 21.6 | 1.4 |
| 1943 | 1,878 | 51.3 | 23.1 | 24.8 | 0.8 |
| 1944 | 3,355 | 60.8 | 18.7 | 19.0 | 1.5 |
| 1945 | 1,191 | 73.8 | . . .* | 25.7 | 0.5 |
| 1946 | 3,266 | 58.6 | 22.7 | 14.1 | 4.6 |
| 1947 | 2,241 | 54.2 | 33.2 | 11.0 | 1.6 |
| 1948 | 1,687 | 58.5 | 28.5 | 11.9 | 1.1 |
| 1949 | 4,213 | 56.6 | 27.6 | 8.8 | 7.0 |
| 1950 | 5,264 | 59.5 | 21.9 | 14.7 | 3.9 |
| 1951 | 3,388 | 60.1 | 29.4 | 7.4 | 3.1 |
| 1952 | 2,560 | 60.8 | 27.5 | 8.6 | 3.1 |
| 1953 | 2,941 | 47.2 | 34.7 | 12.8 | 5.3 |
| 1954 | 4,709 | 56.0 | 27.9 | 9.7 | 6.4 |
| 1955 | 3,587 | 58.7 | 25.5 | 9.2 | 6.6 |
| 1956 | 3,917 | 59.6 | 24.1 | 9.6 | 6.7 |
| 1957 | 3,668 | 54.9 | 22.0 | 14.2 | 8.9 |
| 1958 | 3,639 | 55.5 | 29.0 | 10.4 | 5.1 |
| 1959 | 4,034 | 62.6 | 21.0 | 7.5 | 8.9 |
| 1960 | 3,326 | 59.3 | 24.0 | 8.0 | 8.6 |
| 1961 | 3,986 | 59.2 | 25.1 | 5.8 | 9.8 |
| 1962 | 4,036 | 59.8 | 23.0 | 10.5 | 6.7 |

Source: National Canners Association data.
* Included in other states.

over one-half of the total. It is followed by New York, Washington,
and Oregon.

## Delineation of the Market

A market may be defined as the area within which the price-
making forces of supply and demand operate to establish price, and
transfers of ownership are consummated. The sellers make up the
supply side and the buyers make up the demand side of the market.
It is necessary to identify the buyers and sellers in a given market
in order to make a meaningful analysis of their behavior as related
to the establishment of price. The principal criterion for grouping
firms together in a market is whether or not they are selling
or buying substitute products. A second criterion for grouping
firms is whether or not they have similar structural patterns.

The phrase, similar structural pattern, indicates that the firms have similar technological, market, and organizational problems. In other words, all pertinent conditions confronting the firms are similar. Similar structural pattern groupings fall along product or industry lines. The concept of an industry provides the criteria for narrowing the market to an analytically meaningful size. The market subgroup consists of all the firms that belong to the same market group and at the same time belong to the same industry. It includes all the firms that sell substitute products and have similar structural patterns. The market subgroup becomes a common unit of inquiry. The firms are relatively homogeneous, confronted by similar problems and in relatively close competitive relationships. It is within this unit that sellers actively compete with one another, buyers and sellers actively bargain with one another, and price is formed.

*Apple Sellers.* It will be argued that all apple growers (sellers) in the United States belong to the same market subgroup because they are selling substitute products and are confronted with similar problems. An apple grower may sell his apples through any of the following outlets: buyers of fresh apples, f.o.b., orchard; processor-buyers, f.o.b., processing plant; and one of many central wholesale markets, f.o.b., central market. Usually apples are sold on the basis of U.S. Grades and Standards, regardless of types of outlet (fresh or processor) or market place. Grades standardize apples; that is, they classify apples by variety, quality, and size.

The prices of all grades, varieties, and sizes of apples are closely related and tend to move together due to their high degree of substitution. Also, all market places are tied together because apple sellers substitute one market place for another. For example, if farmer A can realize a higher f.o.b. orchard price for his apples by selling in Chicago than by selling in Atlanta, he will tend to substitute Chicago for Atlanta until returns are the same. In the same way, he determines whether to sell to the fresh or processor outlets. Therefore, all apple growers are selling substitute products.

Technological, marketing, and organizational problems which confront farmer A in the production of apples are similar to those confronting all other apple growers. Although apples are produced over a large part of the United States, the bulk of the commercial crop is produced in four areas (Figure 7.1). The time necessary to establish a producing orchard is about the same in each area. In the various areas, the length of growing season and production costs present a similar problem. Costs are somewhat higher in some areas than in others, but in general, yields in these areas also will be higher.

The weather presents many problems for apple growers. Frost, winter freeze, drought, and hail are some of the major problems. Certainly, the probability of any one of these occurring varies among areas. However, there may be certain offsetting effects. For example, winter freeze seems to be an important hazard in the Pacific Northwest, whereas spring frosts are important in the East. The temperature and amount of sunshine affect the finish of the fruit, and some areas are particularly favored in this respect. This tends to differentiate the fruit of these areas from the fruit of others.

All producing areas sell through the same market places (Table 7.4). Some areas depend more on processor outlets than do others. However, for any grower there appears to be a number of alternative market places. The marketing problems confronting all apple producers are quite similar.

Therefore, all apple growers are in the same industry and sell substitute products. This qualifies all such growers for the same market subgroup, as defined in this study.

Any apple producer is only one among many, and he produces an insufficient quantity of any one variety to influence the price. In 1950, there were over 2,500 commercial apple producers in the Appalachian area. The 1950 Census of Agriculture reported over 1.5 million farms producing apples.

Each grower is a price taker. He may decide how much to produce and sell, but he must take price as given. Even though there are factors which deviate from the purely competitive situation, apple growers in the marketing of their apples act basically as though they were selling under conditions of pure competition. Each seller has such a small volume relative to the market subgroup that he exerts no perceptible influence on the price of apples, new growers may freely enter apple production and their decision to do so is of no concern to those already producing and selling apples, and knowledge of alternatives is rather complete.

*Apple Buyers.* In the United States in recent years, approximately two-thirds of the apple crop is sold to fresh market outlets and the remainder to processors. In Washington State, approximately 85 percent is sold to fresh outlets while, in the Appalachian area, sales are divided almost equally between fresh and processor outlets. Competition among buyers of fresh apples is similar to competition among apple sellers. Growers freely substitute one buyer of fresh apples for another. Buyers of fresh apples have similar problems in that they handle the same product (apples) and perform the same function. Due to the large number of buyers, each taking a relatively small part of the total volume, and due to the high degree of substitution among buyers, any one cannot make an independent price change because he either will lose all his

## TABLE 7.4
### TRUCK UNLOADS* OF APPLES IN 20 CITIES BY STATES OF ORIGIN DURING 1961

| City | Cal. | Ill. | Mass. | Mich. | N.J. | N.Y. | N.C. | Ohio | Oreg. | Pa. | Vt. | Va. | Wash. | W.Va. | Other | Total |
|---|---|---|---|---|---|---|---|---|---|---|---|---|---|---|---|---|
| Atlanta, Ga. | — | — | 1 | 39 | 1 | 29 | 212 | 10 | — | 24 | — | 345 | 3 | 32 | 102 | 798 |
| Baltimore, Md. | — | — | 1 | 2 | 124 | 33 | — | — | — | 216 | 1 | 87 | 8 | 184 | 66 | 722 |
| Boston, Mass. | — | — | 690 | — | 65 | 129 | 2 | — | — | 3 | 30 | 10 | — | — | 293 | 1222 |
| Chicago, Ill. | — | 108 | — | 961 | 5 | 200 | 17 | — | — | 17 | — | 62 | 17 | 23 | 165 | 1575 |
| Cincinnati, Ohio | — | 10 | — | 151 | 2 | 82 | 5 | 138 | — | 2 | — | 26 | 1 | 55 | 54 | 526 |
| Cleveland, Ohio | — | 6 | 26 | 191 | 12 | 202 | 3 | 512 | — | 45 | 28 | 37 | — | 44 | 10 | 1116 |
| Dallas, Tex. | 3 | 1 | — | 39 | — | 1 | 31 | 14 | 3 | 3 | — | 58 | 76 | 8 | 221 | 458 |
| Denver, Colo. | 17 | 9 | — | — | — | — | — | — | 3 | — | — | 1 | 367 | — | 269 | 666 |
| Detroit, Mich. | — | 7 | — | 622 | 2 | 2 | 1 | — | — | 2 | — | 2 | 8 | 17 | 5 | 668 |
| Houston, Tex. | 6 | 24 | — | 94 | — | — | 17 | — | — | 1 | — | 39 | 153 | — | 86 | 420 |
| Kansas City, Mo. | 1 | 12 | — | 145 | — | 2 | — | — | — | — | — | — | 104 | — | 153 | 417 |
| Los Angeles, Cal. | 1101 | — | — | 10 | — | 15 | — | — | 242 | — | — | — | 2364 | — | 877 | 4616 |
| Minneapolis, Minn. | 4 | — | — | 69 | — | 1 | 16 | — | — | 20 | — | 2 | 277 | 9 | 181 | 579 |
| New Orleans, La. | 4 | 11 | — | 33 | — | — | 18 | — | — | 6 | — | 86 | 10 | 12 | 84 | 264 |
| New York, N.Y. | — | — | 351 | 6 | 452 | 3618 | — | — | — | 195 | 456 | 208 | — | 19 | 324 | 5629 |
| Philadelphia, Pa. | — | — | 121 | 1 | 485 | 247 | — | — | — | 325 | 12 | 270 | 12 | 38 | 74 | 1585 |
| Pittsburgh, Pa. | — | 2 | 8 | 22 | 34 | 273 | 1 | 23 | — | 388 | 3 | 56 | — | 129 | 38 | 977 |
| St. Louis, Mo. | — | 176 | — | 331 | 1 | 3 | 5 | — | — | 10 | — | 5 | 32 | 4 | 94 | 661 |
| San Francisco, Cal. | 716 | — | — | — | — | — | — | — | 51 | — | — | — | 815 | — | 90 | 1675 |
| Washington, D.C. | — | — | — | 3 | 24 | 36 | 3 | — | — | 161 | — | 248 | 4 | 55 | 34 | 565 |
| Total | 1848 | 370 | 1205 | 2719 | 1207 | 4873 | 331 | 697 | 299 | 1418 | 530 | 1542 | 4251 | 629 | 3220 | 25,139 |

Source: *Carlot Unloads of Certain Fruits and Vegetables in 100 U.S. and 5 Canadian Cities, also Truck Unloads in 20 U.S. Cities, 1961*, U.S.D.A., AMS, Fruit and Vegetable Div., Market News Branch, AMS-25 (Washington, March 1962).

* Truck unloads in carlot equivalents.

suppliers by lowering price or will be flooded with supplies by increasing price. Again pure competition best describes the situation, although there are deviations from this concept.

Although processors and buyers of fresh apples are substitute outlets for apples, they are in different market subgroups because they are confronted with different problems. Fresh apple buyers purchase for immediate sale without changing the form of the apple, whereas processors buy in a few weeks the amount that they sell over a period of a year or more. Processors also change the form of the fruit. The cost of apples is only a part of their total cost. Containers, manufacturing, storage, and other costs are all factors to be considered by processors. For example, in 1941, total costs for packing applesauce in the Appalachian area were divided as follows: raw materials 27.5 percent, sugar and condiments 7.2 percent, containers 30.6 percent, direct labor 11.7 percent, indirect manufacturing 9.6 percent, labels 2.4 percent, cases 3.0 percent, other warehouse expenses 2.0 percent, selling expenses 3.2 percent, and general and administrative 2.8 percent.[2] Processors depend on local apple supplies, and fresh apple buyers draw their supplies from all producing areas.

Processor-buyers in the Appalachian area are in a different market subgroup from processor-buyers in other areas because the price paid by processors in one area does not directly affect significantly the supply offered to processors in other areas. Processors have their facilities located in specific areas and depend on local producers for their apple supplies. The net cost of marketing processed apple products is less if processed near the point of production in order to reduce their weight, bulk, and perishability.

All processors in the Appalachian area are in the same market subgroup because they are substitute buyers for apples and are confronted with similar production and marketing problems. In a similar manner, all processors in each distinct processing area would be in the same market subgroup. Unlike apple sellers and fresh buyers, competition among apple processors does not fit the purely competitive situation. For a detailed analysis of competition in the apple processing industry, the processors in the Appalachian area market subgroup have been selected because the area is the major processing section in the nation accounting for approximately one-half of the sauce and slices processed and because data are available for the area. Six processors buy most of the apples processed in the Appalachian area. The two largest buy approximately one-half, a cooperative takes about one-sixth, and most of the remaining one-third is taken by three smaller firms. One of the three smaller firms

---

[2] Homer C. Evans, *The Nature of Competition Among Apple Processors in the Appalachian Area*, thesis, Univ. of Minn. (Minneapolis, 1956), p. 92.

operates much like a cooperative, and a second is integrated with the apple production operations of a large grower. The general practice is for one processor to announce a price and for all others to follow with a similar or an identical price. Therefore, it appears that some form of imperfect competition best describes their competitive behavior. Under conditions of imperfect competition on the part of the buyers, economic theory indicates a price lower than the price under conditions of pure competition (efficiency being the same under both conditions).

## Analysis of Processor Price Behavior in the Appalachian Area

*Apple Supply.* Fresh price appears to be established on a national basis under conditions approaching those of pure competition. The quantity of apples received by processors in the Appalachian area is determined largely by the price of apples for processing relative to fresh apple prices. This is outside the control of processors. A rough approximation of this relationship is presented in Figure 7.2. The solid line represents an index of the ratio of processor prices to fresh prices in the Appalachian area, and the broken line represents an index of processor purchases to fresh purchases. The two generally move together.

Processors buy on the basis of United States Grades and Standards. This facilitates the comparisons of offers by the different

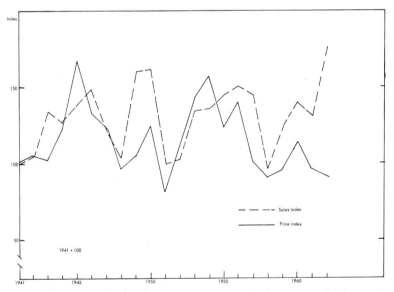

FIG. 7.2—Indices of ratio of processor prices to fresh prices and of ratio of processor sales to fresh sales in the Appalachian area from 1941 to 1962.

processors. In most cases, each grower sells to more than one processor. Consequently, the supply available to any particular processor is dependent upon its price relative to other processors. Therefore, the supply available to any one processor is even more elastic
than that for all processors in the area.

*A Cooperative Firm.* One of the major processors in the Appalachian area is a cooperative firm. Historically, cooperatives are
pictured as a means whereby users increase their returns or decrease
cost, provided present alternatives are inefficient or "excess profits"
are considered as part of total cost and necessary if a firm is to stay
in business. "Excess profit" is the difference between total profits
and "normal profits." In a circular subgroup, excess profits are expected. How does a cooperative as a member of a circular subgroup
affect the price behavior and profits of the group?

An illustration serves to show how a cooperative brings competitive pressure on other members of a subgroup. Assume that the
buyers in a market subgroup of apple processors are made up of
two firms identical in every respect except that firm A is a cooperative and firm B is an ordinary corporation. Since the two firms are
identical, except that one is a cooperative, their costs of processing
and distributing processed products will be identical. To simplify
the illustration, it is assumed that the cost of processing and distributing their products is constant at all outputs, except for the
cost of apples for processing.

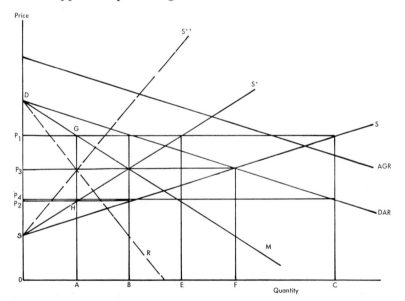

FIG. 7.3—Hypothetical market subgroup situation involving a cooperative.

$AGR$ in Figure 7.3 represents average gross revenue or demand for processed apple products for the subgroup which is composed of two firms. Since the cost of processing and distributing is identical and constant at all outputs for both firms, the derived average revenue or demand for apples of the subgroup lies below $AGR$ by a constant amount. In Figure 7.3, $DDAR$ represents the derived demand curve for apples for the subgroup. The area between $AGR$ and $DDAR$ represents the cost of processing and distributing for the subgroup.[3]

Since each firm has one-half the total derived demand, $DM$ is the demand curve for apples for each of the firms, as it is one-half of $DDAR$. $DM$ is also the average revenue curve for each of the firms, and $DR$ is marginal revenue. It is assumed that $SS$ is the supply curve of apples for the two firms. $SS'$ is the supply curve each firm faces, as it is one-half of $SS$. $SS'$ also is the average cost curve of apples for each firm. Assume that firm B sets a price to be paid for apples. Firm B would set a price at $P_2$, taking quantity $OA$ and selling at Price $P_1$, giving a net profit of $P_1GHP_2$, which is at a maximum. This is also the maximum for firm A.

However, unlike firm B, firm A pays price $P_1$ to its members, returning all profits in patronage dividends. Since growers are indifferent as to which firm they sell, they will be unwilling to sell to firm B at $P_2$ when firm A is paying $P_1$. Consequently, to meet the competition from A, firm B will be forced to raise the price.

This situation leaves the apple sellers dissatisfied. At the price of $P_1$ they are willing to sell a total quantity of $OC$, or $OE$ amount to each firm. However, the processor-derived demand will take only $OB$ quantity at price $P_1$. With $OC$ quantity, the subgroup can only get price $P_4$. This is less than they paid for apples, therefore, processors will reduce the price paid for apples. As processors reduce their price for apples, growers are willing to sell fewer apples and processors can sell a larger quantity of apple products without incurring a loss. This process will continue through successive price reductions for apples until price reaches $P_3$.

At price $P_3$, growers are willing to sell quantity $OF$, and the processors are able to sell that quantity. The processors are making normal profits, or sufficient profits to stay in business. They are not making excess profits as previously. However, if they take a quantity less than $OF$, and firm A continues to return all over cost of operation to growers, the price will be forced back to $P_3$, each firm taking quantity $OB$. Therefore, if we assume that all firms are

[3] For a detailed treatment of the derived demand for an industry see: William H. Nicholls, *A Theoretical Analysis of Imperfect Competition With Special Application to the Agricultural Industries* (Ames: Iowa State College Press, 1941), pp. 31–38.

identical, that growers are indifferent to which processor they sell, and that the cooperative returns all over cost to the apple sellers, profits will be reduced to normal or that amount necessary to keep the processors in business. Average costs will equal average revenue as under perfect competition, provided production costs per unit are the same under imperfect and perfect competition.

With the entry of a cooperative firm, patronage refunds by the cooperative and bonuses by other firms have become part of the final settlement between apple sellers and processors. The introduction of patronage refunds and bonuses may be considered as the equivalent of failure to recognize mutual dependence. If mutual dependence is ignored by firms and they neglect both their indirect and direct influence upon price, the outcome will be the purely competitive price, regardless of numbers. The full effect of patronage refunds is dampened because refunds are made after the grower has decided how he will market his apples. However, the dampening effect will be offset to the extent that such payments were made in the past, thereby establishing a pattern and becoming a factor which the grower will consider in determining how to market his apples. Such considerations on the part of the apple growers partially may explain the fact that there has been a tendency for processors to be handicapped with an oversupply of apples in recent years.

Since the cooperative pays patronage dividends, and other firms pay bonuses to their apple suppliers, it may appear that in actual practice cooperative and noncooperative firms behave in a similar manner. However, the important point is that bonuses were initiated due to price competition from the cooperative in the form of patronage refunds. Consequently, these practices cause competition among the firms resulting in the final price tending to move from the monopsony price toward the competitive price.

*Implicit-Price Deals.* Implicit-price deals, a second factor responsible for competitive pressure, are related closely to patronage refunds and bonuses. The announced price may not represent final settlement between growers and processors because allowances often are paid by processors for hauling, for storage, and for container costs. These allowances are employed when any processor is not getting all the apples he can use at the price offered. Often they start as secret deals between individual growers and processors, but they fail to remain secret and soon become the general practice of all processors. These implicit-price devices are employed for minor price adjustments in an effort by individual processors to attract apples from other processors. Such practices increase the growers' net returns and their sales to processors.

*Entry of New Firms.* Since 1939, three firms have entered the subgroup. Since 1949, they have been doing between one-fourth and one-third of the processing volume in the area. How does this affect competition? An illustration may be helpful in answering this question. The same derived demand and supply relations used in Figure 7.3 are reproduced in Figure 7.4. To simplify the illustration, it is assumed that firm A, a monopsonist, is at first the only firm in the subgroup.

It may be recalled that as a monopsonist, A is faced with the same demand and supply apples as is the subgroup. A's marginal cost and marginal revenue are equal at $G$ and output $OB$. With quantity $OB$, A must pay price $P_2$. After firm B enters (which does one-fourth of the total business in the subgroup), A's relevant marginal cost and marginal revenue are equal at $H$ and ouput $OK$. To obtain quantity $OK$, A must pay price $P_2$, the same as when A was a monopsonist. Firm B also pays $P_2$ and takes quantity $KB$, as this also is B's most profitable price and output as long as B considers its demand and supply to be one-fourth of the subgroup.

Firms A and B together take quantity $OB$ and pay $P_2$. This is the same price and output solution as under monopsony. A's volume has been reduced from $OB$ to $OK$, or an amount equal to $KB$, the purchases of B. A's excess profit has been reduced, but the excess profit for the subgroup remains the same. Therefore, the entry of B has had no effect on the price of apples, on the price of apple products, or on total excess profits for the subgroup. However, firm B has applied competitive pressure to firm A by shifting A's supply curve upward and to the left and shifting A's derived

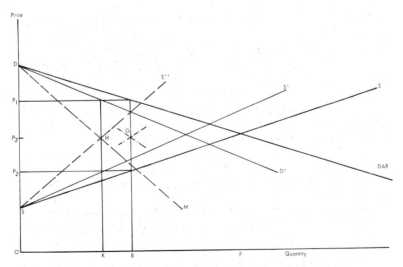

FIG. 7.4—Hypothetical market subgroup involving entry.

demand curve downward and to the left. This in turn has reduced A's profit. Indications are that ease of entry has some effect on the behavior of processors in the Appalachian area, as implied by one processor when he stated, in effect, that newer processors were upsetting the situation, and that his firm was paying a higher price than it otherwise would do to discourage the activities of new firms.

Indications are that there are constant returns to scale of plant, and little if any economy to scale within the range of firms in the area.[4] Also since much of the finished product is sold under buyers' label, entry is not limited by either scale of plant or market outlet. Indications are that one processor is about as efficient as any other processor. Such a situation maximizes the effectiveness of a cooperative and makes the entry of new firms relatively easy.

### Implications

It should be recognized that processors do not have perfect knowledge of demand and of their own costs. Also, resources are not perfectly mobile. Consequently, processors may not be able to establish immediately their best price and output. Therefore, as under perfect competition, price would tend to fluctuate around the equilibrium price. The important question is: Will the equilibrium price for processors in the Appalachian area tend to be in the direction of the monopsony price or of the purely competitive price?

From the analysis of the situation, it may be concluded that the opportunity for excess profits in the market subgroup has been reduced if not eliminated in recent years. The bulk of the evidence indicates that competitive pressure is strong among processors. It appears that there is little opportunity for excess profits over a period of time. The indications are that processor price and output are efficient in the allocation of resources. That is, comparable resources (apples) bring the same returns as in other uses (fresh outlet). From the limited information available on other processing areas, it would appear that the findings relative to competition among processors in the Appalachian area would also be valid for the industry as a whole, with only minor exceptions.

Apple growers may help maintain this competitive market by (1) being in a position to sell their apples through either the fresh or processor outlets and being on the alert to switch supplies to the outlet giving the highest net return, (2) keeping informed about the relative net returns from each processing firm and always being alert to switch supplies to the processor paying the highest net, and (3) supporting and maintaining a strong cooperative processor.

---

[4] For a fuller treatment of costs among firms in the area, see Evans, *op. cit.*, pp. 91–99.

## SELECTED REFERENCES

Chamberlain, Edward Hastings, *The Theory of Monopolistic Competition, A Reorientation of the Theory of Value* (Cambridge: Harvard Univ. Press, 1947).

Evans, Homer C., *The Nature of Competition Among Apple Processors in the Appalachian Area,* W. Va. Univ. Agr. Exp. Sta., Bul. 405 (Morgantown, 1957).

Fellner, William, *Competition Among the Few: Oligopoly and Similar Market Structures* (New York: Alfred A. Knopf, Inc., 1949).

Machlup, Fritz, *The Economics of Sellers' Competition, Model Analysis of Sellers' Conduct* (Baltimore: Johns Hopkins Press, 1952).

Nicholls, William H., *A Theoretical Analysis of Imperfect Competition With Special Application to the Agricultural Industries* (Ames: Iowa State College Press, 1941).

——, *Price Policies in the Cigarette Industry, A Study of "Concerted Action" and Its Social Control, 1911–50* (Nashville: Vanderbilt Univ. Press, 1951).

Papandreou, Andreas G., and Wheeler, John T., *Competition and Its Regulation* (New York: Prentice-Hall, Inc., 1954).

Scitovsky, Tibor, *Welfare and Competition, The Economics of a Fully Employed Economy* (Homewood, Ill.: Richard D. Irwin, Inc., 1951).

Stigler, George J., *The Theory of Price* (New York: Macmillan Co., 1950).

Triffin, Robert, *Monopolistic Competition and General Equilibrium Theory* (Cambridge: Harvard Univ. Press, 1949).

# THE BAKING INDUSTRY[1]

## RICHARD G. WALSH

### AND

## BERT M. EVANS[2]

THE BAKING INDUSTRY is one of the largest in the United States. Its annual sales of more than $4 million are exceeded by only two other food processing industries, meat packing and dairy, and place it thirteenth among all manufacturing industries. Bakery products, while no longer the "staff of life" they once were, still account for almost a tenth of the American consumer's food dollar. Nor is the industry's importance confined to its customers, since the nation's flour millers and, indirectly, its wheat farmers look to it as a primary sales outlet. Of all the wheat flour consumed in the United States, almost half is used by the baking industry to produce bread, rolls, cakes, pies, doughnuts, sweet goods, and other such perishable items.[3] The chief product is white bread which represents over half of the industry's output. We shall focus attention on whole-sale markets for white bread which are illustrative of the industry's market situation as a whole.

### HISTORY AND DEVELOPMENT[4]

Though bread has been a part of man's diet for some 8,000 years, its commercial production has emerged only in the last

[1] The material in this chapter is from a study by Richard G. Walsh and Bert M. Evans, *Economics of Change in Market Structure, Conduct and Performance: The Baking Industry, 1947–58*, University of Nebraska Agricultural Experiment Station and Economic Research Service, U.S.D.A., cooperating. University of Nebraska Studies No. 28 (Lincoln, 1963). Statements not otherwise documented are based on this study.

[2] Richard Walsh is Associate Professor and Bert Evans is Agricultural Extension Economist, Department of Agricultural Economics, University of Nebraska. The assistance of Eleanor M. Birch is gratefully acknowledged.

[3] The baking industry, as used here, excludes the production of biscuits and crackers, which is a separate industry. It also excludes retail bake shops that do their baking on the premises, since these are classified within retail trade, rather than in manufacturing, by the U.S. Bureau of the Census. This usage conforms to the S.I.C. code.

[4] For a more detailed history of the industry, see William G. Panscher, *Baking in America, Volume 1, Economic Development* (Evanston: Northwestern Univ. Press, 1956).

century. In the United States, commercial baking began in the last half of the nineteenth century. During that period, under the stimulus of a growing population with expanding real incomes, consumption of virtually all foods rapidly increased as the nation moved from a mere subsistence level of living to a more abundant way of life. The increasing urbanization of the population was especially favorable to the growth of the baking industry since, outside the cities, home-baked bread was universal. But the baking industry had made some inroads, moving from a contribution of 10 percent of all bread consumed in 1850 to about 25 percent in 1900. Most bakeries were still small retail shops; perhaps only a tenth of them could be called industrial, i.e., operating large plants and selling their output to stores. Few as they were, these bakeries enjoyed about six times the sales of the smaller operations and they were the forerunners of the modern baking industry.

It was during the next three decades that the industry flourished as it adopted mass production and, with the coming of the automobile, mass distribution. Its expansion was something of an anomaly since the very factor contributing to its earlier growth, viz., increasing real income, now proceeded to have the opposite effect. The American consumer began to shift away from starches and to enjoy a much greater variety of foods, especially fruits and vegetables. To the baking industry, the redeeming feature of this changed pattern of demand was that home baking of bread continued to decline. Thus, although per capita consumption of bread was decreasing, the industry's production was rapidly expanding as bread baking was transferred from the home to the commercial bakery. By 1930, the baking industry was supplying 60 percent of all the bread consumed in the United States.

Two other developments occurred during this period that were to have lasting effects on the industry. First, chain grocers began to integrate into baking, producing some of their own bread. This movement started after World War I and, within 10 or 15 years, was important enough to account for about 5 percent of the industry's total output. Secondly, the baking industry shared in the general merger frenzy. This came in two waves: (1) the local consolidations, largely during the first half of the period, and (2) the multi-market combinations, following slightly later and reaching a peak in the 1920's. One of the earliest of the local types was the formation of the American Baking Company in 1907. This was a merger of seven baking companies, each with one plant operating in the St. Louis market. The purpose was to eliminate unfair trade practices and destructive competition, which has a familiar ring more than half a century later. Two of the seven plants were shut down immediately following the merger and, by 1924, three others were closed so that only two plants of the original seven eventually remained in operation. This indicates that excess capacity, a current problem in the industry, was even then rather severe. Since mergers of this local type were not wholly successful in insulating firms against the rigors of competition, bakers, like other businessmen of the day, began to look to other markets for protection. Mergers involving bakeries operating in different markets were sought as a form of insurance through diversification and also to give greater financial strength to the combination than could be found in any single market. One of the earliest examples of this type of merger was the formation of General Baking Company, incorporated in 1911 as a consolidation of 20 baking companies in 17 cities.

The decade of the twenties featured even more sweeping mergers, many of them inspired by William B. Ward whose great-grandfather had started in the bakery business in 1849. The younger Ward opened his own bakery in Buffalo, N.Y., in 1912, but this was only a first step. His major moves began in 1922 when he formed United Bakeries Corporation, a holding company which, within a couple of years, controlled 40 bakeries in 30 cities. In 1923, he organized another holding company, Ward Baking Corporation. The next year, he formed the Continental Baking Corporation which acquired his United Bakeries Corporation. Continental then went on a merging spree and by 1926, it was the largest firm in the industry with 91 plants in 73 cities as well as 9 more plants in Canada. In 1925, Ward and his associates took over General Baking Company, one of the first of the multi-market firms. By 1926, General had 42 bakeries in 32 cities. Ward organized the Ward Food Products Corporation in 1926 as a holding company to control Continental, Ward, and General. At this point, confronted by the prospect of a colossus handling 20 percent of the nation's bakery output, the federal government stepped in with an anti-trust suit, charging Ward, *et al.*, with violation of the Sherman and Clayton acts. A consent decree resulted in April, 1926, by which Ward and his associates were perpetually enjoined from any substantial merger activity in the baking industry, and Ward Food Products Corporation was dissolved. With no further worlds to conquer, Ward soon died, bringing to an end perhaps the most colorful career in the baking business. Although there were other major bakery mergers during the twenties not connected with Ward's empire, his influence on the industry was unique and his imprint remains to this day. The nation's two largest bakery firms today, Continental and General, were his creations.

With increased competition from chain stores during the twenties and with the emergence of giant firms, the baking industry at that time took on many of its present features. It also gained a new sophistication from its frequent price wars. Bakers learned the hard way that theirs was an oligopolistic industry so that the behavior of any one firm affected others and inspired retaliatory actions. As a consequence, there was a new emphasis on nonprice tactics, such as advertising, which has also persisted to the present time.

The depression of the 1930's hit the baking industry hard, all the more because it was not expected to do so. Bread is usually considered depression-proof; when incomes are decreasing, consumers tend to shift away from more elaborate diet patterns and return to the lower-cost staples such as bread. To some extent, this did occur during the thirties but the economic slump was so severe that consumption of all foods, including bread, was adversely affected. Also, unemployed women had more time to bake their own bread and the very low incomes of the period made the small savings gained by home baking significant. Thus, the trend toward commercial baking was arrested for the first time in more than 80 years. Integrated chain stores, with their lower-priced bread, made some relative gains during the depression.

Fortunately for commercial bakers, before the nation's housewives had many years in which to sharpen their baking skills, World War II came along and drew millions of them back into the labor force. Higher wartime income, coupled with rationing that restricted spending, also helped to create a salubrious climate for the baking industry which rapidly regained the ground it had lost in the thirties. The war indirectly aided the industry in another way by settling some of its internecine disputes. A War Food Order prohibited consignment selling to minimize wastage and a Defense Transportation Order restricted the expansion of routes as a means of conserving tires and gasoline. Since both consignment selling and route expansion were particularly aggressive and predatory competitive practices, the industry as a whole had reason to be grateful for this "government interference."

The net effect of the war was an enormous expansion in demand for bakery products until, by the end of 1946, commercial bakers were supplying about 85 percent of all bread consumed. This proportion rose to almost 90 percent by 1950. Looking back at this century of development, one sees an almost uninterrupted growth. But as one looks forward, the picture becomes less rosy. The basic inelasticity of demand for bread has for years been masked and offset by the substitution of commercial for home baking, but this process is fast approaching its upper limit. The industry must soon face the prospect of a stable, or even declining, total demand for bread, though, of course, there remains the possibility of expanding the consumption of specialty products such as snack foods—cakes, cookies, and other sweet goods.

## CONTINUING PROBLEMS

The discouraging demand outlook is one of the industry's major problems. The general rise in consumer incomes since World War II has brought in its wake no improvement in the demand for bread. In fact, investigators typically find that income varies inversely with bread and flour consumption, suggesting a negative income elasticity.[5] Moreover, the demand for bread is highly insensitive to price changes. A price elasticity of demand of zero seems to be a reasonably close estimate; that is to say, consumption responds very little, if at all, to any change in price.[6] This has serious implications for the competitive behavior of firms already in the industry and also for potential entrants. Any firm that cuts the price of bread cannot, by so doing, enlarge bread sales *in toto;* the best it can do is reduce another firm's sales by the amount of its own gains. Similarly, a potential entrant contemplating the introduction of cost-reducing innovations, and hence lower prices, cannot hope to expand total demand this way. Since the total pie cannot be enlarged, any slice the newcomer can capture must correspondingly reduce the size of the other slices.

The inelasticity of total demand, coupled with a rapidly advancing technology, has created a severe problem of excess capacity, or underutilization of plant, in the baking industry. Since the beginning of the industrial revolution in baking at the turn of the twentieth century, the scale of operations has dramatically increased as new machinery has been adopted at a rapid pace. Early mechanization involved the development of machines to supplant repetitive hand operations. Mixing machines were introduced around 1880 followed by special machines for dividing, slicing, and wrapping.[7] By 1930, the largest bread plants which in 1900 produced 1,000 pounds of bread per hour often surpassed 2,000 pounds hourly in a single production line, and some multi-line plants produced more than 100,000 loaves daily.[8] By 1958, the median bread plant operated at a capacity of about 3,000 pounds per hour and some of

---

[5] Lars Jureen, "Long-run Trends in Food Consumption: A Multi-Country Study." *Econometrics,* Volume XXIV, 1958, pp. 1–21; also *Household Food Consumption Survey, 1955,* Reports 1–10, U.S.D.A. (Washington, 1956).

[6] Wilfred Melenbaum, *The World Wheat Economy, 1885–1939* (Cambridge: Harvard Univ. Press, 1953), p. 72.

[7] Herman J. Rothberg, *Studies of Automatic Technology, A Case Study of a Large Mechanized Bakery,* Bur. of Labor Stat. Rept. 109, U.S. Dept. of Labor (Washington, 1956), p. 1.

[8] Panscher, *op. cit.,* pp. 123–24.

the larger ones had bread lines capable of producing 8,000 pounds per hour or as much as 192,000 pounds on a single production line every 24 hours.

Technological advance in recent years has continued unabated. With the end of World War II, nearly all bread plants changed their bread formula, increasing the ratios of sugar, shortening, and skim milk to flour. This change, coupled with oven modifications such as stepping up heat and improving performance of existing ovens, is estimated to have cut average baking time for a pound of bread from about 35 to 18 minutes.[9] These moves resulted in an increase of approximately 100 percent in the capacity of practically all bread ovens in the United States during the postwar years.

While advances in baking technology have been made to a limited extent in small plants, most of the recent innovations have been readily fitted into the operations of medium and large plants. This is partly due to the lower investment and labor costs per unit of output of large versus small machines. The significant innovations are in the production process and the handling of materials. Moreover, each stage of bread production has been subject to output-increasing mechanization and to labor-saving automation of the station-to-station movement of product.

Foremost among recent technological developments are those that have made possible a shift from batch operations to continuous mixing. The conventional batch method of bread production necessitated periods of dough fermentation, intermediate proofing, and considerable hand labor, moving the product in process into or out of machines or rooms at each of 12 production stages. Now baking has become an organized and partly automated assembly line. Under typical conditions, the shift to automated baking in any given plant is only partial, with several of the operations carried on as before, and thus many bread plants have not achieved the optimum level of equipment adoption. Although the changeover is not complete, the equipment is available and its efficiency and output-increasing potentials are felt in nearly every bread market.

## MARKET STRUCTURE

### Seller Side

The general trend in food processing industries is one of declining numbers of rival firms, and bakeries are in the lead. Be-

---

[9] *Administered Prices Bread Hearings,* Subcommittee on Antitrust and Monopoly, 86th Cong., 1st Sess. (Washington, 1959), p. 6189 (hereafter referred to as *Hearings); Administered Prices Bread Report,* Subcommittee on Antitrust and Monopoly, 86th Cong., 2nd Sess. (Washington, 1960) (hereafter referred to as *Report).*

tween 1947 and 1954, bakeries went out of business at a rate more than double the failure rate of all food processors. The baking segment accounted for more than half of the early postwar decline in numbers of processors among the 30 major food industries.[10] Thus, for the nation as a whole, the number of bakeries decreased from 6,796 in 1947 to 6,103 in 1954, to 5,985 in 1958, and to 5,003 in 1963. Some of this decline represents shifts within the industry, as indicated in Table 8.1. The general trend is toward increased size with greater volumes moving through large-scale grocery outlets. The chief losers have been the multi-unit retail bakers and those offering home delivery. Many small bakeries that formerly distributed their products via high cost house-to-house routes have shifted to restaurant and grocery store outlets and are now classified as wholesale bakeries. In the other segments of the industry, too, it is usually the smaller firms that are disappearing. Among the wholesale bakers, the number of multi-plant companies is declining, but those that remain, and especially the larger ones, are operating more plants. Thus, the largest companies have expanded their operations horizontally into more and more markets. This horizontal integration brings under unified control bakeries engaged in very similar production and marketing functions in a widening circle of bakery markets.

Thus, while the baking industry as a whole has suffered a high casualty rate, the largest companies have attained an increasingly dominant position. Table 8.2 shows that the share of all bakery business done by the four largest companies rose markedly—from 16 percent in 1947 and 1950 to 20 percent in 1954, and to about 23 percent in 1958—so that it is now half again as great as it was in 1947. While the rest of the industry (excluding integrated grocery chain bakeries) grew at an annual rate of about 2 percent per year, the growth rate of the four largest wholesale baking companies was 11 percent annually.

Concentration in wholesale baking, the largest and most important segment of the industry, is, as one would expect, higher than in the industry as a whole. While the eight largest baking companies account for almost a third of the bakery business, they share about 42 percent of wholesale bakery sales. Smaller, independent bakeries still do more than half (58 percent) of the wholesale bakery business, but many of these have combined into management cooperatives to achieve some of the advantages of large-scale buying and merchandising available to the major companies. Although such organizations date from 1922, they have

[10] Forest E. Scott, "The Food Marketing Industries—Recent Changes and Prospects," *The Marketing and Transportation Situation,* U.S.D.A. (Washington, Nov. 1957), p. 21.

TABLE 8.1

NUMBER OF ESTABLISHMENTS, TOTAL VALUE OF SHIPMENTS, VALUE OF SHIPMENTS
PER ESTABLISHMENT, 1947, 1954, 1958, AND 1963, PERISHABLE
BAKERY PRODUCTS INDUSTRY

| Bakery Segment | Number of Establishments | Total Value of Shipments | Average Value of Shipments Per Establishment |
|---|---|---|---|
| | | ($1,000s) | ($1,000s) |
| Wholesale | | | |
| 1947 | 5,019 | $1,764,968 | $ 351.7 |
| 1954 | 5,426 | 2,385,721 | 439.6 |
| 1958 | 5,199 | 2,807,650 | 540.0 |
| Vertically Integrated Grocery Chain | | | |
| 1947 | 90 | $ 150,174 | $1,668.6 |
| 1954 | 142 | 265,851 | 1,872.2 |
| 1958 | 178 | 371,941 | 2,089.6 |
| Home Service | | | |
| 1947 | 624 | $ 281,937 | $ 451.8 |
| 1954 | 217 | 297,551 | 1,371.2 |
| 1958 | 361 | 363,937 | 1,008.1 |
| Retail Multi-unit | | | |
| 1947 | 1,064 | $ 219,812 | $ 206.6 |
| 1954 | 318 | 117,892 | 370.7 |
| 1958 | 247 | 155,945 | 631.4 |
| Total Bread Product Industry | | | |
| 1947 | 6,796 | $2,404,000 | $ 353.7 |
| 1954 | 6,103 | 3,067,000 | 502.5 |
| 1958 | 5,985 | 3,556,000 | 600.0 |
| 1963 | 5,003 | 3,790,000 | 757.8 |

Source: *1947, 1954, 1958,* and *1963* (Preliminary Report) *Census of Manufactures, Bakery Products,* Bureau of the Census, Department of Commerce (Washington, D.C.).

Note: Excludes products purchased and resold without further processing. Also, excludes 11,901 retail bakeries in 1958 and 12,611 in 1954 which were covered in the *Census of Business, Retail Trade.* In current dollars, they had annual sales of $649.4 million in 1958 and $581.9 million in 1954. While output may have increased slightly, the number of retail bakeries declined by 710, or about 6 percent in this recent four-year period. Also excluded from the above tabulation are bakery product stores with no paid employees. In 1958 there were 4,752 such stores with sales of $79.3 million compared to 3,932 stores in 1954 with sales of $59.7 million, both in current dollars. Combined, these small retail bakeries account for about 16.5 percent of the estimated total bakery product sales of $4,428.1 million in 1958, a decrease from 17.3 percent of the total of $3,708.6 million in 1954, and about 19 percent of the total of $2,966.4 million in 1947.

become increasingly important in recent years until, in 1958, around $570 million, or more than 36 percent, of the sales of the smaller wholesale bakers were made by the 258 members of three cooperatives.[11] These buying groups rival in size the largest wholesale baking firms. For example, the 120 members of Quality Bakers of America, the largest bakery cooperative, have combined sales of more than $280 million. If the annual sales of the eight largest

[11] *Hearings, op. cit.,* pp. 6036–38.

## TABLE 8.2

CHANGES IN CONCENTRATION AMONG THE EIGHT LARGEST BAKERIES AND COMPARISONS OF THE SALES OF THE EIGHT LARGEST BAKERIES WITH TOTAL SALES OF THE PERISHABLE BAKERY PRODUCTS INDUSTRY, 1947, 1954, AND 1958

| Bakery Group | 1947 | | | 1954 | | | 1958 | | |
|---|---|---|---|---|---|---|---|---|---|
| | Total bakery sales* | Percent of 8 bakeries | Percent of all bakery sales | Total bakery sales* | Percent of 8 bakeries | Percent of all bakery sales | Total bakery sales* | Percent of 8 bakeries | Percent of all bakery sales |
| | ($ million) | | | ($ million) | | | ($ million) | | |
| Sales of Top Two Bakeries† | 253.7 | 40.6 | 10.6 | 346.6 | 36.5 | 11.3 | 506.2‖ | 44.5 | 14.1 |
| Sales of Top Four Bakeries‡ | 384.6 | 61.6 | 16.0 | 613.4 | 64.5 | 20.0 | 820.7 | 72.2 | 22.9 |
| Sales of Next Four Bakeries | 240.4 | 38.4 | 10.0 | 337.3 | 35.5 | 11.0 | 315.9 | 27.8 | 8.8 |
| Sales of Eight Largest Bakeries§ | 624.9 | 100.0 | 26.0 | 950.7 | 100.0 | 31.0 | 1,136.6 | 100.0 | 31.7 |
| Total Industrial Sales | 2,403.5 | ... | 100.0 | 3,067.0 | ... | 100.0 | 3,579.0 | ... | 100.0 |

Source: *Concentration in American Industry*, Report of Subcommittee on Antitrust and Monopoly, 85th Cong., 1st Sess. (1957); *Census of Manufactures, op. cit.*, p. 4; *Moody's Industrials*.

* Industry value shipments, bread and related products; does not include products sold but not produced, nor nonbakery products.
† Continental Baking Co. and General Baking Co. in 1947; Continental Baking Co. and American Baking Co. in 1954 and 1958. *Moody's Industrials*.
‡ Add to † above, Campbell Taggart Baking Co. and American Baking Co. in 1947; Campbell-Taggart Baking Co. and General Baking Co. in 1954 and 1958. *Moody's Industrials*.
§ Includes in addition to the foregoing, Ward, Interstate, Langendorf, and Purity Bakeries in 1947; Ward, Interstate, Langendorf, and Omar in 1954; Interstate, Ward, Langendorf, and Southern in 1958. *Moody's Industrials*.
‖ Includes estimated sales of firms acquired by Continental in 1958. Excludes nonbakery sales.

wholesale baking companies are added to those of the 258 bakeries affiliated with the three largest management cooperatives, these 11 organizations together have about half of the bakery industry sales and about two-thirds of all wholesale bakery sales.

The baking industry follows an organizational pattern typical of many food processing industries in that it consists of a small number of large firms which operate on a nationwide or at least regional basis and a large number of firms of limited geographic scope which distribute their products only in their own local area. It would be a mistake to assume, however, that the baking industry is typical of all food industries since the former has some unique peculiarities. Even the very largest baking firms cannot be said to have a nationwide market, owing to the high transportation costs as well as to the bulk and perishability of their products. These rigid restrictions on movement give rise to almost 100 separate and semi-independent bakery markets.[12] The radius of these market areas has widened from an estimated 50–100 miles in 1946 to about 150–300 miles in 1963, but this development has not altered the fact that bread markets consist, typically, of a metropolitan area and a rural-urban fringe. It is true that a small portion of the industry's specialty items are frozen and transported farther than white bread but even for these products, with lower bulk-to-value ratios, market crossover can be accomplished only within very strict limits.

Consequently, even though the industry has more than 5,000 firms, its market structure conforms more closely to oligopoly than to the competitive model. Since there is little or no inter-penetration of markets and each consists of a small group of rival sellers supplying highly substitutable products to many buyers, a particular company can have an insignificant share of the U.S. bakery business and yet be an important force in those markets in which it operates. For example, Continental Baking Company, the nation's largest, has less than 10 percent of the U.S. industry's sales, but it does more than a third of the bread business in many of the markets where it sells. This situation is illustrative of most bread markets where, typically, the bakery with the largest sales does more than 30 percent of the business, the two largest together about 50 percent, and the four largest more than 65 percent (market estimates range from 46 to 92 percent).[13]

Large firms tend to dominate bakery markets in most sections of the country. In virtually all markets, sellers consist of a con-centrated core of a few dominant companies surrounded by a fringe

[12] *Distribution: The Challenge of the Sixties*, Rept. to the Amer. Bakers Assn. (Cambridge, Mass.: Arthur D. Little, Inc., Dec. 1960), p. 73.
[13] *Report, op. cit.*, p. 123.

of many small firms. The core usually includes from one to three of the largest multi-plant wholesalers and one or two locally owned independent companies that have grown large in terms of their relevant market. Vertically integrated bakeries owned by grocery chains are usually not among the "big four" in particular bread markets. The smaller firms comprising the fringe often depend for their success on a specialty product or specialized distribution channel. Consequently, they are often not strictly competitive with the large wholesale bakers distributing primarily at wholesale through grocery stores.

### Buyer Side

Perhaps the most important change in the structure and organization of bread markets since World War II is the increased concentration on the buyer side. Whereas in the 1930's and early 1940's wholesale bakers dealt primarily with independent grocers, today the bulk of their output is channeled through corporate and voluntary grocery chains. Moreover, an increasing number of these large-scale buyers are in a position to "bake their own" whenever this policy seems potentially more profitable than buying from existing wholesale bakeries. This places baking companies under what is probably the most severe economic pressure of their history. Grocery chains control the terms under which outlets for most bread products are made available and possess the added leverage of actual and potential vertical integration into baking.[14]

In typical U.S. cities, the retail grocery market for bread products consists of a concentrated core of a few large chains (corporate, cooperative, and voluntary) and a fringe composed of a large number of small unaffiliated independents. Stores of the largest grocery chain generally account for about 30 percent (ranges from 14 to 49 percent) of the city's retail food sales and those of the four largest chains for 63 percent (ranges from 39 to 90 percent),[15] the rest being distributed through a large number of smaller firms essentially in different economic markets owing to convenience of location or specialization of function. Indeed by 1958, market concentration on the buyer side of wholesale bread markets was very high, yet, it should be recalled, not appreciably higher than on

[14] Willard F. Mueller and Leon Garoian, *Changes in the Market Structure of Grocery Retailing, 1940–58,* Res. Rept. 5, Agr. Exp. Sta., Univ. of Wis. (Madison, Apr. 1960).

[15] The Federal Trade Commission studied concentration in 15 urban markets. Federal Trade Commission, *Economic Inquiry Into Food Marketing,* Part I, *Concentration and Integration in Retailing* (Washington, 1960), p. 248. Mueller and Garoian found very nearly the same concentration levels in 133 U.S. cities in 1957. Willard F. Mueller and Leon Garoian, *Changes in the Market Structure of Grocery Retailing* (Madison: Univ. of Wis. Press, 1961), pp. 35–36.

the seller side previously discussed. Thus the market structure can now be characterized as one of *bilateral oligopoly*.

The potential integration of retail groups into the baking industry is more significant than the current actual level would indicate. Retail grocery groups bake only a tenth of total U.S. output of bread products, according to the *1958 Census of Manufactures,* but corporate grocery chains produce about 39 percent of the bread products sold in their own stores.[16] Moreover, of the very largest supermarkets, those with annual sales of at least $1 million, about 38 percent in 1959 had bake shops on their store premises, half of which were owned by the retail food firm.[17] With the rapidly expanding scale of retail operations, more and more grocery buying groups have become large enough to do their own baking. Whereas during World War II only 11 of the top 20 chains were integrated into baking and only three more were large enough to be potential integrators, by 1957, 19 of the top 20 chains were baking their own products and all of the top 40 chains were large enough to do so.[18] While affiliated independents apparently do much less of their own baking than corporate chains, it is clear that retail buying groups generally possess considerable leverage over terms of trade with wholesale bakers.

## Product Differentiation

Product differentiation refers to the extent to which consumers distinguish between competing products. Where this differentiation is low, consumers substitute one product for another relatively freely; where it is high, they develop preferences for a particular brand. The brand thus favored can often command a higher price and make grocers eager to stock it. Thus, product differentiation can influence the competitive relations between firms. The common bases for product differentiation in most industries are (1) the ability to produce significantly different designs and qualities of the item, (2) the relative ignorance of buyers concerning the merits of competing products, and (3) the susceptibility of buyers to persuasive appeals about the alleged superiority of a particular item.[19] All these factors have special relevance to the bakery industry.

White pan bread is a homogenous product in physical quality, nutritive value, and palatability (or lack of same, as our European critics would say). The output of one firm is highly, if not wholly,

---

[16] Calculated from sales data in *Report, op. cit.,* p. 103; and, Federal Trade Commission, *op. cit.,* p. 30.

[17] *Annual Report, 1959,* Super Market Institute (Chicago, 1959), p. 19.

[18] Mueller and Garoian, *Changes in the Market Structure of Grocery Retailing, 1940–58,* Res. Rept. 5, *op. cit.,* p. 16.

[19] Joe S. Bain, *Industrial Organization* (New York: John Wiley & Sons, 1959), p. 219.

substitutable for that of other firms in any given market. There is widespread dissemination of technical and business know-how in the industry, so that general uniformity has been achieved in the quality of ingredients and formulas used, in the cleanliness and timing of production and delivery operations, and in the enrichment and subsequent nutritive value of white bread.[20] Product specifications vary slightly between regions of the country, but within any given region, products of competing firms are virtually identical.

Another important aspect of bread quality is its perishability. The widespread addition of calcium propionate as a mold inhibitor and lecithin as an emulsifier, combined with rapid cooling and immediate wrapping, is characteristic of the heroic effort to minimize bread "staling," which nevertheless remains one of the industry's major headaches. In spite of all attempts to prevent it, within two or three days after baking, the crumb of all bakers' bread becomes dry and hard, the crust leathery, and the flavor less desirable.[21]

Although she ordinarily buys bread at least every few days, the typical American housewife does not know enough about quality to make a reasoned choice between alternative brands, as many consumer preference surveys have demonstrated. A 1955 study of 300 families in Rockford, Illinois, tested five experimental white pan breads, purposely made of distinctly different formulas, and found that consumers' powers of discrimination were almost nil.[22] How much lower then must they be in a real market situation where the competing brands are made from essentially the same formula!

Whatever basis there is today for product differentiation of white bread results chiefly from sales promotion. Each baker tries to make his product something special in the consumer's mind, and the effort to accomplish this involves many factors such as attractiveness and convenience of the display including location, size, and height above the floor; differential loaf size and/or weight; differences in wrapping material; driver courtesy; and other such intangibles sold along with the product itself. Of course, the main weapon in this struggle is advertising. A recent study indicated

[20] L. C. Taylor and M. C. Burk, *Review of Cereal Food Enrichment in the United States, 1950–53,* Nat. Food Situation No. 69, Agr. Mkg. Serv., U.S.D.A. (Washington, 1954), pp. 17–20.

[21] *Bread Staling,* Consumer Serv. Dept., Amer. Inst. of Baking (Chicago, 1954); as quoted in *Bread Facts for Consumer Education,* Agr. Res. Serv., U.S.D.A. (Washington, 1955), p. 19.

[22] Hugh P. Bell, *Consumers' Preferences Among Bakers' White Breads of Different Formulas—A Survey in Rockford, Ill.,* Rept. 118, Agr. Mkg. Serv., U.S.D.A. (Washington, May 1956).

that even consumers themselves realize advertising is more important than physical quality in shaping their preferences for bread.[23]
Consumers apparently suffer from monotony with such a staple
food and are peculiarly susceptible to the appeal of something new
or different—a weakness dear to the hearts of advertisers everywhere,
and one not lost on bread manufacturers. This effort to achieve
product differentiation usually has a nonrational, emotional basis.
While bread advertising could be made informational in nature
and thus achieve certain socially desirable goals, it would not serve
to maximize short-run profits of bakery firms. In fact, informing consumers of the physical uniformity of competing breads
would tend to destroy whatever consumer franchise a particular
brand has, and so reduce an important source of market power held
by some bakery firms.

### Barriers to Entry

In the baking industry neither outright legal restrictions nor
trade secrets seem to be obstacles to the entry of new firms. Factors
of production and technological know-how are freely available.
Kaplan puts it this way: "Competent bakers can be found anywhere
in the country and little is required in the way of working capital
with which to get started. Machinery and equipment can frequently
be obtained on credit and financed by installment payments. Trucks
can be leased. Raw material inventories are relatively low because
of rapid turnover. Little or no finished-goods inventories exist because of perishability."[24]

These permissive factors are largely offset by higher market
barriers such as the existence of preferential agreements between
grocers and certain established bakers. The allocation of shelf
space in the typical supermarket is a classic illustration of the
adage, "Them that has gits," since newcomers are not ordinarily
granted display space on an equal footing with established firms.
Besides the nuisance value to the grocer of adding a new brand to
his already crowded shelves, there are other considerations behind
this discrimination. Established bakery firms often furnish display
cabinets to the grocer in exchange for dominant display space and
position as well as restriction of other brands.

Until shortly after World War II, many bakers sold in small
cities and rural communities effectively isolated from the largest
baking companies and from chain store private label bread. Small-
and medium-sized bakeries prospered in such environments until

---

[23] Nathanael H. Engle, "Bread Buying Habits," *Journal of Marketing* (Oct.
1956), p. 193.
[24] David Kaplan, president, The Economics of Distribution Foundation, New
York, testimony before, *Hearings, op. cit.*, p. 6494–95.

recently when two major displacements occurred. Either a major chain acquired a small local grocery chain and introduced private label bread, or a large city baking firm set up a delivery system in the outlying community and launched an extensive advertising and promotional campaign that local companies could not match. The costs of entering such an outlying area are affected by its distance from the central city market. The extent to which bakers in large cities can expand their market by drop shipment to outlying area depots and subsequent delivery to stores by driver-salesmen is limited by the relationship between the slope of the production cost curve and the rising costs of distribution. Roughly estimated, these balance at 150 miles. Grocery chains which distribute their private label bread via common carrier to store docks can venture much further before distribution costs become prohibitive, an estimated 400–500 miles.

The increased importance of regional and national brands often means that a smaller company cannot effectively compete with the largest firms and affiliated cooperatives in advertising. For a new company attempting to gain a foothold in a market, the problem is even more severe. It is caught in a vicious circle, viz., it must be able to demonstrate consumer acceptance before a grocer will stock its product; it must advertise to gain consumer acceptance especially against entrenched rivals, but it must enjoy a large sales volume before it can justify the costs of large-scale advertising. Because of this, many potential entrants abandon the contest before it begins.

Perhaps the most significant single barrier to entry into wholesale baking is the ability of an increasing number of grocery chains to bake their own products if they so choose. Widespread consumer acceptance of retailer labels has enabled grocery chains to integrate into many lines of food processing, the most extensive of which has been baking.[25] Moreover, preferential display of a store's own brand of bread restricts the shelf space remaining for wholesaler brands, reduces their sales volume, and increases their unit delivery costs. This forces some wholesalers to abandon the outlet. Also, some chains have limited the number of wholesaler brands allowed in the store, so it is easy to imagine how they would greet a brand that was not only additional, but new and untried as well.

Under static demand conditions which, as we have seen, characterize the bread industry, all potential entrants face a scale effi-

---

[25] In 1958, the total value of shipments by food manufacturing plants owned by chains (with 11-or more stores) was $1.3 billion, about 30 percent of which was bread products. Of the $288.6 million increase in the product of chain food plants from 1954 to 1958, about 40 percent was bread products. Federal Trade Commission, *op. cit.*, p. 30.

ciency barrier with respect to plant and distribution systems. Entry at the optimum point is virtually foreclosed except to already existing grocery chains that have enough stores to take all the output of such a bread plant. For example, a grocery chain serving about 360,000 people within a 150-mile radius could enter bread production and distribution at near-optimum scale with an investment of about $1.1 million and estimated average total costs of about 8.5 cents per pound. But a potential entrant into wholesale baking would find it just about impossible to accomplish this feat since he would need an enormous share of the market to justify such a large plant. In the Omaha, Nebraska, market with 450,000 people, for example, the required share for entry at optimum levels of efficiency would be roughly 70–90 percent. Given the further fact that five operating plants now share the bulk of that market and operate at varying levels of undercapacity such that any one of them with full plant utilization could almost supply the entire market, the height of the entry barrier is further raised. Thus economies of scale and existing excess capacity effectively foreclose entry at optimum operating levels.

The barriers to entry discussed thus far apply primarily to wholesale bakeries. Although other segments of the industry may not share these particular woes, they have their own problems. For example, bakers who provide home delivery or who distribute through a chain of retail bake shops face a higher selling cost barrier. An important obstacle to chain store entry into the bread industry is the one mentioned previously, viz., that the firm must have enough stores to take all the output of an optimum-sized bakery plant. This is something of an overstatement, however, since the modern distribution methods practiced by the chains are so superior to the driver-salesman system employed by regular wholesale bakers that the chain can actually operate at lower-than-optimum levels as far as production is concerned and yet achieve lower total unit costs than a potential wholesale baking entrant. Some grocery chains have integrated into the baking industry by acquiring an existing bread plant which was smaller than optimum size and had correspondingly higher unit production costs, but they have offset these disadvantages by their relative efficiency in distribution.

## MARKET CONDUCT

Industries differ not only in market structure but in the ways the firms within them carry on their business. The tactics they use to compete with each other are encompassed under the general heading of market conduct. This includes various forms of nonprice competition as well as pricing policies. The bakery industry provides a particularly favorable environment for the study of these competitive weapons, owing to its oligopolistic structure. Since the conduct of individual firms is not given or predetermined by outside forces, some strategic or discretionary action is permitted the firm, and the particular courses of action chosen can effect further changes in market structure. They may sustain underutilization of plant and distribution facilities and may influence delivery and selling costs as well as prices.

### Price Leadership in Large City Wholesale Markets

Collusive price fixing is infrequently discovered in bread markets because it is illegal as well as difficult to enforce. Price leadership provides analogous results and has the advantage of being acceptable in the eyes of the law. In large city wholesale bread markets, some form of price leadership is almost universally observed. Businessmen freely testify to its prevalence. Evidence of price leadership is the occurrence of virtually simultaneous price increases of equal magnitude and it is overwhelming in the bread industry. For example, between 1953 and 1958, bread producers in Seattle, Washington—including two large companies, Continental and Langendorf—raised their prices simultaneously on five separate occasions.[26] In New York City, on February 11, 1957, the large firms, General, Ward, and Continental, raised their prices simultaneously. A recital of further detailed illustrations would be merely soporific, but suffice it to say that during the years 1952–58, there was a total of 80 price changes in 24 cities surveyed by a Senate subcommittee. In only three cases did the large baking companies reduce prices of their principal brands of bread and, in nearly every instance, all large baking firms adjusted their prices to the same level within four days of an increase by a price leader.[27]

Even where these price changes occur simultaneously and are of equal magnitude, they do not necessarily imply collusion because firms in the bakery industry commonly know in advance what the price leader will do and can thus plan to make a similar move. As the president of a large baking company testified before a Senate committee, prenotification several days prior to a price change is required by grocery chains which pass the information along to other bakery route men servicing the stores.[28] The subsequent unanimity of action does not result in a uniform price for all bread sold in a given market owing to the increase in private label and secondary brands, although these also tend to sell at uniform though somewhat lower prices. Within any of these product

---

[26] *Hearings, op. cit.,* p. 6123.
[27] *Report, op. cit.,* pp. 146–47.
[28] *Hearings, op. cit.,* p. 6121.

classes, however, actual price competition rarely occurs and then usually only when the market is distressed, as when a firm is going bankrupt and acts out of desperation.

The existence of nearly 100 distinct, geographically separated bread markets complicates the analysis of the industry's price policy. Most industrial products can be readily transported over great distances, although, in some cases, only at substantial cost; for such products, it makes sense to discuss the industry's price policy. However, in the bread industry, one must always be aware of the segmented nature of the markets, which means that pricing policies can vary from one market to another. In large city wholesale bread markets, price leadership seems to be generally of the "cost-barometric" variety. The role of price leader may rotate among a few companies but it usually falls to the larger firms in the market. Other large rivals follow because they believe the leader to be more expert at assessing costs and some smaller firms also follow for this reason. Usually changes in average input prices occur simultaneously for all firms in a market area, and the price leader is thought to be watching costs closely—both his own and those of his competitors.[29] In markets where the oligopoly core is sufficiently dominant, the smaller companies have little choice. Yet they, too, welcome price leadership by the major firms which, they feel, have the greatest interest in preventing price cutting and disorderly marketing as well as superior ability to enforce their policies owing to their substantial productive capacity and financial resources.[30]

While one might expect that the price chosen by the leader would conform pretty closely to his production costs, in practice it turns out to be an umbrella price that covers the average unit costs of all members of the oligopoly group regardless of plant size and

---

[29] *Hearings, op. cit.,* p. 6124. This assumes that all baking companies act as separate entities. A number of large wholesale companies have interlocking directorates with each other and with potential suppliers of bakery inputs. An F.T.C. study of interlocking directors among the 1,000 largest manufacturing companies in the U.S. showed that Continental, General, American, Interstate, and Ward had direct or indirect ties with each other and/or with several suppliers of bakery inputs. For example, Continental interlocked with General through Midland Trust, and with Swift (which produces shortening) through Underwood, and with Wilson (also produces cooking oil) through Guarantee Trust. General Baking Company interlocked directly with National Sugar Refining and indirectly with National Dairy, American Sugar Refining, Anheuser-Busch, General Mills, and Best Foods. These ties provide channels for a meeting of minds among the top companies in the baking industry and some of their suppliers. It was reported that interlocking directorates in baking were much more numerous than similar relations in any branches of the food industry previously studied. Federal Trade Commission, *Interlocking Directorates* (Washington, 1951), pp. 64–73.

[30] *Report, op. cit.,* pp. 167–69.

utilization of the price followers. This arises from the variation in market shares and plant sizes from one market to another. For example, while company A may be the price leader in market I because it has a substantial share of that market and as a consequence is producing with a large plant at a high level of utilization, it may face company B in market II under conditions such that size of plant, market share, and plant utilization of company B are far superior in that market to those of company A. The prevalence of excess capacity in the baking industry as a whole places most bakers in a vulnerable position with respect to the point at which they produce on their average total unit cost curve. Thus, the price level resulting from cost-barometric price leadership is partially determined by the relative cost structures of the oligopolists within any single market. But when the aggregate industry level of analysis is considered, it is apparent that price is also influenced by their recognition of mutal dependence on a broader intermarket basis.

Most wholesale bread producers quickly adjust their prices to that of the price leader. There are sound bases in economics for their action. Most bakers have learned that they cannot materially increase their share of total bread sales through an openly aggressive pricing policy because each price decrease is met with at least similar cuts by competitors. They are forced to go down with the leader when he drops his price if they are to maintain volume. Moreover, when the leader raises his price, they have good reason to follow suit. If the price rise is due to cost increases, the follower firms may need the additional revenue even more than the leader firm which may be operating at a lower cost level. In addition, all firms stand to gain from increased revenue in the short run as aggregate sales remain substantially the same. If they do not follow, the price leader can simply drop his price again, and little has been gained or lost.

### Differential Pricing in Outlying Wholesale Markets

Wholesale prices for bread in outlying market areas served by large city plants are typically 1 to 4 cents per pound lower than those in the large city as the U.S. Senate investigation showed.[31] Most territorial price differentials are the result of the historic failure of large city bakers to raise their prices in outlying areas the same way they do in the city. In its effects, this has approached

---

[31] Differential pricing "assumes its most striking form when the price charged at a distant community is *lower* than that charged at the plant where the bread is baked. This was found to be a very prevalent practice among the larger wholesale bakers. . . ." *Ibid.,* p. 39. This finding is supported by extensive testimony of company management and is documented by market area maps with prices, plants, and mileage shown. *Ibid.,* pp. 38–66.

discriminatory price cutting—it was, in fact, defined as "route price discrimination" in the Senate subcommittee report[32]—and it is one of the factors explaining the increased concentration among large baking companies and the correlative declining number of whole-sale baking firms. The practice has the advantage of generally being considered legal, whereas outright price discrimination has been held to be against the law.[33]

Until the end of World War II, most outlying areas in small cities and rural communities had been dominated by smaller in-dependent bakers. At that time, with wartime distribution re-strictions eased, the major bakers with plants in large cities began to look with renewed interest upon the possibilities of expanding into these outlying markets. The adoption of new machinery of greater capacity created a need for larger volume which could be realized through wider distribution. This inspired many of them to initiate semitrailer delivery to depots set up in outlying areas some 100 or 150 miles from their large city plants. Driver-salesmen delivery systems operate out of these depots much the same as they do from large city plants.

The one thing that changes when large city firms enter an out-lying area is their pricing policy. Their objective in these fringe areas is to capture a substantial share of the market rather than merely to hold their own and rely upon population growth for gradual sales accretion, which is the best they can hope for in metropolitan markets. It follows that their pricing policy is con-siderably more aggressive than it is in large city wholesale markets. Their competitors in the new area are sharply different, too. The polite, gentlemanly ways of the large city oligopolists are notably lacking in the outlying independent firms which are desperately attempting to hold their sales volume against the inroads of these powerful invaders. Their natural reaction is one of hostility.

Thus, when a major baker attempts to penetrate an outlying area, it no longer faces the community of interest typically shared by the oligopoly group in large city markets. For if price leader-ship had been exercised in the outlying market prior to the large firm's entry, it is doubtful that the market participants would be willing to accept a new leader without serious price competition. Or if there had been little earlier experience with price leadership, the market participants may very well react by using price as a com-petitive weapon since they are unlikely to know the rules of the game. Many of these outlying independents apparently believe price competition is the only means of preserving their market

---

[32] *Ibid.,* p. 38.
[33] Corwin D. Edwards, *The Price Discrimination Law: A Review of Expe-rience* (Washington: The Brookings Institute, 1959), p. 458.

shares and it is one of the few tactics as freely available to them as to the large companies. They are prone to use it in last-ditch attempts to stay in the baking business. They are in a peculiarly vulnerable position since, like the majors, they, too, have adopted volume-increasing equipment and need a larger market to maintain efficient production levels. However, they are virtually foreclosed from entering the large city markets of the major bakers, owing to the possibility of severe retaliation by them, as well as their superior access to advertising and retail outlets.[34] About the only way an independent baker in an outlying area can invade the large city wholesale market is by the use of private label contracts and drop shipments. Some small grocery chains have secured their private label bread in just this manner when the oligopoly group in the large city refused to supply it.

Differential prices in outlying market areas usually arise out of the refusal of large city companies to raise prices there as large city prices are increased. Although there are a few notable examples of open and hidden price cutting by large city companies in the process of entering outlying markets, the typical case is pricing at a level "to meet competition" in the initial stage and then refusing to participate in efforts to raise prices as costs increase. This pricing tactic can succeed because they are relatively secure from retaliation above the single market level, owing to the one-plant, one-market nature of most independent baking firms operating in these areas. Their security vis-à-vis the outlying independents is in marked contrast to their vulnerability in large city markets which are dominated by an oligopoly core of wholesale bakers. A big company may gain in one large city market through price tactics but would lose to its retributory rivals in another, so price is much less apt to be used in these cities than in outlying bread markets. The power to retaliate in another market is not usually available to independents operating in outlying areas; large city bakers are therefore not so reluctant to use price tactics there where they can do so with relative impunity.

Notwithstanding the economic facts of the matter, the practice of differential pricing has thus far been successfully defended by large multi-plant baking companies as not being "area price discrimination." It can be argued that differential pricing reflects real cost differentials in marginal terms. The defense rests on realized returns to scale in production, advertising, and other overhead costs;[35] the relatively small increase in unit costs of delivery over greater distances; and the assumption that *bread produced for ship-*

---

[34] *Report, op. cit.,* p. 64.
[35] E. A. G. Robinson, *The Structure of Competitive Industry* (Chicago: Univ. of Chicago Press, 1932), p. 72.

*ment to the outlying area is the marginal product.* Although this assumption would be consistent with marginal economic analysis at the firm level, its use as a justification of differential bread pricing is questionable. As the Attorney General's Committee To Study the Antitrust Laws suggests, "the idea that the cost of serving a given buyer is less than that of serving other buyers, for no other reason than that this buyer's additional volume spreads the overhead, imputes arbitrarily to a particular buyer the savings of larger volume."[36] Adelman also points out in this connection that the buyer in the outlying area might with equal logic have been considered the first buyer and have the entire overhead imputed to him as to be called the marginal buyer and bear none of it.[37]

### Grocery Chain Bread Pricing

Grocery chain bread pricing policy is a very important part of bread market behavior. The private label price policy of grocery chains affects the market structure and behavior of wholesale bread producers in two ways. First, the bakers have few alternatives to marketing an increasing share of their production through the grocery chains, many of which are integrated into bread production. By 1958, the 10 largest grocery chains had about 27 percent of total retail food store sales. All were integrated into bread production and, on the average, their private brands represented about 40 percent of total bakery product sales in their stores.[38] Second, there is a differential impact of vertical integration by grocery chains upon large versus small wholesale baking companies.

Recent bread market behavior of grocery chains is based on their ability to exploit opportunities for technological and organizational changes in bread distribution. Shortly after World War I, the fast-growing grocery chains sought to secure quantity discount prices from wholesale baking companies consistent with the economies of large-volume deliveries and elimination of special services to smaller stores. Also, in this period of rapid chain growth, many chains failed to follow the resale price maintenance policy of wholesale baking companies and used bread as a "price leader." By and large, bakers refused to sell to chains under such conditions. As a result, most large grocery chains integrated vertically into bread production. Two distinct bread marketing practices have emerged: (1) the curtailment and simplification of service associated with chain label bread, and (2) the policy of selling at lower prices than

[36] *Report of the Attorney General's National Committee To Study the Antitrust Laws* (Washington, 1955), p. 334.
[37] M. A. Adelman, *A & P: A Study in Price-Cost Behavior and Public Policy* (Cambridge: Harvard Univ. Press, 1959), p. 180.
[38] Calculated from sales data in *Report, op. cit.,* p. 103; and *Economic Inquiry Into Food Marketing, op. cit.,* p. 30.

primary wholesale brands, thus allowing consumers some price-product alternative. These principal features of grocery chain price policy permit some variety in their marketing strategy such as the use of bread as a promotional item or the establishment of a grocery chain as a price leader.

In most markets, integrated grocery chains establish private label bread prices below those of wholesale brands. According to Census data, the average difference between these prices in 1958 was 3.3 cents per pound, or 17 percent, for the nation as a whole.[39] For representative markets, the price differential tends to be greatest in central and northeastern United States, and least in the South and the West where the price of private label bread follows very closely price levels for wholesale brands.

Price differentials of a few cents may be sufficient to achieve consumer acceptance of private label brands because wholesale bakeries have no alternative but to supply integrated grocery stores with wholesale brands under nonprice terms that are relatively unfavorable. These include adverse shelf location, stacking, and size of display, all of which tend to limit the sales of wholesale bakery brands in large chain stores. The extent of this restriction varies considerably. For example, in 1958, A & P private label bread products represented about two-thirds of total bread product sales in A & P stores.[40] But this is a unique case. A & P is the second largest producer of bakery products as well as the largest food retailer. Safeway Stores and National Tea are more typical of the 10 largest grocery chains, as a whole, in that private label products are about 40 percent and 25 percent, respectively, of total bread product sales in their stores. Yet consumer surveys in 27 large city markets have shown that, in over three-fourths of the markets, chain store brands account for less than 10 percent of consumer preferences.[41] There are indications that several of the largest grocery chains may have reached the upper limit in restriction of wholesale brands. With these brands in their stores, they can offload some of the inventory and production problems associated with heavy weekend demand onto wholesale baking companies. Moreover, through the acquisition and construction of new stores, they have gained a greater share of total grocery sales, including bread, and have thus achieved fuller utilization of their existing bakery plants.

On occasion, integrated grocery chains have temporarily set their private label bread prices at a level far below those of whole-

---

[39] *1958 Census of Manufactures, op. cit.,* 20E–12–13.

[40] Authors' estimates based on A & P bakery production shown in *Report, op. cit.,* p. 109. Margin of 17% applied to this to obtain retail sales. Total A & P bakery sales estimated as 6.23 percent of A & P total sales, based on *The Dillon Study* (New York: Progressive Grocer, May 1960), p. D–9.

[41] *Report, op cit.,* p. 106.

sale brands, resulting in a differential much wider than normal. Company replies to a U.S. Senate investigation of retail bread prices by the 10 largest grocery chains between July 1, 1958 and June 30, 1959 revealed 290 cases of special sales in one or more stores at prices of 10 cents or less.[42] These promotional prices were usually less than half the prevailing retail price of wholesale brands in the market areas involved. They were usually continued for three to six days and were confined to chain stores located in one or two cities at a time. Cut-rate bread sales in some markets, however, continued for nine months and one large chain held simultaneous sales throughout all its stores. However, no bread sales of 10 cents per pound or less were reported in regions west of the Rocky Mountains.

As long as this practice occurs infrequently and briefly and is restricted to a few markets, its effects on major wholesale bakers with plants in a number of states may not be severe. The large multi-plant wholesalers apparently can absorb temporary losses in markets affected by these promotions by offsetting them with profits in other markets where chains abstain from such practices. An important point is that integrated grocery chains *can* set bread prices relative to input costs in such a way that single-market, wholesale baking companies are squeezed and have to operate with a minimal profit or a loss, while the integrated, multi-market grocery chains which produce and deliver their own private label bread at average costs below those of the nonintegrated firms can at the same time prosper.

## Nonprice Competition in Bread Markets

The primary competition between wholesale baking companies distributing bread to grocery stores is on a nonprice basis. Instead of price competition, the usual market conduct pattern seeks improvement in the consumer franchise of individual wholesale brands by preferential product display in retail outlets, product advertising and promotion, and product variation. In contrast to their pricing behavior, these oligopolists apparently do not achieve spontaneous coordination of their nonprice practices.[43] Independent action is preferred if it is expected to achieve advantages that are unlikely to be matched in the short run, if at all, by other wholesale baking companies. Thus, the nonprice conduct of firms in bread markets closely conforms to the theory of monopolistic competition.[44] These nonprice practices have two principal results: (1) they alter the relative competitive strength of small and large

---

[42] *Ibid.*, pp. 115–18.
[43] *Ibid.*, p. 106.
[44] Edward H. Chamberlin, *The Theory of Monopolistic Competition* (Cambridge: Harvard Univ. Press, 1956).

baking companies, and (2) they create a cost-push effect on prices. The concept of "cost push" as used here refers to the tendency toward rising costs resulting from the various nonprice practices in distribution and selling as well as from capital investment in new equipment. These rising costs can be tolerated under the protective cover of cost-barometric price leadership practiced in bread markets. The basic factors contributing to rising costs and prices in bread markets are very difficult for any one firm to control, but it should be noted that they are primarily endogenous to the industry.

*Product Display.* Perhaps the most widely used and significant nonprice practices in the wholesale bread market in postwar years have been the various tactics of firms to win favored display positions for their brands in retail outlets. Under the umbrella of cost-barometric pricing, firms resort to the purchase of rack position with cash[45] or, in lieu of cash, give free bread, building improvements, special entertainment, and management service. They also try to dominate display shelves with "massed displays."[46] The term "massed display" is defined as the overloading of display space in retail outlets beyond expected sales. Its purpose is to appeal to consumers through what has been colorfully termed "pile psychology." It is used for this purpose by grocery chains with private label bread, and by driver-salesmen with wholesale brands, to gain or maintain preferential shelf space in retail outlets.

The bread industry came out of World War II with government controls over some market practices. Under the War Food Administration the consignment of bakery products to grocery stores and the removal of day-old products were prohibited. With the end of controls in 1946, consignment selling was again introduced by wholesale bread producers. Consignment selling facilitates the domination of distribution outlets by firms who overload limited display shelves with their bread and thus force competitors to accept disadvantageous display space. Largely as a result of this form of nonprice competition, average costs of "stale return" loss increased from 1947 to 1958 at a rate second only to distribution labor costs. In a sample of 105 baking companies affiliated with a management cooperative, bread returns as a percentage of route

---

[45] An example of buying out distributive shelf display is provided by the president of an independent bakery in Lincoln, Nebr., who submitted a sworn affidavit to the House Committee on Small Business dated Nov. 3, 1955. Affiant stated that at Sutton, Nebr., in Oct. 1955, Colonial Baking Company of Des Moines, Iowa (an affiliate of Campbell-Taggart), gave Oscar Griess Grocery Store $50 worth of bread, and as a result Wendelin Baking Co. was eliminated as a seller of bread in the store. House Committee on Small Business, *Price Discrimination, the Robinson-Patman Act and Related Matters,* Part I, 84th Cong., 1st Sess. (Washington, 1956), p. 370.

[46] For a discussion of other of these practices, see *Report, op. cit.,* pp. 67–84.

sales increased from 1.3 percent in 1947 to 7.4 percent in 1958. Even though a small part of these was recovered through sales of day-old products, the remaining loss rose from 1.1 percent of sales in 1947 to 4.8 percent of sales in 1958.[47] This experience is typical of the industry as a whole. Moreover, in a specific case of retaliatory overloading of grocery bread display in a single mid-western market, "stale return" loss of a medium-large single-plant baking company almost doubled in four years, increasing from 4.9 percent of sales in 1954 to 9.5 percent of sales in 1957.[48] A careful study of the stale bread problem in the baking industry estimated that net loss from stale bread in the 1920's averaged about 2.5 to 3 percent of sales.[49] It concluded that stale loss not in excess of 0.5 to 1 percent of production is an attainable standard in wholesale bread markets.

When effective, these nonprice competitive tactics can result in making grocery outlets no longer available on equal terms to all wholesale baking firms in a market. When nonprice concessions are given in the form of merchandise and services of indefinite value, it is difficult for grocers and competing bakers to decide which company's product would be most profitable. This facilitates the intended result of dominating distributive outlets. However, while various nonprice tactics may be introduced by one firm as offense weapons, they are almost invariably adopted by others as defense weapons. The introduction of one or more of these tactics into a market rarely goes unnoticed by competitors but is adopted or matched in value by all. When this happens, they typically neutralize each other and no single firm is better off than before, while all have experienced increased costs. Higher costs may be more difficult to bear for independent firms in competition with one or more large firms in the outlying area of a market. Moreover, by their nature, some nonprice tactics, e.g., buying up shelf space, foreclose the possibility of adoption by rivals. Thus nonprice practices as well as overt price policies facilitate the expansion into outlying markets of large companies and the corollary demise of smaller firms.

*Advertising.* Among the food industries, baking was one of the first, and is today one of the foremost, users of advertising.[50] In the postwar years, the ratio of advertising to sales has been about a third higher for baking corporations than for all corporate manu-

[47] *Hearings, op. cit.*, p. 6593.
[48] *Report, op. cit.*, p. 71.
[49] J. S. Davis and Wilfred Eldred, *Stale Bread Loss as a Problem of the Baking Industry,* Publication No. 1, Food Res. Inst., Stanford Univ. (California, Feb. 1923), p. 7.
[50] E. J. Sperry, "65 Years of Bakery Advertising," *Baking Industry Magazine* (Apr. 12, 1952), pp. 149–50.

facturers of food products. In absolute terms, bakery corporations' advertising expenditures have been increasing faster than those of all food corporations but their real product sales have not responded in kind. According to the U.S. Internal Revenue Service, corporate food processors spent 1.1 percent of their sales on advertising in 1947 and 2.0 percent in 1957. By comparison, advertising expenses of bakery corporations represented 1.6 percent of their sales in 1947 and 2.8 percent in 1957. Or, to look at it another way, the bakers' share of all food corporation advertising rose from 12.1 percent to 14.6 percent in the 10-year period.[51] Since food processors are generally heavier advertisers than other manufacturers, these results would be even more dramatic were the comparison drawn between bakery advertising and that of nonfood manufacturers.

Wholesale bakers do virtually all the advertising in the bakery industry. Among these companies, the ratio of advertising to sales varies considerably.[52] House-to-house and multi-unit retail baking baking companies use other means to isolate their markets. These include special service in the case of house-to-house delivery. Multi-unit retail bakeries use a differentiated product, location, and service. All of these involve selling costs which, as suggested by the theory of monopolistic competition, are incurred primarily to secure a degree of market isolation, i.e., protection from cross elasticity of demand.

Evidence of private label selling expenditures by the 10 largest chain store bread producers indicates advertising expenditures in 1958 amounted to about $1.2 million or less than one percent (0.68) of their bread sales.[53] This ratio was one-fourth of the industry average and about one-sixth of that of the largest four wholesale baking companies. Lower advertising expense for private label bread reflects, in part, less total advertising effort; in part, economies of joint-product advertising of about 50 items with bread in newspaper ads; and, in part, the tendency to advertise the chain name rather than specific food items. Moreover, to the extent that conventional bread advertising is intended to influence the managers of grocery stores as well as consumers, advertising is of less importance to private label bread producers.

Advertising is one of the most obvious forms of bread promo-

---

[51] Data for food firms from U.S. Int. Rev. Serv., *Statistics of Income, Corporation Income Tax Returns, 1947–48 and 1957–58*. Data for bakery firms from U.S. Agr. Mkg. Serv., AMS–399; and "Advertising Expenditures by Food Manufacturing Corporations, 1947–57," by Roberta Lamb (reprinted from *The Marketing and Transportation Situation*, July 1960).

[52] The largest wholesale baking company spent about 5 percent of sales on advertising; the remaining members of the big four and big eight wholesale bakery groups spent approximately 3 percent. *Hearings, op. cit.*, pp. 6055, 6062, 6580–91.

[53] *Report, op. cit.*, pp. 113–14.

tion. It usually includes expenditures on television, radio, magazines, newspapers, and billboards. In addition to these, sales promotion policy may include "consumer deals, premiums, coupon offers, menu-related item promotion, contests, sample and demonstration programs, special displays, various trade deals, and special promotion associated with the introduction of new products."[54] Estimates of the costs of nonadvertising promotion practices are not available for the bakery industry. But it is not unreasonable to expect that for many large wholesale baking companies these costs are as great or greater than advertising expenses. To an increasing extent, subsidization of grocery store outlets with in-store facility and promotional allowances is becoming a major instrument of sales promotion policy. While costs of in-store facilities are usually hidden in broad ill-defined categories of a firm's operating statement, there is evidence that promotional allowances to chain stores amounting to 3 to 5 percent of sales are not uncommon.[55] Thus they frequently double the promotion expenditure on bread sold through these stores.

In its early days, advertising undoubtedly performed an informational function that helped to expand the market for bakery bread relative to that baked at home. Through advertising, consumers were made aware of the existence and the convenience of this new form of mass-produced, wrapped bread. By the end of World War II, however, commercially produced bread was an established and well-known staple of the American diet. It is doubtful that bread advertising has contributed significantly to any further increase in the aggregate demand for bread.

*Product Variation.* There is considerable evidence that product variation policy is a significant aspect of firm behavior in bread markets, both in its impact on costs and on the competitive relationship between bakery firms. Product variation can be defined as the "periodic alternation of products, of the sort not necessarily identifiable as improvements, in order to stimulate a consumer demand."[56] The regular introduction of superficial changes in product and/or packaging such as variety breads, diet breads, and "new" loaves of white bread exemplify this policy. On the individual firm level, product variation has a rational basis in recent studies of consumer behavior. Engle, for example, found that bread consumers tend to shift their brand or product loyalties every three to five years, reflecting a sense of monotony and a desire for something new or different.[57] He urged baking companies, as a matter

[54] Sidney Hoos, "The Advertising and Promotion of Farm Products—Some Theoretical Issues," *Journal of Farm Economics* (May 1959), p. 355.

[55] *Hearings, op. cit.*, pp. 6344, 6641–51.

[56] Bain, *op. cit.*, p. 323.

[57] Engle, *op. cit.*, p. 195.

of policy, to adopt rates of product variation and selling outlays consistent with the noted consumer turnover cycle. Product variation by baking companies generally has taken three forms usually not associated with significant improvements in bread quality. In the postwar years, firms have periodically introduced one or more selling "features" such as variation in loaf size, texture, and wrapper.

## MARKET PERFORMANCE

Thus far we have considered several important structure and conduct conditions of bread markets. The important consideration remains to combine these criteria and estimate the performance of bread markets. In other words, how well does the market activity of baking companies contribute to the public welfare?

It is often assumed by observers of industrial markets that changes in the product, price, and profit criteria of market performance are of primary importance. If it can be shown that the available economic improvements in product quality have occurred, if prices have a reasonable relationship to average total unit costs, and profit levels are not higher than experienced in all manufacturing, then performance of an industry may be said to be adequate (although perhaps less than optimum) and contributing satisfactorily to the general material welfare. Indeed the evidence with respect to bakery profits supports the assumption that average profit levels of wholesale baking companies are not appreciably higher than those in all manufacturing and, at 1958 levels, had little impact on the general material welfare. While bread prices have advanced rapidly since World War II, they are closely related to changes in average total unit costs, at least in large city markets (70 percent of U.S. consumption). Moreover, consumers often have the opportunity to purchase alternative private label brands in grocery chains at lower prices than wholesale brands. While real improvements in product quality have been very limited, there is little or no evidence that quality has deteriorated since World War II.

A consideration of these few performance criteria, however, is not sufficient to understand the performance of bread markets. In fact, changes in the product and profit criteria may be secondary rather than primary determinants of performance in these markets. The conduct of firms in individual markets with respect to product quality seems to be largely predetermined and prices of wholesaler brands are quite similar as profit levels tend to be protected by a pattern of price leadership. Individual companies are therefore more concerned with varying costs and output.

The performance of bread markets with respect to cost and output primarily reflects the market power of oligopoly groups and

changes in technology. The oligopoly market structure in wholesale bread markets is associated with interdependent conduct of
enterprises with respect to pricing policies, nonprice practices, and
plant utilization. In large part, no individual firm can independently have a beneficial effect upon market performance without
risking serious economic repercussions for itself or for the oligopoly
market group in question. Yet, technical advance in bakery equipment, in the transport and handling of bakery products, and in food
merchandising in general are dynamic variables tending to bring
about economic changes in bread markets.

⌐ The performance of bread markets with respect to the introduction of efficient equipment and techniques of production, while
less than optimum, has probably approached adequacy. Yet in
oligopolistic bread markets, consumers have thus far realized little
or no benefit from the progressive adoption of more efficient bread
production technology.

Moreover, there is a tendency toward *chronic* underutilization
of capital equipment and failure to achieve economies of scale in
the baking industry. There are important potential savings in
bread production and distribution. The "efficiency gap" between
actual and necessary costs (in relation to given input prices) to provide the consumer with bread products suggests the performance
of wholesale bread markets in 1958 was adequate except for the
average retail price of bread which, at 19.3 cents per pound, was
about 50 percent higher than would be required to cover the necessary costs. This measure between where the industry is and where
it could be if the economy were to make full use of its resources
without straining productive capacity is in part a measure of the
aggregate costs of oligopoly.

A comparison of the existing system with an optimum market
organization suggests the *direction of possible adjustment* of undesirable market conditions which annually cost the American public
more than one billion dollars. The more than $520 million po-
tential production cost reduction could be realized by long-run adjustments in size of plant to 8,000 pounds per hour capacity, by
adopting automatic continuous-mix machinery, and by operating
the remaining plants at practical capacity levels (dependent in
part on consumer willingness to benefit from early-week shopping).
The estimated $530 million potential distribution and selling cost
reductions could be realized by reorganization of the wholesale
driver-salesman delivery system to semitrailers and dock delivery.
Some progress is being made toward achieving these potential economies, but there are important institutional barriers at work that
seem to account for the sizable lag in bread market performance.

While individual baking companies often have good economic

reasons for technological adoption and plant expansion, such developments may be a mixed blessing for consumers, farmers, and some bakery companies. New output-increasing equipment and techniques of production have considerable potential for reducing costs as noted above. But levels of cost and output are not autonomous forces; in bread markets, they are largely determined by the conduct of the industry itself. The alternatives open to bakery management include some variation of the following market conduct patterns: (1) price competition to force bread prices to cost levels consistent with the increased efficiencies of larger plants and with a decrease in the number of bakeries (perhaps his own included); or (2) price leadership which provides an "umbrella" covering production and distribution costs experienced by existing plants operating at considerably less than capacity.

Firms participating in oligopolistically structured markets generally have chosen the latter form of market conduct. Firms tend to orient interfirm conduct around nonprice competition to increase their shares of bread markets. The resulting increase in selling costs has little or no beneficial effect on consumers. Per capita demand for the industry's products has declined by about 1 percent per year, and whatever changes in market share distribution have occurred among the oligopoly market groups have not been associated with lower costs and prices. This is because if some firms in oligopoly-structured markets increase their efficiency or gain fuller utilization of capital equipment, their success tends to shift excess capacity among other participants in the market whose costs are increased. It is also due to mutual interdependence of oligopolists with respect to advertising, product variation, special packaging, and servicing. Immediate imitation or retaliation usually occurs, with the result that selling costs in bread markets increase with little or no beneficial shift in output between participants.

The general pattern of price leadership within oligopolistic groups of wholesale baking companies is usually of the cost-barometric type, and is designed to keep market price comfortably above costs experienced by the group. Illegal price collusion and discrimination are seldom found in bread markets, for price leadership tends to protect the industry from destructive price competition and has the advantage of being legal. High-cost firms have raised prices to cover costs of inefficient production and distribution with virtual certainty that other members of large city market groups would follow, even though they may be more efficient. Price leadership has not usually provided the competitive discipline to drive out the higher-cost producers, or to force the remaining firms to operate at efficient levels of utilization of production and distribution facilities. Quite the reverse tends to occur. The market power of oligopoly groups in large city bread markets tends to shield inefficient baking companies and sustain inefficient market practices.

The few exceptions to this practice are largely short run, intersegmental rivalry, or a part of pricing tactics used by members of the oligopoly group in large city markets to invade outlying areas of these markets. These modify but do not alleviate the more general price conduct and market performance pattern. As a result of increased plant capacity and grocery chain integration into baking, members of the large city oligopoly core have encroached upon outlying areas. Large city bakers have practiced differential pricing and various nonprice share-gaining techniques in outlying areas beyond those practices common within the oligopoly core of large city markets. The single-market firm in outlying areas is often unable to match these increased distribution and selling efforts, and usually dares not compete on price because of its vulnerability to price retaliation. Thus, there has been a gradual encroachment of the outlying market areas by the major wholesale bakers and an increase in concentration in the baking industry.

## POLICY IMPLICATIONS

We can expect continued adjustment to fewer and larger bakeries. Just how far this adjustment will go is not yet clear, but potential economies are sizable. Company growth in markets already served would better approach optimum economies of scale in bread distribution than further geographic expansion into additional market areas. Although we have not attempted here an exhaustive study of the economies of large multi-plant and multi-market company organizations, we have demonstrated that as these firms meet in several individual markets their rivalry expressed through price competition tends to diminish.

If company growth occurs in markets already served, concentration which often is already high may become higher, yet costs may decrease as aggressive nonprice competitive rivalry may diminish, a development which is a necessary (but not sufficient) condition for price reduction. It is our judgment that public policy toward maintaining competitive market structures through placing certain restraints on growth via merger should consider these different single- and multi-market effects.

What of the performance of the grocery retailing industry? Grocery chains have achieved marked efficiencies in distribution and selling without, however, consistently passing these savings on to the consumer in the form of higher quality or lower price. A degree of bilateral oligopoly behavior often develops between an oligopolistic group of wholesale baking companies and an oligopsonistic group of corporate and voluntary grocery chains in which the chains often follow in both price and quality. Certainly, the private label bread price differential in many bread markets more nearly reflects general grocery chain price policy than necessary bread production and distribution costs.

This opens a large area of legal-economic research. While we have dealt specifically with bread markets, the potential gains to the public from reorganization of bread market structure and conduct may not be unique among food markets in the American economy. Other studies have demonstrated similar technological and organizational problems. These studies provide some of the information necessary to focus the forces of public opinion and of the law on the whole problem of attaining optimum market organization.

# 9

# THE SOYBEAN PROCESSING INDUSTRY

## LEHMAN B. FLETCHER[1]

### AND

## DONALD D. KRAMER[2]

THE SOYBEAN is a relatively recent addition to commercially important farm crops in the United States. Prior to 1930, soybeans were grown primarily for seed, hay, animal feeding, and crop rotation purposes. For the first time, in 1935, more than half of the crop was processed into oil and meal. Production and processing increased afterwards; their rate of growth was especially rapid during World War II in response to increased demands for oil and high protein livestock feed. Consequently, the soybean processing industry is a comparative newcomer among agricultural industries.

The industry's growth has continued in the postwar period. Also, major changes in processing technology, plant size and location, transportation facilities and costs, and business organization of firms have occurred. These changing conditions raise the main questions to be answered in this chapter. How has the structure of the industry changed? What external, conduct, and performance factors have been associated with the observed changes? How well has the industry adjusted to changing conditions? This analysis attempts to describe and evaluate the performance, conduct, institutional, and technological developments that have led to the specific structural changes.

## HISTORICAL DEVELOPMENT OF SOYBEAN PRODUCTION AND PROCESSING

Soybean production in the United States has expanded from about 50,000 acres in 1907 to over 27 million acres in 1962. This acreage increase coupled with yield increases that have doubled

---

[1] Associate Professor of Economics, Iowa State University.
[2] Formerly Research Associate, Department of Economics, Iowa State University.

production per acre have made the United States the most important soybean producer in the world.[3] Production has increased
from less than 10 million bushels prior to 1930 to about 700 million bushels in recent years.

Before 1920, soybean production was concentrated along the
South Atlantic coast. By 1940, soybean production had moved
westward; states in the North Central region accounted for more
than 90 percent of that year's crop. This region still produces almost 80 percent of the nation's soybean crop, although increasing
production in the South has diminished somewhat the extreme importance of the Midwest. The southern states now account for
practically all of the remaining 20 percent of production.

The development of soybean production in the Midwest was
influenced by various factors, including

1. Improved varietal selection and breeding coupled with favorable
   climate and soil conditions leading to higher yields and oil
   content.
2. Soybean adaptability to midwestern crop rotations.
3. Reduction of corn acreage under various farm programs.
4. Adaptability of soybeans to (a) harvesting with small combines
   and (b) existing grain storage and marketing facilities.
5. Favorable location with respect to livestock feeding demands
   and export markets.

Biological environment has been a significant factor in regional development of production.[4] Soybean production in the
Midwest was influenced in part by that area's relative advantage in
yield and oil content. Higher yields favor both the farmer and the
processor as well by insuring adequate soybean availability to maintain high plant utilization. The oil content of the soybeans affects
the relative quantities of the end products, and this content may
vary appreciably among geographic areas. Oil is valued at several
times that of the meal for a given quantity of each, although about
four times more meal is obtained from each bushel crushed. As
long as the ratio of the price per pound of oil to the price of meal
per pound is greater than one, a higher yield of oil will increase
processors' margins.

The relative quantities of oil and meal recovered from processing soybeans have been influenced by processors in recent years by
shifting from the mechanical to the solvent method of processing.
One mechanical method, the hydraulic press, has not been of any

---

[3] *Soybean Blue Book* (Hudson, Iowa: Amer. Soybean Assn., annual editions).
[4] Klare S. Markley, *Soybeans and Soybean Products,* Vols. I and II (New York,
1950).

importance in processing since 1943. The other mechanical method, the screw press (expeller), has had declining importance since 1941 and, since 1948, has been less important than the solvent process. The screw press method differs from the hydraulic in that expellers are rotated through ground soybeans while the hydraulic method uses intermittent pressing. Both processes require the soybean to be heated and properly conditioned. The solvent method is a chemical process in which soybeans are washed with hexane to remove the oil. In recent years it has accounted for over 90 percent of the soybeans crushed.[5]

Not only has solvent processing affected the relative quantity of end products, but it has also changed the efficiency of recovery which has had important repercussions on developments in the industry. Solvent processing results in a higher revenue per bushel processed, due to the greater quantity of oil recovered and the higher price of oil.[6] For smaller plants, both the per-bushel cost and investment per bushel is slightly higher for solvent plants.[7] However, both the per-bushel cost and investment disadvantage of solvent mills declines for successively larger mills so that large solvent plants can process a bushel of soybeans just as cheaply as a screw press and have a definite revenue advantage.

The relatively higher rate of recovery of oil by the solvent process varies among years as well as locations, depending on the chemical characteristic of the soybean processed. In 1949, the solvent process yielded nearly 20 percent more oil than the screw press and 30 percent more than the hydraulic press, at the same time yielding 3.5 percent and 4.6 percent less meal than the respective mechanical processes. These characteristics of the various types of crushing processes take on increasing importance in the subsequent analysis of structural change in the industry.

### Utilization of Soybean Oil

Soybean oil has increased in popularity both for food and nonfood uses. Food uses presently account for about 90 percent of the soybean oil used in the United States. The increasing substitution of soybean oil for other oils and the increase in demand for margarine, shortening, and salad and cooking oils have been important factors in the total increase in consumption of oil. Research in re-

---

[5] Hiroshi Nakamura, "Structure of the Soybean Processing Industry in the United States: Economic, Institutional, and Technical Factors in Its Development," Ph.D. thesis, Univ. of Ill. (Urbana, 1963).

[6] Clifford H. Keirstead, *Marketing Study of Factors Affecting the Quantity and Value of Products Obtained From Soybeans*, P.M.A., U.S.D.A. (Washington, 1952).

[7] *Size of Soybean Oil Mills and Returns to Growers*, Agr. Mkg. Serv., MRR No. 121, U.S.D.A. (Washington, Nov. 1956).

fining oil in the 1920's produced the hydrogenation process that eliminated much of the oil's adverse smell and thus enabled it to compete favorably with other oils.[8] The oil's hydrogenated form is now the major component of practically all margarines and vegetable shortenings. About three-fourths of all soybean oil consumed for human food is in these products. Soybean oil in recent years has been far more important as an ingredient of food products than the other substitute oils.

Industrial uses developed in the early twentieth century when crude soybean oil was used by soap and paint manufacturers when competing products, cottonseed and linseed oils, were in short supply. The chemical composition of soybean oil renders it eminently suitable for many nonfood uses following certain chemical modifications. However, since the latter 1930's, both increasing food uses for the oil and the replacement of soybean oil by synthetic resins for nonfood uses has diminished the relative importance of nonfood oil utilization.

Soybean oil has been subject to vigorous competition from substitute fats and oils but, through its adaptability to numerous food and nonfood uses as well as low price, it has maintained a strong market position. However, in recent years, the demand for meal has increased relative to that for oil so an abundant supply of oil has caused prices to trend downward.[9]

### Utilization of Soybean Meal

The utilization of soybean meal as a protein source in feeds for livestock and poultry accounts for almost all the total disposition of meal. In recent years, the use of soybean meal has increased greatly both in terms of absolute volume and relative to competing meals.

Thus, the growth of the feed manufacturing industry, both domestic and foreign, has been essential to the growth of the processing industry. Not only has the number of protein-consuming animals increased, but the quantity of high protein feed fed per animal has increased as well.[10] Poultry have long been the primary consumers of soybean meal and utilization for poultry feed has increased greatly. In recent years, swine, the second largest consumers of soybean meal, have made the greatest increases in utilization, while dairy and beef cattle and sheep are of lesser importance. As a consequence of the domestic and foreign demand for meal, the

---

[8] Earl C. Hedlund, *The Transportation Economics of the Soybean Processing Industry* (Urbana: Univ. of Ill. Press, 1952).

[9] Walter G. Heid, *Changing Grain Market Channels*, Econ. Res. Serv., U.S.D.A. (Washington, 1961).

[10] *Consumption of Feed*, Prod. Res. Rept. 21, U.S.D.A. (Washington, Nov. 1958).

soybean processing industry's increasing crush has been readily absorbed at prices which have tended upward in recent years.

## Location of Processing and Product Markets

Geographic location of processing plants has paralleled regional production changes since plant location is decentralized into regions of production and market outlets for meal. Until 1944, the increase in plant numbers occurred primarily in the Midwest. Between 1944 and 1950, the increase in number of plants was primarily due to increasing processing in the South. New plants were built but cottonseed processing plants also were diversified for soybean processing. Since 1950, both the South and the Midwest have experienced a decline in the number of processing plants and a corresponding increase in the average size of plant.

The location of both margarine and shortening manufacturers is in high consumption areas. Their plants are centralized in large cities in the East, Midwest, West, South, and Southeast. About 60 percent of these plants are owned by multi-plant firms, many of which are integrated backward into processing. Distant oil markets are in contrast to the generally local meal markets for plants located in livestock-producing areas.

## The Crushing Margin and Industry Structure

The most notable performance characteristic of the soybean processing industry in the period since World War II undoubtedly is the narrowing of the margin between the price of soybeans and the value of the processed products (Figure 9.1 and Table 9.1). This is possibly also the most important performance criterion from the viewpoint of marketing efficiency. This margin is the aggregate "price" of all the services provided by handlers and processors in transforming the soybeans sold by farmers into oil and meal. It is determined by the myriad of economic factors, including industry structure and firm conduct, which affect price behavior of soybeans and the processed products. But the margin is also a determinant of firm conduct and resulting structure as well. Since the focus here is on the changing economic structure of the industry, performance will be viewed in its dual role as "effect" and "cause."

The narrowing of crushing margins in the last 15 years has occurred because the price of the two processed products, meal and oil, has dropped.[11] In recent years meal prices have been on the upswing due to increasing demand by livestock feeders while oil prices have tended downward. The demand for meal is primarily

[11] *Agricultural Prices*, Annual Summary, Crop Reporting Board, Stat. Reporting Serv., U.S.D.A. (Washington, yearly bulletins).

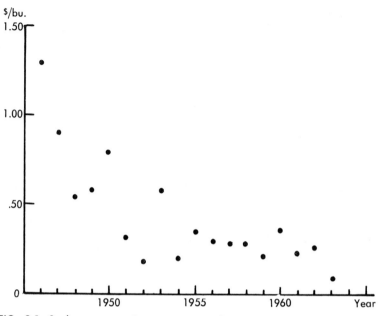

FIG. 9.1—Soybean processing margins in the United States from 1946 to 1963. (Source: Table 9.1.)

national while demand for oil is international. Although meal prices have increased since 1956, soybean prices also have increased since 1959. Thus, over the last 15 years, the crushing margin in the aggregate of all firms has become smaller. The relative degrees of margin "shrink" for individual mills depend on the particular firm's supply and market areas as well as organizational and operational efficiency. Advantages of various mills may reflect more favorable supply and market outlets; the particular rate structure for rail, water, or truck transportation in the area; soybean quality; use of production technology; or managerial proficiency.

Large processing plants have a slightly less per-bushel processing cost, but slightly less total revenue per bushel, than do small plants.[12] The existence of economies of scale explain the former characteristic while the fact that many small plants operate in more favorable time periods and market locations explains the latter. Thus, plants of minimum optimal scale achieve higher per bushel net revenue than do large plants, but a lower return on investment. Further, the economic advantages of solvent processing has led the industry to intensify processing operations in larger solvent plants.

Thus, the processing industry today has in existence both large and small firms and plants.[13] Plants smaller than minimum optimal

[12] *Size of Soybean Oil Mills and Returns to Growers, op. cit.*
[13] *Soybean Blue Book, op. cit.*

TABLE 9.1

PRICE SPREAD BETWEEN SOYBEANS AND END PRODUCTS

| | (1) | (2) | (3) | (4) | (5) | (6) | (7) | (8) | (9) |
|---|---|---|---|---|---|---|---|---|---|
| | Soybean* Average Price Rec'd by Farmers | Soybean Oil | | | | Soybean Meal | | Value of Products (cols. 4 +7) | Spread Between Price Rec'd by Farmers and Value of Products (col. 8—1) |
| | | Yield† | Price‡ | Value (cols. 2×3) | Yield§ | Price‡ | Value (cols. 5×6) | | |
| Year Beginning October | ($ per bu.) | (lbs.) | (¢ per lb.) | (dollars) | (lbs.) | (¢ per lb.) | (dollars) | (dollars) | (dollars) |
| 1946 | 2.52 | 9.0 | 23.2 | 2.10 | 48.0 | 3.56 | 1.71 | 3.81 | 1.29 |
| 1947 | 3.39 | 9.5 | 23.8 | 2.26 | 47.5 | 4.08 | 1.94 | 4.20 | .81 |
| 1948 | 2.29 | 9.8 | 13.1 | 1.28 | 47.1 | 3.29 | 1.55 | 2.83 | .54 |
| 1949 | 2.19 | 9.9 | 12.3 | 1.22 | 48.0 | 3.22 | 1.55 | 2.77 | .58 |
| 1950 | 2.49 | 9.7 | 18.1 | 1.76 | 47.6 | 3.21 | 1.53 | 3.29 | .80 |
| 1951 | 2.77 | 10.0 | 11.4 | 1.14 | 47.6 | 4.11 | 1.96 | 3.10 | .33 |
| 1952 | 2.78 | 10.8 | 12.1 | 1.31 | 48.5 | 3.40 | 1.65 | 2.96 | .18 |
| 1953 | 2.79 | 11.0 | 13.5 | 1.48 | 48.4 | 3.90 | 1.89 | 3.37 | .58 |
| 1954 | 2.52 | 10.9 | 11.9 | 1.30 | 46.8 | 3.03 | 1.42 | 2.72 | .20 |
| 1955 | 2.29 | 11.1 | 12.6 | 1.40 | 47.2 | 2.62 | 1.24 | 2.64 | .35 |
| 1956 | 2.23 | 10.9 | 12.7 | 1.38 | 48.5 | 2.37 | 1.15 | 2.53 | .30 |
| 1957 | 2.15 | 10.7 | 10.8 | 1.16 | 47.8 | 2.67 | 1.28 | 2.44 | .29 |
| 1958 | 2.06 | 10.6 | 9.5 | 1.01 | 48.3 | 2.79 | 1.35 | 2.36 | .30 |
| 1959 | 2.01 | 11.0 | 8.3 | .91 | 47.5 | 2.78 | 1.32 | 2.23 | .22 |
| 1960 | 2.32 | 11.0 | 11.3 | 1.24 | 48.0 | 3.03 | 1.45 | 2.69 | .37 |
| 1961 | 2.33 | 10.9 | 9.5 | 1.04 | 48.1 | 3.18 | 1.53 | 2.57 | .24 |
| 1962 | 2.39 | 10.7 | 8.9 | .95 | 47.9 | 3.56 | 1.71 | 2.66 | .27 |
| 1963 # | 2.63 | 10.9 | 8.4 | .92 | 51.4 | 3.50 | 1.80 | 2.72 | .09 |

* Prices received by Illinois farmers and include an allowance for unredeemed production loans at average loan value. From *Agricultural Statistics* & *Agricultural Prices*, U.S.D.A.

† U.S. average from *Soybean Blue Book*, 1964.

‡ Spot price, crudetank cars, f.o.b. Midwestern mills weighted by volume crushed, from *Soybean Blue Book*, 1964.

§ U.S. average from *Soybean Blue Book*, 1964.

‖ Spot price, bulk, 44 percent protein (41 percent before July 1950) basis Decatur, weighted by volume crushed, from *Soybean Blue Book*, 1964.

# Preliminary.

scale are declining in number as firms faced with declining crushing margins attempt to minimize costs by attaining both the optimum scale and rate of utilization. Scale relationships are important in attaining increased efficiency, as are technological change to solvent processing and increasing emphasis on soybean quality. The existence of firms operating at less than full capacity, the extent of which depends on location, has led to nonoptimal volume for particular scales.[14] However, higher cost operators are unable to shift this inefficiency to consumers due to industry competition. The resulting absorption of higher processing costs has thus led to further narrowing of crushing margins for these firms and subsequent exit.

The existence of vertically and horizontally integrated firms has not increased appreciably the return on investment. Firms so organized may or may not obtain appreciable savings and thus above-average profits, depending again on the firm and its plants in specific supply and market settings.[15] At this time, neither integrating vertically into refining, shortening, margarine, or feed manufacturing alleviates the competitive pressure on firm profits since competition is intense in the related activities as well. It does, however, through diversification, reduce the uncertainty of processing margins since soybean processing is only one part of the utilization process. Multi-plant operations leading to increasing returns depend on the entire complex of vertical and horizontal organization of the firm, including spatial separation of component plants. Thus, successful horizontal integration in soybean processing is more prevalent when the firm is vertically integrated as well.

## STRUCTURAL CHANGES IN SOYBEAN PROCESSING

The most important structural characteristic to be discussed is the rapid decline in the number of plants since 1950. In 1950 there were 250 mills, an increase of more than 100 since World War II. Since 1950, the number of mills has been declining and stood at 144 in 1963. However, processing capacity has continued to increase as plant numbers have declined. This continuing increase in capacity is due to expansion of existing facilities as well as the construction of larger plants at new locations to realize the economic advantages associated with solvent processing.

From World War II to the mid-1950's, industry processing capacity increased more rapidly than crushings. This resulted in

---

[14] *Ibid.*; and *Marketing Margins, Practices, and Costs for Soybeans and Cottonseed Oils,* Agr. Mkg. Serv., MRR No. 231, U.S.D.A. (Washington, May 1958).

[15] Don Paarlberg, *Prices of Soybeans and Soybean Products,* Agr. Exp. Sta. Bul. 538, Purdue Univ. (Lafayette, 1949).

TABLE 9.2

FIRM CAPACITY-CONCENTRATION OF SOYBEAN PROCESSORS IN THE UNITED STATES

| Size Group | Percent of Industry Capacity* | | |
|---|---|---|---|
| | 1947 | 1955 | 1963 |
| Largest 4 | 42 | 27 | 33 |
| Largest 8 | 58 | 44 | 50 |
| Largest 20 | 75 | 65 | 70 |

* Based on *Soybean Blue Book, Moody's*, NCM-30 interviews, and estimates by the authors.

excess capacity, which was undoubtedly a contributing factor to the narrowing of the crushing margin in that period. Between 1955 and 1963, industry capacity increased about 20 percent while crushings increased by 53 percent. Thus, excess capacity in the industry has been reduced although it still exists to a lesser degree. Its extent varies geographically with the distribution of production and plant locations. Midwest plants have an advantage relative to plants in southern states due to the concentration of production in the Corn Belt states. This is offset in part by the diversification of southern plants to crush cottonseed as well as soybeans.

In this period of decline in numbers of plants, both average plant and firm size (capacity) have increased. The median firm in the processing firm size distribution in 1947, 1955, and 1963 had daily capacities of 121 tons, 200 tons, and 400 tons, respectively. Average plant sizes for these years were 88 tons, 160 tons, and 284 tons. The average number of plants per firm has remained constant at about 1.4 for over 15 years. The great increase in plants until 1950 was due to both single-plant firm entry and plant additions by multi-plant firms. Since 1950, the largest firms have added plants, both by merger and by building plants. A mass exodus of smaller firms in the industry has occurred since 1950.

This would seem to imply increasing concentration of processing capacity in large multi-plant firms. However, several multi-plant firms have halted processing operations at most of their plants. This is attributed primarily to the postwar soybean product shortage ease that caused many refiners, margarine and shortening manufacturers, and feed manufacturers to relinquish backward integration. This integration was initially begun to maintain adequate supplies in the war shortage period.[16]

Table 9.2 presents a picture of concentration in the soybean processing industry. Using Bain's criteria, the industry would be classified as showing low-moderate concentration.[17] This suggests

[16] Nakamura, *op. cit.*
[17] Joe S. Bain, *Industrial Organization* (New York: John Wiley & Sons, Inc., 1959).

that the conduct and performance of the industry is to some degree oligopolistic in nature. This implication will be developed subsequently.

The illustrated deconcentration from 1947 to 1955 was due to the increase in number of plants and firms that increased industry capacity. This postwar deconcentration has reversed since 1955 due to industry adjustments and maturing of the industry through more stabilized demand and supply of soybean products. The increasing interfirm competition, both local and interregional, as well as the use of more efficient solvent processes had led to horizontal and vertical integration through mergers and erection of new facilities. For these reasons, the increasing size of surviving firms and elimination of small firms have resulted in increased concentration in recent years. The firms leaving the industry have primarily been the owners of small, less efficient, hydraulic press plants.

To add another dimension to the major structural change in the postwar period, analyses both of firm rank mobility and distribution variance were made for 1947, 1955, and 1963. The 1947–55 transition illustrates the immediate postwar industry expansion while the 1955–63 period shows the net effects on the size distribution due to more recent structural adjustment of the maturing industry.

The mobility analysis is indicative of the fluidity of industry structure and is suggestive of the success of new or established firms in securing stable market positions. The net increase of 49 firms from 1947 to 1955 was composed of 96 births and 47 deaths. The 63 surviving firms had a rank correlation coefficient of .87. This correlation was computed by grouping firms into rank classes of increasing width, beginning with width two for largest firms and ending with width five for smallest firms.

The 1955 to 1963 transition illustrated increasing rank stability, the correlation coefficient being .90. There were 72 surviving firms, 26 births and 73 deaths, a net decline of 47 firms. Thus, it is apparent that a great deal of industry stability exists for large survivors while there is an ever-present but declining number of small firms. Since 1955, the small firms have faced increased competition and, depending of course on their location, were unable to maintain adequate processing margins.

From 1947 to 1955, the variance of the firm size distribution doubled and, from 1955 to 1963, it increased again by two and one-half times. The 1947–55 variance increase was due not only to an increase in average plant size and an increasing number of multiplant firms to exploit economies of scale, but the survival and birth of many small firms. In this period, adequate anticipated margins induced relatively inefficient firms to operate. Since 1955, the continued increase in relative inequality of size distribution was due to an increased tendency to exploit economies of scale associated with large, solvent plant operation. The average firm size increased greatly and processing margins narrowed, so many smaller, less efficient firms halted operation. Many of the plants and firms which withdrew from processing were vertically integrated firms that ceased processing when meal and oil were available for domestic use and processed products were no longer in short supply and high priced.

Future tendencies of concentration depend not only on changes in production of soybeans and future demand for the processed products but on operational economies at both the plant and firm level. The presence of vertically and horizontally integrated firms tends to insure the long-run existence both of relatively inefficient small and very large plants and firms. Thus, the number and size distribution of processing firms is determined in part by the inter-industry firm relationships involving technical and market complementarity among products. Further, the cost and revenue variations among different sized plants and firms also help explain the continuation of an unequal size distribution. These intra- and interfirm characteristics will be analyzed in the context of geographic and institutional influence to determine their effect on the existing as well as future market structure.

## Economies of Large Plants

For a complete analysis of economies of size in the soybean processing industry, both the revenue and cost components must be explored to indicate the economic advantages accruing to plants of various sizes.

The details of the Decatur pricing system will be discussed in the pricing analysis but, as will be shown, the f.o.b. mill marginal revenue for sales in spatially separated markets declines with distance, due to transportation costs. The rate of decrease depends on the marginal costs of delivery as well as competition in the market area. Large processors must sell in the broader geographic markets since their local market is soon saturated. The decreasing marginal revenue for sales in geographically dispersed market outlets must be offset with cost economies of size if the entire operation is to be profitable relative to small plants and to help explain the structural tendency toward larger plants.

The traditional cost categories, fixed and variable, are useful for the analysis. The variable class includes two components of particular significance to size economies: procurement costs of soybeans, and disposition cost of the products. Disposition costs are both delivery costs and brokerage fees incurred between the plant and the market, while procurement costs include (1) price of the soybeans, (2) intermediary handling charges, and (3) transportation costs to the mill. Lack of complete cost data on all unique operations of firms in the industry forces this analysis to emphasize general cost characteristics and their apparent effect on the existing structure.

Scale economies are important for processing plants smaller than 300 tons daily processing capacity. Increases in scale produce the greatest reduction in average costs up to 300 tons. Plants larger than this have declining costs with an increase in size of mill, but successively larger plants show cost declines at rapidly decreasing rates. These relationships are true for both the solvent and screw press method with one exception. Screw press processing results in no appreciable cost economies beyond the 300-ton size while solvent plants have continually lower costs. Thus, it is apparent that solvent plants assume profit advantages relative to screw press plants for successively larger plants. However, the average cost per bushel crushed is higher for solvent plants than for screw press plants for capacities from 25 tons to 800 tons. Solvent plants larger than about 800 tons have lower per-unit processing costs than the same size screw press mills.

The two cost components that can be singled out as the costs determining relative efficiencies are capital and labor. Capital costs can be broken down into depreciation, taxes, and interest, all of which are higher for solvent plants. The per-bushel total cost advantage of screw presses diminishes as the scale of plant increases due to the more rapid decline in capital costs components for solvent plants.

However, as previously emphasized, solvent plants yield more oil from a bushel of soybeans than do screw presses. Since oil is typically worth several times as much as meal, a total revenue advantage accrues to solvent plants. The total value advantage per bushel less the total cost disadvantage determines the net per bushel advantage of various size solvent plants. The net advantage begins at a daily capacity of 50 tons and increases progressively with size.[18] The investment per bushel processed is higher for solvent plants than screw presses but, once again, the disadvantage narrows with size. When net return per dollar invested is compared between the two methods, the advantage accrues to solvent processing and increases with size of plant.

Inclusion of procurement and disposition costs does not invalidate the previous comparative analysis between processing methods since these costs are about the same for either type of proc-

[18] *Size of Soybean Oil Mills and Returns to Growers, op. cit.*

essing. These total cost components offset the continually declining long-run average cost curve since the larger the plant the more it becomes necessary to process soybeans and market meal in the general rather than local market. The varying use of rail, barge, or truck transportation, depending on their availability and relative costs, makes it impossible to determine specifically the levels of transportation costs for various size plants. However, the obvious saturation of local supply and market outlets by large plants dictates increasingly higher marketing costs for larger plants. These cost diseconomies primarily determine the spatial limits of supply and market areas as well as the size of plant. Further they point to horizontal integration through multi-plant operation as a growth alternative to expansion of plant size.

### Economies of Multi-Plant Integration

Advantageous horizontal integration through multi-plant operations depends importantly on the nature of the existing firm organization in determining multi-plant economies as well as the size of plants combined. Thus it is desirable to delineate pure multi-plant economies accruing to a nonvertically integrated firm from those economies obtained by firms that are vertically integrated. Multi-plant economies that depend on the vertical complex rest primarily on the processing plant as a necessary link for a more economical and stabilized supply of processed products as an input in the forward-integrated activity.

Considering horizontal multi-plant economies, it must be kept in mind that not only do internal economies of scale exist in soybean processing, but rising acquisition costs as well. To build an additional processing plant, size and location depend primarily on the specific locational supply-price relationships. This is one factor inducing horizontal integration. Specifically, the costs of soybean acquisition and product disposition are diseconomies for a single plant. Horizontal integration decentralizes the firm into more favorable supply and market outlets and reduces acquisition and disposition costs. Unless these firm costs can be substantially lowered by plant decentralization, plant location will be centralized.

These economies of multi-plant operations are important for the continued existence of industry structure that is decentralized.[19] These economies are important in high soybean production areas and for serving the various regional demands for processed products, especially meal. Thus, areas of high production and meal utilization are attractive locations for decentralized multi-plant processing firms. Strategically located plants with respect to supply of soy-

---

[19] Nakamura, *op. cit.*

beans and demand for processed products stabilize the firm's industry position, while permitting the firm to operate in areas of relatively favorable margins.

## Economies of Vertical Integration

The analysis of vertical integration broadens the scope of plant and firm interrelationships to include economies to be achieved by combining two or more stages of soybean marketing under a single ownership. These relationships between separable and distinct industry links have led to the present structure of the diversified and integrated firm complexes in soybean processing. The scarcity of soybean meal and oil during World War II and the associated desire by both feed mixers and oil refiners to secure and stabilize inputs contributed to the rapid integration of soybean processing. This backward integration was terminated by many firms when soybean product supplies were no longer short. However, much of the war-induced integration has persisted for reasons other than supply shortages.

The most important form of vertical integration has been that combination of soybean processing with feed manufacturing. This integration has developed through firm and plant mergers, new plant construction, and diversification of existing processing facilities. It results in increased flexibility in directing the flow of meal to more profitable outlets.

The tendency for feed mixing plants to be decentralized and their close marketing links and complementary attributes to soybean processing lend themselves to the concept of a single, integrated, profit-maximizing combination. These complementary attributes are basically the more economical flow of separate products and inputs, since meal disposition costs are minimized for the processor as are meal processing costs for the feed mixer. Not only is physical movement reduced but the operations of both activities can better be adjusted to supply and demand conditions. The crushing operation and storage can be adjusted to feed requirements and enable the firm to adjust to its optimum scale and output. Excess capacity has been the primary deterrent to the attainment of optimum firm operations, and integration permits maximum use of facilities. Ease of procurement on the basis of expected returns on the processed products is also affected. Firms can be more competitive in supply areas and secure adequate stocks of soybeans if the integration brings higher and more certain returns on the processed products.

The above discussion indicates the general advantages of integration with feed manufacturing and explains why about 50 percent of soybean processors today have combined operations. It does not explain why there has been no increase since 1950 in the number of feed-integrated firms. Of course, the proportion of feed-integrated firms to total firms has increased since the latter have declined in absolute number.

Both internal technical restrictions as well as marketing problems complicate the combination and provide barriers to increased integration. Backward integration from mixing into processing involves an investment much greater and more technically complex than for feed manufacturing. Further marketing problems in oil merchandising face the backward integrated feed plant. Forward integration of processing to feed mixing transfers the marketing problems from merchandising meal to selling feed, which itself is a very competitive industry. If the processing plant is at least minimum optimal size, the feed plant may not be large enough to use all the produced meal and the feed mixer must market meal as well. Large corporate processors have a network of feed and processing plants designed to allocate meal supplies to areas of higher demand and to have more efficient plant operation and product movement. However, this usually involves spatial separation of supply and demand and certain integration advantages are lost if high interplant transportation costs are incurred.

Vertical integration has also developed on the oil utilization side. About two-thirds of soybean oil goes into food products while the other one-third goes to export and nonfood uses. Margarine and shortening utilization account for about 70 percent of the food use. Integration developed as backward integration of manufacturers of soybean oil products into the soybean processing industry.

Crude soybean oil for margarine and shortening generally moves to consumption areas for refining. Over 70 percent of refined oil is utilized either for final products or is further processed into final products very close to the refinery. Refinery locations include large cities such as Chicago, New York, Los Angeles, Atlanta, and Minneapolis. The primary reason for backward integration by margarine and shortening manufacturers is to stabilize the supply of oil and reduce the necessity for large storage inventories. As of 1958, about 30 percent of margarine and more than 50 percent of shortening plants were operated by firms also operating soybean and cottonseed oil mills.[20] In recent years of plentiful oil production, there has been less need for backward integration to stabilize oil supplies.

The nature of marketing channels for shortening and margarine as well as the established brand names of existing manu-

---

[20] *Marketing Margins, Practices, and Costs for Soybeans and Cottonseed Oils,* op. cit.

facturers have generally precluded forward integration by soybean processors into manufacturing. However, although most refining facilities now are owned by edible foods manufacturers, some processors have found integration into refining to be advantageous. The increasing size of processing plants has helped make at-plant refining more economically feasible than previously. Some transportation cost advantages accrue as a result of weight losses in the refining stage. If at-mill refining becomes attractive for independent and cooperative processors, the competition for market outlets will shift to the manufacturing level. Here the existing high degree of backward integration involving large refineries located at population centers and owned by manufacturers will deter forward integration by processors into refining.

Cooperative processing firms differ from private and corporate firms in that certain vertical integration economies can be obtained without ownership investment through the association of cooperatives performing different functions. Local elevators can become members of regional processing firms, thus providing both backward and forward integration links for processors. Soybeans are typically shipped to the mill and soybean meal hauled to the local association for bulk feed mixing and retail sales.

In summary, large, multi-plant processing firms rely on both horizontal and vertical integration. Horizontal integration through multi-plant operations in decentralized locations is the primary structural response to the diseconomies of acquisition and disposition. Diseconomies associated with rising supply prices of soybeans for large plants is to some extent controlled by backward integration into local and terminal elevator operation, although the disadvantage persists.

### Transportation Costs and Structure

Transportation is one of the major factors accounting for the decentralization advantages that have been involved in the changing market structure. Rail, truck, and barge movements of soybeans and the processed meal have each affected the location and size of existing plants in various ways. Rail movement has been the primary mode of transportation for soybeans and meal in the United States. Decentralization of processing facilities has led to the increasing importance of truck shipments as well as advantageous waterways locations and barge shipments. The relative importance of the various modes varies with plant size, available transportation facilities, and existing rate structures. The varying use of different types of transportation has tended to equalize the competitive advantage accruing to firms of different sizes. Also, rate structures have tended to intensify interregional competition and lead to more efficient processing operations. One such rate structure policy is the in-transit processing privilege.

The transit privilege is an institutional device designed to make rail transportation more competitive with other modes for movement of agricultural commodities.[21] This privilege, granted chiefly by railroads, was developed long before the soybean processing industry, and the industry has grown with it. Transit permits interrupting a shipment of soybeans between origin and destination for purposes of milling. The entire movement of raw grain and processed meal moves at a through freight rate instead of a higher combination of two local rates.

The characteristic weight loss due to processing is about 20 percent of a given quantity of soybeans. This average weight loss includes both a 15 percent loss in weight due to oil and 5 percent loss due to moisture, waste, etc. The 20 percent total weight loss of the inbound total does not move under the transit privilege. Export rates on overseas shipment of oil are the only way to lower oil transport costs unless the oil is sold in local markets. Actually, the oil has its own in-transit rate but, unless the processor is also the refiner, he receives none of the advantages. The specific rules of transit use vary among railroads; thus, only the general principle and its effects on competition will be discussed here.

The tendency for plant location to be raw-material oriented, as previously discussed, is primarily due to transportation economies in areas of adequate supplies of soybeans and high-consumption meal markets. This tendency is lessened by transit privilege, and plant locations intermediate to soybean supply and spatially separated meal markets become feasible. This intermediate-location tendency is partly reduced in favor of production-area location when the relative advantages of transit are compared between intermediate and production-area locations. Since rail rates increase less than proportionally with distance, a production-area mill receives a greater percentage decrease in the local rates combination than does the intermediate mill.

In-transit privileges influence the merchandising behavior of processors with respect to acquisition and disposition, and thus effect the degree of competition in the industry. Under transit, a general broadening of both firms' supply and market areas occurs. Widening of both supply and market area limits contributes greatly to the competitiveness of the existing market structure. Concentration of processing volume among a few firms in given areas has less significance as an indicator of competitive market performance. This develops because the institutional transit privilege affects

---

[21] Hedlund, *op. cit.*

market conduct in such a way as to prevent regional collusive pricing activities by allowing firms access to spatially separated markets, thus intensifying competition. This, of course, assumes the availabilities of transit billings. Processors use less costly truck transportation for local movements of soybeans and meal and balance incoming and outgoing interstate billings for meal shipments to distant areas at reduced costs.

Transit privileges have also increased the economic feasibility of large-scale processing. They assist operators of large plants to compete for soybeans with smaller, spatially separated mills and to sell successfully in the market areas of plants located at consumption points. This permits expansion of total volume to take advantage of the relative efficiency of processing in large plants.

## PRODUCT DIFFERENTIATION

Product differentiation refers to the extent to which outputs of competing sellers are regarded as close substitutes by the buyers in the market. That is, the degree of substitutability among outputs of various processors reflects the extent of product differentiation in the industry.

Differentiation is present only to a slight degree in the products of soybean processors. This does not mean that the products are necessarily physically homogeneous. Meal produced by the solvent process has higher protein content; oil may vary in the content of several of its components. But these products are usually sold on the basis of the proportion of specified ingredients. Thus, although meal of higher protein content may sell for a premium, sale on the basis of guaranteed minimum protein content means the meal of one processor is regarded as a very close—if not perfect—substitute for that of another. Thus, little competitive advantage in sales can be obtained by processors through brand names and advertising.

Location of plants is another aspect of product differentiation which does exist in soybean processing. When a processor is selling meal in nearby markets and prices are established f.o.b. plant, buyer substitutability is low for price changes which do not lead to shipments into the area by other processors. As will be discussed later, the diminishing importance of basing-point pricing of meal has increased the ability of plants to secure and hold local markets. Service and reputation among local buyers are other factors which may reduce the substitutability of the products of spatially separated plants.

## BARRIERS TO ENTRY

Entry barriers refer to advantages which established processors have over potential entrants. These barriers are structural dimensions that retard firm entry which would develop from anticipated profits. Not only are established buying and selling markets deterrents to entry but also the achievement of higher returns of the entire processing operation through horizontal and vertical integration are deterrents as well.

With changing processing technology and the existence of economies of plant size, the surviving entrant must be sufficiently large to obtain the minimum optimal scale. The initial investment for an optimal scale is moderately high—from one to five million dollars. However, the minimal scale, in the setting of the entire industry today, would add less than one percent to total processing capacity. Thus necessary investment is high in absolute terms, but in relation to the entire industry, minimum optimal scale for entry is not an important barrier.

Established processors, because of their secured position in the industry, have greater plant-entry potential than new firms since processing experience minimizes many risks of plant entry. Capital requirements are more easily met due to the presence of processor equity, technical know-how, market position, possible economies of multi-plant operations, and other factors. Thus growth of existing firms should predominate over firm entrants for industry growth in the future, especially in view of narrow crushing margins. Both vertical and horizontal integration by established firms will continue to diversify investments and achieve potential economies.

Institutional barriers are practically nonexistent in the soybean processing industry. The significant entry impediment at present is the low expected crushing margin, and hence low anticipated profits. This barrier varies with location, but interregional competition has made it increasingly difficult to find potential markets free from intense competition. Competition among existing firms establishes the upper limit to price bids for soybeans and the lower limit for meal and oil prices at levels which do not attract entry by profit-seeking firms.

## MARKET CONDUCT

Analyses of the market conduct of soybean processors will emphasize the determination of processor prices. Thus the analysis will consider processing operations with particular reference to the pricing policies and power of processors and their economic effects on performance.

Soybeans are crushed by processors, in total, in somewhat uniform quantities through the year. Typical processor purchasing activities entail an accumulation of several months crushing requirements at harvest time when soybeans are marketed at seasonal low prices. The bulk of soybean purchases come from local and terminal elevators, although in some marketing channels soybeans may pass through various intermediaries. The particular supply path depends on the size of the processor in determining necessary quantities of soybeans and the distance of the shipment. Accumulation of soybean stocks develop not only at the mill, depending on the availability of storage facilities, but at local elevators as well. In recent years, however, the harvest time accumulation has been proportionately lighter since on-farm storage has increased by farmers' storing soybeans in anticipation of higher prices. This on-farm storage restricts seasonal price changes and makes satisfactory crushing margins increasingly difficult to attain.

As mentioned earlier, processors bid for soybeans according to oil content, means of transportation billing, orders to be filled, and prospects for plant utilization. Soybean purchasing involves numerous risks, only one of which is price. Storage of soybeans involves risks associated with fire, quality deterioration, and shrinkage, as well as financing. The larger the processing plant, depending on availability of local soybeans and local markets, the more acute become problems associated with acquiring, storing, and financing necessary crushing supplies. Vertical integration may transfer many of these risks from the immediate processing operation to the various integrated functions. Still, the price risks exist due to the necessity of securing an adequate margin for the entire operation cost.

The success of a processor in profitably performing the processing operation and maximizing processing margins depends a great deal on the success of handling the risks associated with ownership and marketing products through a complex and changing pricing structure. A brief discussion of the existing pricing system will indicate the nature of competition that develops under the basing-point price system. Following this, a discussion of future markets will indicate the policies employed to maximize net margins under existing price risks.

Due to the initial development of soybean processing in Decatur, Illinois, soybean products prices usually are quoted f.o.b. Decatur. Under the strict Decatur basing-point system, "phantom freight" rates or transportation costs from Decatur to the mill are incorporated in selling prices. These theoretical rate inclusions represent no cost to the firm and are a direct result of the single basing-point system. Since the phantom rate added a considerable amount to meal prices in various areas, the increasing narrow margins and excess capacity of many firms have led to intense interregional competition and a general washing out of the "phantom freight." Thus, the strict Decatur pricing system has eroded although some firms still quote prices on that basis.

The Decatur pricing system for many mills and buyers is pri-

marily a convenient basis for price quotations, but implies no particular price leadership by Decatur-located firms. Most of the sales
in the industry are made on the basis of f.o.b. plant prices so that
more distinct local market areas exist due to the impact of transportation costs. Although these more secure and distinct local
market areas have developed through competition, large processors
saturate local markets and must encroach upon other firms' markets
through price competition and absorption of marginal delivery
costs. The geographical limits are determined by transportation
costs to outlying markets. That is, interregional competition will
develop to the extent that the marginal revenue of additional crushing and disposition of meal is greater than the marginal cost of
production and delivery. If economies of scale are anticipated or if
firms are operating at less than full capacity, marginal production
costs decline to offset to some extent the increasing marginal delivery costs and thus extend the market area.

The nature of interregional competition provides an answer to
the question of why some firms persistently price on the strict
Decatur basing point. Firms doing so are those in advantageous locations unaffected by sufficient competition in their market areas
to eliminate the "phantom freight." This discriminatory pricing
results in a higher price for the nearby markets of less elastic demand. That is, the advantage of strict Decatur basing-point pricing
depends on the elasticity of the various markets served.

Commodity futures are widely used in the processing industry
and the larger the firm, the greater the necessity to hedge its vast
inventory against price changes. The use of commodity futures in
soybean processing operations is an attempt to shift price risks
associated with ownership of soybeans and soybean product inventories.[22] These operations complicate the pricing mechanism and
offset the processor's competitive behavior by stabilizing uncertainty
associated with price changes. The existence of futures markets for
soybean meal and oil, as well as soybeans, changes price relationships such that the actual price level is of lesser importance than
the changing *basis*.

The three basic merchandising operations of soybean processing that hedging facilitates are soybean buying, oil selling, and meal
selling. Hedging in each of these areas or intermingling of futures
trading depends on the whole complex of price relationships involving soybeans and soybean products.

The rate of accumulation of soybeans at favorable prices depends on the storage facilities, the existing supply of soybeans

---

[22] Dean W. Malott, *Grain and Its Marketing* (Chicago: Grain Exchange Inst.,
1951); and Merrill, Lynch, Pierce, Fenner, and Smith, Inc., *How To Hedge Commodities*.

relative to optimum plant utilization, and the relationship of spot to futures quotations. Thus basis behavior revolves around the supply and demand situation for storage space. The storage facilities relative to plant capacity are an important characteristic of the optimum organization of a processor. This factor dictates tendencies for backward integration and stabilization of supply in an attempt to offset increasing costs of soybean acquisition.

Both the meal and oil merchandising operations utilize futures markets not only for shifting the risk of price fluctuations but for facilitating optimum use of existing warehouse facilities. Futures quotations in relation to spot oil and meal prices determine, in part, the tendency for processors to store oil and/or meal to earn carrying charges.

Crushing margins are determined by the relationship between cash and future market prices. A processor fixes the processing margin by futures transactions, while cash purchases and orders are scattered through the year.[23] Generally, the *basis* for soybeans is wider earlier in the season than for oil and meal. The competitive advantage of hedging depends on successful analysis of futures and spot quotations as well as correctly forecasting subsequent changes. Exact methods used vary among processors seasonally, and from year to year.

Competition as a result of futures trading is likely to result in increased gross margin uniformity between processing areas since price factors become international rather than local. Futures price levels are determined by world supply and demand, and local spot prices in disadvantageous locations become of secondary importance. Less risk is assumed since the purchase price for soybeans, sales price for meal and oil, and the associated margin can be fixed at the most advantageous time regardless of what local prices are. This risk reduction may or may not narrow the processors margin, it reduces the necessary size of working capital, and it separates speculation from processing operations. This latter characteristic permits processors to restrict profits or losses solely to processing. Buying and selling through futures markets increase the number of individuals effectively establishing margins, and oligopolistic price interdependence between several competitors is partly eliminated. World supply and demand conditions become more of an integral part of the price-taking firm's margins. Pricing interdependence is partially eliminated although there is not complete elimination of market interdependence in cash sales.

---

[23] *Commodity Markets and the Public Interest*, Proceedings, Eighth Annual Symposium, Chicago Board of Trade (Sept. 1955).

## MARKET PERFORMANCE AND PUBLIC POLICY

The soybean processing industry has little product differentiation, few and low entry barriers, and has increased efficiency of resource utilization as reflected through a narrowing of the processing margin. Major changes in number, size, and location of plants, and in vertical and horizontal integration have taken place. The resulting industry structure and firm conduct in pricing and adjusting to risk are important and are determinants of observed performance.

At the same time, market structure should be—and in *this* study was—viewed as an adjustment to fundamental conditions of the market. One important performance criterion, and perhaps *the* most important for this industry, is how well the industry has adjusted to changing conditions. Analytically, the answer to this question requires that we understand how specific structural changes have been conditioned by conduct, performance, and technological and institutional variables and factors. Our tools for analyzing and evaluating these relationships are themselves largely in a developmental stage. The results presented here are tentative, but do support the conclusion that observed changes are in the right direction.

The rate of change is another matter and raises the question of "perfection of competition" in this industry in the large sense. Restrictive practices and predatory behavior are not at issue nearly to the extent of efficiency of resource use and possible market foreclosure through vertical integration.

Are firms building the size of plants and choosing the locations which are optimal from the viewpoint of industry production and marketing efficiency? Are private investment decisions leading to replacement of obsolete facilities or expansion of small plants consistent with overall minimization of processing costs? What information is available to private decision makers and is the right kind and amount being supplied by public agencies?

Is vertical integration necessary for successful entry into the industry, thus constituting a rising barrier for potential entrants? Does horizontal integration permit adjustments to demand and supply conditions, pricing, and risks which maximize gains or minimize losses to large firms while insuring large losses for small firms in unfavorable periods?

There is not sufficient evidence at present to award "final marks" to the industry on any of these points. They represent critical and interrelated dimensions of structure, conduct, and performance. Public policy must be alert to the evolution of the industry in these dimensions and responsive to its malleable characteristics. Research workers must further our understanding of the dynamic processes in this industry as a basis for positive policies to insure performance in the interests of farmers and consumers.

## SELECTED REFERENCES

Armore, Sidney, *The Demand and Price Structure for Food Fats and Oils,* U.S.D.A. Tech. Bul. 1068 (Washington, 1953).

Emory, William, and Wolf, J. S., *A Study of Practices Affecting the Use of Major Vegetable Oils for Refining and Processing,* Graduate School of Business and Public Administration, Washington Univ., and Agr. Mkg. Serv., U.S.D.A. cooperating (St. Louis, July 1960).

Gold, Gerald, *Modern Commodity Futures Trading* (New York: Commodity Res. Bur., Inc., 1959).

Goldberg, Ray A., *The Soybean Industry* (Minneapolis: Univ. of Minn. Press, 1952).

Gray, George Douglas, *All About the Soya Bean* (London: John Gale, Sons and Danielson, Ltd., 1936).

Jordan, G. L., *What Determines Soybean Prices?* Univ. of Ill. Agr. Exp. Sta. Bul. 546 (Urbana, 1951).

Pahigian, Noriar, *Marketing Study of the Oil Content of Soybeans as Related to Production Areas and Climate,* U.S.D.A., P.M.A. (Washington, 1950).

Schonberg, James S., *The Grain Trade: How It Works* (New York: Exposition Press, 1956).

*The Soybean Digest* (Hudson, Iowa: Amer. Soybean Assn., monthly editions).

Thompson, William H., *Transportation of Poultry Feed Ingredients From the North Central States,* S. Dak. Agr. Exp. Sta. Bul. 485 (Brookings, 1960).

# 10

# THE GRAIN PROCUREMENT INDUSTRY

## PAUL L. FARRIS[1]

THE PRICING of agricultural commodities has long been a topic for study and comment. For grains, along with a number of other commodities, the tradition has prevailed of an open competitive market at one or more points in the marketing channel. At such markets the basic forces of supply and demand meet and price is determined. The pricing process is usually assumed to work quite automatically and impartially. Prices generated at open markets not only perform the traditional pricing functions of guiding resources and distributing income, but they also provide benchmarks for establishing prices at other points in the marketing channel.

Market structure changes, technological developments, government activities, and other factors have in recent years forced changes in traditional exchange processes. As a consequence, the pricing process for many commodities is a changing one. Central market pricing for some commodities is declining. Whether the role of price is a generally declining one has been actively debated but not convincingly decided.[2]

Nevertheless, the important issue really is not whether price is becoming more or less important as a coordinator of economic activity. Market outcomes are increasingly being subjected to scrutiny and, where the results are unsatisfactory in one sense or another, alternative exchange processes and arrangements are being sought and found. The real question is whether, regardless of the

---

[1] Professor of Agricultural Economics, Purdue University.
[2] Norman R. Collins, "Changing Role of Price in Agricultural Marketing," *Journal of Farm Economics,* Vol. XLI, No. 3 (Aug. 1959), pp. 528–34; Jimmye S. Hillman, "Collins' Changing Role of Price," and Norman R. Collins, "Collins' Changing Role of Price—A Reply," *Journal of Farm Economics,* Vol. XLII, No. 2 (May 1960), pp. 385–89; Roger W. Gray, "Some Thoughts on the Changing Role of Price," *Journal of Farm Economics,* Vol. XLVI, No. 1 (Feb. 1964), pp. 117–27.

form that exchange processes take, such processes work effectively to promote improved economic performance.

Thus it is increasingly important that we understand our exchange processes. The idea has strong support that market prices should be relied upon primarily to coordinate economic activity in our enterprise system. Critical analysis is necessary not only to assure that traditional pricing systems are given opportunity to flourish wherever they may have comparative advantages, but also to improve the market performance of any exchange process.

This chapter, therefore, has dual objectives. The first is to set forth the essential features and characteristics of the pricing process for grains, which are an important group of commodities in American agriculture. Emphasis is focused on the country elevator level. The second objective is to draw from the empirical analyses of grain pricing processes some conclusions and inferences to illustrate the kinds of problems and issues involved in improving exchange processes for other commodities as well as grain.

## PERFECT COMPETITION AND THE PRICING PROCESS FOR GRAINS

Grain markets are generally considered to represent the best empirical examples of pricing processes under conditions approaching perfect competition. Such reference is ordinarily made but not limited to futures markets. A high degree of pricing efficiency is assumed to prevail at other stages in grain marketing channels.

The key concepts and definitions underlying the empirical results presented in this chapter are briefly outlined below.

*Pure* competition is here defined as absence of any monopolistic element or absence of control over supply and, therefore, over price. A purely competitive market is one in which there is (1) a large number of buyers and sellers so that the influence of any one or of several in combination is negligible and (2) a homogeneous or standardized product.

*Perfect* competition requires, *in addition* to the requirements for pure competition, such "perfection" as the particular theorist finds useful and convenient to his problem.[3] Absence of friction in some sense is usually implied. This means perfect knowledge about current market conditions, the future, and the product, and further, perfect mobility of factors so "that adjustments to changing conditions which actually involve time are accomplished instantaneously in theory."[4]

This concept is similar to Shepherd's definition of the perfect

---

[3] Edward H. Chamberlin, *The Theory of Monopolistic Competition* (Cambridge: Harvard Univ. Press, 1948), pp. 6–7.
[4] *Ibid.*, p. 6.

market in time, place, and form, which carried to the abstract limit assumes "(1) a particular commodity, (2) a point in space, and (3) an instant of time."[5] Obviously, there is only one price in such a market.

Perfection may exist, however, even if the commodity is not strictly homogeneous, or if there are space or time periods involved. This is true provided that price differentials accurately reflect (1) differences among commodities and among grades of a given commodity, (2) transportation costs, and (3) storage costs and correct discounting of the future.

Because these rigid requirements of perfect competition do not hold in reality, the relative efficiency of the process of "price discovery" becomes highly important. This process, state Thomsen and Foote, has two distinct phases: "(1) evaluating the conditions of demand and supply and determining the general level of prices for the commodity which will result from these conditions and around which prices for particular lots of the commodity in different locations, of different qualities, and in different transactions will fluctuate; (2) determining the value of a specific lot of the commodity being exchanged relative to the general market level."[6]

Though we have long known that actual market prices conform only approximately to prices which would prevail under abstract conditions of perfect competition, we have not always recognized what implications follow. There is a tendency to assume that even though individual deviations between actual and theoretical prices may be considerable, when all the actual prices are averaged together the departures from some theoretical base may be relatively small. This reasoning goes on to assume that, consequently, competition assures that the law of one price will tend to prevail.

The fallacy in this reasoning is that most buyers and sellers are interested in outcomes of individual transactions involving particular products they buy and sell. Resources are allocated and incomes distributed by terms of trade established in millions of individual transactions involving thousands of buyers and sellers and hundreds of markets. Only when the range of imperfection in the pricing process is quite narrow can we safely deduce results which we can assume will hold for individual market participants and for general performance of the pricing system.

An important objective of many public education and service programs has been to narrow the range of deviation of individual market prices from prices dictated by underlying supply and de-

―――――――
    [5] Geoffrey S. Shepherd, *Marketing Farm Products* (Ames: The Iowa State College Press, 1955), p. 18.
    [6] F. L. Thomsen and R. J. Foote, *Agricultural Prices* (New York: McGraw-Hill Book Co., 1952), p. 120.

mand conditions.[7] In terms of the traditional horizontal price line facing the firm under perfect competition, the range of deviations can be visualized in the form of bands above and below the horizontal price line.[8] The wider the band, the more serious are the imperfections; the narrower the band, the more closely do actual prices agree with perfectly competitive prices.

It is not known just how wide these bands are for various commodities. There undoubtedly is a great amount of variation, both among commodities and for individual commodities at different markets and at different points in the marketing channel. Reasons for differences lie in variations in knowledge of current market conditions, knowledge of the future, difficulties in judging product quality rapidly and accurately, and lags in the adjustment of products and factors to changed supply and demand situations. Programs aimed at reducing such imperfections can be expected to contribute to overall pricing effectiveness. Studies of particular commodities and particular markets are needed in order to determine the more important sources of market imperfections so that appropriate corrective programs can be prescribed for specific market situations.

## MARKET STRUCTURE CHARACTERISTICS OF COUNTRY ELEVATORS

Grain is produced on numerous farms widely scattered throughout the United States. Nearly all food grains, soybeans, and large volumes of feed grains are transported mainly to country elevators which are the initial assembly points and points of first sale. In 1959, for example, an estimated 83 percent of wheat and feed grains sold off farms went to country elevators.[9] The remainder went directly to terminal elevators, CCC-owned storage, processors and other agencies, and secondary elevators.

Most of the grain received at country elevators is bought by the elevators, and the elevators, in turn, sell most of the grain they purchase to terminal elevators or grain processors. Country elevators, therefore, are major price-making points in the grain economy.

Pricing grain at country elevators is a process which reflects (1) the influence of basic price-making forces throughout the United States and the world and (2) local competitive conditions and practices. Grain prices tend to be determined by aggregate sup-

---

[7] See, for example, Harold F. Breimyer, "Fifty Years of Federal Marketing Programs," *Journal of Farm Economics*, Vol. XLV, No. 4 (Jan. 1963), pp. 749–58.

[8] This conceptualization is illustrated in Paul L. Farris, "The Pricing Structure for Wheat at the Country Elevator Level," *Journal of Farm Economics*, Vol. XL, No. 3 (Aug. 1958), pp. 607–24.

[9] Walter G. Heid, Jr., *Changing Grain Market Channels*, ERS–39, Econ. Res. Serv., U.S.D.A. (Washington, Nov. 1961), p. 5.

plies and demands for grains throughout the world and modified by trading policies and arrangements, both national and international. They are discovered in a myriad of local and central market environments, each with its own particular institutional characteristics and practices. The large grain futures markets are focal points for the meeting of demand and supply forces. Prices generated at futures markets tend to govern but not to control nor discover prices at local markets and central cash markets. It is necessary to analyze the market structure and behavior of local markets in order to understand the pricing process at the local level. It is also necessary to analyze the structure of the buying and selling sides at central markets in order to understand the pricing process at this level.

Some of the key market structure and institutional characteristics of country elevators are as follows:

1. Country elevators are relatively numerous in grain-producing areas, and the average size of business tends to be relatively small. In 1959, there were an estimated 6,000 country elevators in the United States, down from 9,000 in 1939. The average capacity of the elevators increased from somewhat less than 30,000 bushels in 1939 to an estimated 90,000 bushels in 1959.[10] In the 1961–62 marketing year, the average Indiana elevator purchased approximately 300,000 bushels of grain.[11]

2. There is a relatively high fixed cost in country elevator physical facilities and, partly due to the seasonality of grain harvest, there is a general problem of underutilization of grain-handling facilities. Recent studies indicate that country elevator grain merchandising costs per bushel decline rapidly from about 10 cents to around 5–6 cents per bushel as total volume merchandised increases from 100,000 to around 600,000 bushels. Merchandising cost per bushel then declines more slowly—by another cent or two per bushel as volume merchandised increases to one million or more.[12]

---

[10] *Ibid.,* p. 4.

[11] The variability about this average was fairly large as reflected in the standard deviation being slightly larger than the average. This information is from a survey of Indiana country elevators conducted in 1963. Results are reported in Truck Shipments of Grain From Indiana Country Elevators, 1961–62 Marketing Year," by Paul L. Farris, Res. Progress Rept. 105, Purdue Univ. Agr. Exp. Sta. (Lafayette, Mar. 1964).

[12] Francis P. Yager, *Country Elevators—Cost-Volume Relations in the Spring Wheat Belt,* Serv. Rept. 63, Farmer Cooperative Serv., U.S.D.A. (Washington, Sept. 1963), p. 11; Thomas E. Hall, Walter K. Davis, and Howard L. Hall, *New Local Elevators—Cost-Volume Relations in the Hard Winter Wheat Belt,* Serv. Rept. 12, Farmer Cooperative Serv., U.S.D.A. (Washington, May 1955), p. 79; and V. L. Sorenson and C. D. Keyes, *Cost Relationships in Grain Plants,* Tech. Bul. 292, Mich. State Univ. Agr. Exp. Sta. (East Lansing, 1963), pp. 24, 26.

3. Many physical facilities are relatively old. As time has passed, locations have become less and less desirable; and space, structures, and equipment have become increasingly inadequate. Thus in spite of the general decline in elevator numbers, there have been new and modern elevators constructed to replace older, outmoded facilities. But the trend is not rapid. In a large representative sample of Indiana country elevators it was found that about 8 percent of the elevators were constructed between 1955 and 1963. Fourteen percent of the elevators had undergone a change in management during the same period. This indicates an average ownership change of around 2 percent per year.[13]

4. Most country elevators, particularly in the Corn Belt, are independently managed and operated firms. Only a relatively small proportion (less than half) are line or branch elevators that are operated from a central office. The independently operated elevators consist of both cooperatives and privately owned stock firms.

5. In many areas the income from sideline business and custom service is much larger than the income from handling grain. For example, a 1952 study of 18 Indiana elevators selected from a 35-county area showed that gross income from marketing grain made up only 23 percent of the total gross income from all sources.[14]

6. In grain-producing areas there are commonly several elevators within a county, and trade areas overlap considerably. Most farmers are within easy transportation distance (often 10 miles or less) of two or more elevators.[15] Nevertheless, there are product, service, and location attributes of country elevators which provide some insulation from the competition of other elevators. This differentiation appears to be buttressed by the propensity of most farmers not to shop around in search of better places to buy or sell.[16]

---

[13] Paul L. Farris, *op. cit.*, p. 6.

[14] Perry S. Richey and Thew D. Johnson, *Factors To Be Considered in Locating, Planning and Operating Country Elevators*, Mkg. Res. Rept. 23, U.S.D.A. (Washington, June 1952), p. 4.

[15] The trading area varies by section of the U.S. The above-mentioned study by Richey and Johnson indicated that farmers bringing grain to the elevators studied normally traveled an average of about seven miles to reach them. *Ibid.*, p. 8. A study of 48 cooperative grain elevators in Montana reported that elevators received grain from farms within an average radius of 20 miles. Francis P. Yager, *Cooperative Country Elevators in Montana*, Gen. Rept. 64, Farmer Cooperative Serv., U.S.D.A. (Washington, July 1959), p. 8.

[16] R. L. Kohls, *Farmers' Behavior and Decisions in Purchasing Farm Supplies, Feed, Machinery, Fertilizer*, Res. Bul. 749, Purdue Univ. Agr. Exp. Sta. (Lafayette, Oct. 1962).

7. There are problems associated with the two main phases of price discovery in the pricing process for grains. Imperfections result partly from lack of market knowledge on the part of buyers and sellers (or failure to acquire and use market knowledge) and from technical difficulties or time-consuming aspects of accurate quality determination.[17]

These attributes combine to produce a market structure among country elevators which has some characteristics of monopolistic competition and some of oligopoly. In comparison with the perfectly competitive model, we find that entry into the industry is not blocked, but is partially discouraged by location and goodwill advantages of existing elevators. Elevators are few enough in their trading areas to be mindful of actions and reactions of competitors, that is, interdependence is recognized to some extent. Competition is partly on price and partly on service, although the imperfections associated with the pricing process help limit the amount of direct price competition, and the apparent loyalty of many customers to particular firms seems to moderate the rigor of competitive activity.

The fact and persistence of this combination of structural characteristics of country elevators strongly affect their behavior and performance. In respect to grain pricing, empirical results show there are substantial variations in prices paid to farmers for grain, even after adjustments are made for location and quality differences. This type of performance, in turn, tends to perpetuate an industry structure in which firms are not rapidly forced to adopt new technology nor reduce unit operating costs in order to survive. There is a great deal of inertia in the existing structure which acts as a substantial restraint on the ability of innovating firms to capture business from competitors by reducing margins, competing on the basis of price, and/or improving service. Changes are occurring, but progress is not rapid.

## EMPIRICAL OBSERVATION OF THE PRICING PROCESS FOR GRAINS AT THE COUNTRY ELEVATOR LEVEL

Results of the empirical studies reported here are not intended to depict completely the pricing process for grains at the local market level in every area. Rather, the findings are presented to illustrate the kinds of market structures which tend to prevail at the local market level and the consequent implications of these structures for one important performance attribute, the pricing of grain.

The results are based on research conducted at the Purdue

---

[17] The nature of these imperfections is brought out more fully in the following section.

University Agricultural Experiment Station in the late 1950's.[18]
The two phases of the pricing process evaluated are (1) paying
prices for grain of standardized quality among firms in particular
geographic areas and (2) adjustments in prices for quality variations
of specific lots of grain, both among elevators in particular geographic areas and within individual elevators.

### Analysis of Quoted Paying Prices for Grains of Standardized Quality

Country elevators usually post their paying prices for grains
in terms of standardized quality.[19] Daily paying prices among
elevators were compared within selected counties during the harvest
seasons for corn, soybeans, and wheat. There were frequent day-to-
day variations of a few cents per bushel in quoted paying prices.
These ranged as high as 6 cents on particular days. No elevator
consistently paid either the high or low daily price, although some
elevators consistently paid higher prices than other elevators within
the same county. The number of elevators per county ranged from
five to fourteen.

For wheat, special notice was taken of 10 towns which had two
or more elevators. On over half the days there were differences in
paying prices by elevators within the same town. The differences
were usually 1 to 2 cents per bushel, but ranged up to 6 cents. In
only one town did one elevator consistently pay a higher price than
the other elevator in the same town on days when a difference
existed. In one of the wheat areas, line elevators were a major influence in the pricing structure. Paying prices for line elevators
were set at the central office, and other elevators in the area tended
to follow.

These comparisons indicate considerable uniformity in *quoted*
paying prices for grains within particular geographic areas. Although evidence is limited, there were greater differences for corn
than for soybeans and wheat. There also seemed to be a tendency

---

[18] The results have been reported in more detail in the following publi-
cations: Paul L. Farris, "The Pricing Structure for Wheat at the Country Elevator Level," *op. cit.*, pp. 607–24; David A. Storey and Paul L. Farris, *Corn Price
Variations in One Indiana County*, Res. Bul. 694, Purdue Univ. Agr. Exp. Sta.
(Lafayette, May 1960); Monte E. Juillerat and Paul L. Farris, *Soybean Pricing
and Grading at Indiana Country Elevators and Processing Plants*, Res. Bul. 700,
Purdue Univ. Agr. Exp. Sta. (Lafayette, Aug. 1960).

[19] The quoted price of corn usually refers to a bushel of No. 2 corn with a
minimum moisture content, usually $15\frac{1}{2}$ percent, and other specifications.
There was found to be variation among elevators, however, in the number of
pounds required to equal one bushel. Soybean prices referred to a bushel of
No. 1 soybeans with specified minimum tolerances for split soybeans, damaged
soybeans, and foreign material. Wheat prices were for bushels of No. 2 wheat,
again with certain minimum tolerances for moisture, test weight, garlic, and
other factors.

for the widest spreads in daily paying prices to coincide with fluctuating general levels of grain prices.

The daily prices which country elevators quote are based predominately on daily bid prices which are received from terminal buyers and processors. Country elevators can usually obtain bids from several buyers if they desire.[20] There is usually not much variation in bid prices received by elevators in a given area, and many sell most grain to only one or a few regular buyers. Independent elevators tend to sell grain to more different buyers than cooperatives. Each line elevator, of course, buys for its parent organization.[21]

The daily difference in bid prices for corn among elevators within one county ranged from 1 to 4 cents. In this county the differences in elevator paying prices were not strongly associated with differences in bid prices received by the elevators. Quoted price differences among elevators appeared to be attributable mainly to differences in operating margins and not to differences in bid prices received by the elevators.

The bid prices are closely related to cash grain prices at central markets and, in turn, are strongly influenced by futures markets prices for the near month. The spread between cash grain prices and futures prices (basis) varies somewhat among markets and over time in accordance with current supply and demand conditions for cash grain, changes in storage costs, future expectations, and the like.[22] Nevertheless, many country elevators follow futures market prices closely by radio and they sometimes adjust their quoted prices by current changes in futures market prices.

Quoted prices, however, are usually not the prices that farmers receive, although they are the prices which get publicized and to which competitors presumably react. One might suggest that the existence of similar quoted prices indicates competition is working and producing results in accordance with the law of one price. Alternatively, one could hypothesize that oligopsonistic interde-

---

[20] There are several merchandisers and processors to which country elevators sell grain. A 1960 survey of 11 North Central states covered 586 plants owned by 301 firms. L. B. Fletcher, *Market Organization of the Grain Industries in the North Central Region*, N. Cen. Reg. Publ. 155, published as Res. Bul. 847, Univ. of Mo. Agr. Exp. Sta. (Columbia, Jan. 1964), pp. 7, 21. The four largest firms accounted for about 22 percent of the volume of grain handled in the region and the eight largest, 33 percent. Although no firm bought all grains in every geographic area, country elevators appear to have several alternative outlets.

[21] Grain merchandising and processing plants in the North Central region acquired 10.7 percent of the grain from facilities owned by the same company. Vertical integration was higher in disposition in that 18.5 percent of the grain and 17.6 percent of grain products disposed of by the plants surveyed were handled through company-owned facilities. *Ibid.*, p. 20.

[22] T. A. Hieronymus, *Uses of Grain Futures in the Farm Business*, Univ. of Ill. Agr. Exp. Sta. Bul. 696 (Urbana, Sept. 1963), pp. 22–52.

pendence tends to encourage quoted price uniformity and to shift competitive actions away from quoted prices. The important point is that one can not generalize on the basis of quoted prices alone. It is necessary to determine actual paying prices for specific lots of grains and to analyze the processes and adjustments which are made to arrive at actual prices. Comparison of quoted prices is only the starting point in determining actual prices.

### Analysis of Price Adjustments for Quality Variations

When farmers sell grain to country elevators, a sample of each lot is usually obtained, the sample is graded, and the quoted price is adjusted (usually discounted) in accordance with a price discount schedule. The processes of sampling, grading, and applying a discount schedule are important steps in pricing individual lots of grain. These processes were analyzed in the pricing of corn, soybeans, and wheat.

The research was accomplished by laboratory grading of samples of grain which had been graded by elevators and by making comparisons of the results. For soybeans, additional samples of grain were drawn and compared with samples drawn by elevators. Price discount schedules actually used by the elevators were used to determine differences which would have occurred in paying prices if laboratory-grading results had been used instead of elevator-grading results.

Inasmuch as there was some variation in procedures and characteristics among the three grains, the results are summarized by grain.

*Corn.* In addition to comparing quoted paying prices for corn, it is also necessary, in order to determine actual prices, to consider (1) the weight per bushel used in the elevator calculations, (2) sampling procedure, (3) inconsistencies in testing, (4) the type of price discount schedule used, and (5) the accuracy of applying the discount schedule to the determined quality of the corn.

When adjustments indicated through detailed study of five elevators in one county were made for each of these sources of variation, it was found that the difference in *average* quoted price among elevators for the harvest season was 8.6 cents per bushel. That is, the *average* daily paying price for one elevator during the season was 8.6 cents per bushel higher than the *average* daily paying price for another elevator. Before adjustments, the difference between the high and low average quoted prices was 3.1 cents per bushel. Moreover, the two elevators which had the lowest average *quoted* prices paid the highest *actual* prices when all adjustments were made.

For individual loads at particular elevators, the differences were also striking. The differences between actual elevator discounts and indicated laboratory discounts were as much as 12 cents per bushel. Differences of 3 cents or more were frequent. Since the laboratory-indicated discounts were both above and below actual elevator discounts, a given farmer's corn, adjusted to a comparable quality basis, might frequently be priced 6 cents or more per bushel above or below that of his neighbor. These differences arose from two sources: inconsistencies in moisture determination, and variations in calculating the discount. In some cases the difference was in favor of the elevator, in some cases in favor of the farmer. At four elevators the *average* difference was in the elevator's favor, and at one elevator the *average* was in the farmer's favor.

**Soybeans.** To determine the extent of price variation associated with sampling, grading, and discounting, soybean samples were obtained from 19 country elevators and four processing plants. The samples (two from each load whenever possible—one duplicate sample and one control sample) were from 20 loads of soybeans received by each of the elevators and processing plants. The samples were graded for split soybeans, damaged soybeans, and foreign material. The only grading factor of importance during this season was foreign material.

Price discounting variations due to grading and sampling either could cancel each other, so that the actual price paid would be about the same as if both grading and sampling were completely accurate, or they could accumulate. Both situations occurred in the study. About one out of three times, the discount on a given load would have differed 4 cents or more per bushel from the discount indicated by laboratory procedures. Since elevator discounts were both greater and smaller than discounts indicated by laboratory procedures, the discount on any given load might differ several cents per bushel from the discount on another load because of variations in the combined effects of grading and sampling. At soybean processing plants there appeared to be about half as much price uncertainty due to such variations as at country elevators.

Again, for individual loads there were extreme differences in prices indicated by laboratory results and those actually paid by the elevator. At country elevators the difference ranged up to 9 percent foreign material. For soybeans at $2 per bushel, this extreme difference would amount to 18 cents per bushel.

**Wheat.** In the study of wheat the analyses were based on the samples drawn by the elevators. Separate samples were not drawn by standard sampling procedure to determine sampling accuracy. The elevator samples, 30 samples for each of 23 elevators and 17 samples each for two elevators, were tested for moisture, test weight, foreign material, damage, garlic, smut, and other grading factors. Test weight, moisture, and garlic were found to be the important factors in this study. Comparisons between laboratory and elevator findings were made and evaluated for these grading factors.

The elevators were located in two areas of the state where wheat growing is relatively important. They were within a three-county area in north central Indiana and in a four-county area in southwestern Indiana.

The average indicated laboratory discount for individual elevators in the northern area ranged from 4 cents per bushel more than the average elevator discount to 3 cents per bushel less. For four elevators, the average indicated laboratory discounts were higher and for eight elevators, lower.

In the southern area, the average indicated laboratory discount for all elevators was higher than the average elevator discount, indicating a general tendency toward lenient elevator discounting in this area. The range in the average differences was from about 1 cent per bushel to about 8 cents per bushel.

But again, striking in both areas was the relatively wide variation in discount differences among individual samples within elevators. A few of the discount differences in the northern areas were more than 10 cents per bushel, and in one instance, 17.5 cents. In the southern area, the greatest difference for an individual sample was 46 cents per bushel. Variations of 10 cents or more were frequent.

The standard deviation of the laboratory-elevator differences ranged from 1.1 to 4.3 cents for individual elevators in the northern area. This means that, at the elevator with a standard deviation of 4.3 cents per bushel, there was roughly a probability of 68 percent that the price to an individual farmer would have been within plus or minus 4.3 cents of the laboratory standard or within a range of up to 8.6 cents of what his neighbor received. However, this left a fairly higher probability of even more variation, depending on how the elevator happened to grade and discount each particular sample.

In the southern area, the range in standard deviations was from 2.1 to 10.7 cents among individual elevators. At most elevators in this area farmers faced a fairly higher probability of 10 or 12 cents per bushel variation depending on how their samples happened to be graded and discounted and, of course, a possibility of much more.

### Evaluation of Grain Pricing Practices at the Country Elevator Level

For each of the three grains, variations in actual paying prices to farmers which arose from variations among elevators in quoted prices were relatively small compared with price variations arising from sampling, grading, and discounting practices. There were frequent day-to-day variations of several cents per bushel in elevator-quoted paying prices. But no elevator consistently quoted a high or low price on each day throughout the harvest season. The tendency was for prices paid by all elevators in an area to be grouped together. The general level of prices tended to follow near month futures prices.

Many considerations enter into the establishing of quoted prices. In a given area, prices for a product of uniform quality tend to move toward a single price except for differences in associated services and transportation rates. However, even with effective competition, such a price equilibrium among elevators in an area may not exist at any one time. If, for example, an elevator has a special outlet for a given quality of grain, it will probably raise the price to farmers in order to attract the grain needed. During the time required for farmers to respond with increased deliveries, this elevator's price is likely to be higher than those of other elevators in the area. If, on the other hand, an elevator's storage facilities are full and it cannot handle additional grain, the manager will probably lower the price to discourage farmers from bringing in grain. Similarly, time is needed to dispose of the grain and a lower price would be expected at this elevator than at others.

In these circumstances, prices guide the flow of grain through the marketing channel. Our enterprise system relies upon prices to perform this function, but the farmer plays a key role in the process. The farmer must be informed about price differences and buying practices among elevators and he must act on the basis of this knowledge in his own best interest. Furthermore, he must realize that an elevator that pays a high price one day may not the next day. His information must be current.

This logic applies equally to country elevator managers. By keeping informed and transacting business with the most profitable outlets, they, like farmers, not only contribute to a smooth-running and effective marketing system, but to their own profit as well.

Insofar as short-run paying price fluctuations among elevators result from lags in the transfer of information and other imperfections caused by a general lack of market knowledge, the outlook is for improvement. The development of more rapid communications, improved pricing and marketing information, improved transportation facilities, and increased alertness of farmers should help further to reduce price variations resulting from these imperfections.

Nevertheless, there appears to be considerable room for increasing the effectiveness of the pricing system at the country elevator level through more accuracy in grading and price discounting. It did not appear that elevators were deliberately attempting to take advantage of farmers through grading and discounting practices. During the harvest season, there is little time for absolute accuracy in pricing, sampling, grading, and discounting each individual lot of grain received. The problem arises in part from the rather tedious technical processes involved, and points toward the need for more simplified techniques and procedures. There appeared to be some carelessness in performing current processes. This probably contributes to a tendency to overvalue low-quality grain and not adequately to reward producers of high-quality grain. In addition, to avoid farmer dissatisfaction, elevators were reluctant to discount grain as much as testing results indicated, and many followed a practice of grading leniently.

The country elevator, of course, is not only a place for farmers to sell grain but also a place to buy farm supplies. The country elevator has the constant problem of building and maintaining sufficient volume of business. The price paid for grain, therefore, reflects not only supply and demand factors for grain but also efforts to attract sideline business. In such a situation the price actually paid for grain is not just for grain only. It is for grain and "something else"—the "something else" including a number of diverse things among which would be a certain amount of subjective feeling on the part of the elevator managers.

In terms of pricing accuracy, several institutional factors give rise to uncertainty as to how accurately any particular sample will be graded and discounted. Such uncertainty would likely not provide the incentive to producers to make a determined effort to deliver high-quality grain. If quality grain is really preferred by terminal elevators and processors, the present grading and discounting methods and practices do not permit the pricing system adequately to reflect such preferences to producers.

The variation among elevators in a county in average paying prices, discounting practices, selling prices, and margins did not appear to be associated with any particular type of business organization studied (independent, line, or cooperative). There were, however, differences among elevators resulting from patronage refunds. For example, patronage refunds paid by cooperative elevators ranged from 2 to 6 cents per bushel for soybeans sold through the cooperatives. In turn, the cooperative country elevator received patronage refunds of an estimated 2 cents per bushel for soybeans sold by them through Indiana Grain Cooperative, the organization to which cooperative elevators sold most of their grain.[23]

---

[23] Regional grain cooperatives, including Indiana Grain Cooperative, have handled an increasing share of grain leaving the farm, reaching 15 percent in 1961–62, compared with around 7 percent in the late 1930's. Daniel H. McVey, *Regional Grain Cooperatives, 1961–62, 24th Annual Report*, Serv. Rept. 64, Farmer Cooperative Serv., U.S.D.A. (Washington, Aug. 1963), p. 7.

## CHARACTERISTICS OF THE PRICING STRUCTURE AT GRAIN FUTURES MARKETS

The pricing of grains at futures markets does not involve questions of quality determination, price adjustments for quality differences, nor quality standards. Trading is on a basis of standardized uniform quality. Evaluation of competitive performance, therefore, involves only those structural questions relating to number and size distribution of firms, ease of entry and exit, and market knowledge. There is no product differentiation nor need for product knowledge. The issue comes down to the questions of (1) whether the numbers of buyers and sellers are large enough so that the influence of one or several in combination is negligible and (2) the adequacy and accuracy of available market knowledge.

In respect to numbers, it is generally believed that the requirements of perfect competition are usually approximated. There have been periodic instances of price manipulation. Nevertheless, a great deal of attention is given by the exchanges themselves and by public regulatory agencies to improving practices and to preventing opportunities for traders to manipulate prices to their advantage. As continuing effort and study is given toward better understanding of the structures of buyers and sellers and of the functioning of the exchanges, it would appear that ways can be found to improve further the competitive price-making processes at these markets.

Market knowledge, of course, is never adequate to assure that the discovery of prices at futures markets, nor at any market, meets the rigid requirements of perfect competition. There is always, as Professor Taussig observed many years ago, a "penumbra" within which actual prices will fall.[24] As market knowledge is made more complete, more accurate, and more timely, we can expect that the zone of the "penumbra" will tend to be narrowed. Furthermore, such speculative price gyrations as are based on ignorance, rumor, fear, and misinformation would be moderated and more quickly brought in check. There would seem to be less opportunity for speculative fever to feed on itself as more cold, hard facts of reality are showered on traders. The world, of course, remains uncertain and perfection is not possible. But there are opportunities to improve knowledge and thereby enable futures markets more accurately to discover the prices that are tending to be determined by underlying supply and demand conditions.

## IMPLICATIONS OF PRICING UNDER CONDITIONS OF PURE BUT NOT PERFECT COMPETITION

It is commonly assumed that the pricing process in most agricultural markets tends to yield results not greatly different from re-

---

[24] F. W. Taussig, "Is Market Price Determinate?" *Quarterly Journal of Economics*, Vol. XXXV (May 1921), pp. 394–411.

sults under our theoretical ideal of perfect competition. If one makes this assumption, he can go on to deduce the proposition that the pricing system effectively allocates agricultural resources. But if the empirical existence of a high or low price fails to indicate that more or less of a commodity of particular quality is demanded, he cannot safely assert that the price signals to producers will call forth the quantities and qualities of products that consumers and the trade really want at these prices.

We have long known that the markets for grains, as well as the markets for other agricultural commodities, do not conform to our abstract model of perfect competition. But we have known little about the magnitude or the kinds of imperfections. The results presented in this chapter show substantial departures from perfect competition and the kinds of imperfections that are most serious in the pricing of grains at country elevators. The findings suggest that in the pricing of any product there are important questions not only of variations in quoted prices, including services and intangibles associated therewith, but also in the determination of quality, the value to be placed on quality, and even of the quality standards themselves. There are a number of sources of imperfections. Only by studying their nature and extent can one properly evaluate the performance of the pricing system for a product or market and determine appropriate corrective policies and procedures.

There is a broader question. Can the organization and operation of open markets in general be improved in terms of guiding producers, satisfying consumers, and rewarding effort? Upon the answer to this question hinges the kind of role that traditional pricing procedures will have in our agricultural economy of the future.

More and more of our traditional marketing processes are being questioned as methods of exchanging goods. Exchange processes are developing outside traditional markets. Integration, for example, ties businesses together so that products move through production and distribution channels without going through markets. Government is being asked by many groups, agricultural and nonagricultural alike, to step in and change market environments.

As various forms of administrative arrangements for exchanging goods and services succeed, the market system as we have known it will gradually lose ground. This is not to be deplored if our traditional markets are really replaced by something better. It would be unfortunate, though, if they are replaced because they are not doing what they are really capable of doing.

The answer to the question of the role the traditional market system will have is not clear. It is not clear because we still have some latitude in determining how effective we want traditional markets to be. The most important step, if we want such markets to continue to have a major role in our agricultural economy, is to recognize that they need intelligent guidance. They will not improve much automatically. Like any man-made social invention, a market has defects which can cumulatively grow worse unless corrected. That is the reason we have historically modified in various ways the conditions under which supply and demand meet. Our tradition has been to keep the market system as our dominant method of exchanging goods and correct its faults rather than to throw it out because it had faults. Though our market system was imperfect, it was the best we had, and it could be improved.

Organizational changes, technology, and other influences seem to be bringing changes in some instances which may so completely transform existing market structures and marketing institutions that we can not expect an open competitive pricing system, as we have known it, to survive. In such instances we face a challenge to develop new ways of effectively and impartially determining terms of trade as goods move through the marketing channel from producer to consumer.

There are at least two other reasons why our traditional markets may not get a fair chance to survive. One is that persons unfriendly to them may be influential enough to overcome the influence of those who like them. The other reason, and the more important, is that those who favor traditional open markets may not themselves try to make them better. The attitude of this group especially will be crucial. More and more, we shall need to develop our thinking and provide leadership in solving the increasingly complex problems of industrial organization and market structure and behavior in many particular market situations. The market system can be improved by study, critical analysis, and the will to accept and initiate change.

# 11
# THE MIXED FEED INDUSTRY

## DANIEL I. PADBERG[1]

EARLY in the 1900's, the feed business consisted essentially of a merchandising channel for milling by-products, livestock protein sources such as tankage, and a few formula supplements. At this time, much livestock was fed straight feed grains with no protein supplement. In this type of feeding program and in this state of development of livestock nutrition, the opportunity and latitude for development of a formula feed industry was rather restricted.

The institutional framework which carried out the feed business under these conditions ranged from grain-handling agents such as country elevators in some areas to general country stores in other areas. At the manufacturing end of the channel the feed business was essentially the by-product business of the milling industries with these institutions serving as handlers of feed ingredient sources such as tankage, oyster shell, and others.

As the quantity and scope of nutrition research increased, the latitude of formula feed manufacturing and sale was rapidly expanded. Animal nutrition became a more sophisticated problem requiring more than feed grains for a balanced ration. This technical know-how was incorporated in the manufacturing phase of the feed business and also was disseminated to the farmer, facilitating demand for these more sophisticated products.

Following World War I, the use of protein supplement began to increase. Figure 11.1 shows a gradual increase in feeding rates of feed grains[2] per animal unit since the drought-depression period of the 1930's and a much more rapid increase in availability of protein supplement per animal unit during the same period. Increases in high-protein feeds have been especially pronounced since World War II. These changes in the agricultural production complex created opportunities for widespread growth and specialization in the feed industry.

---

[1] Associate Professor of Agricultural Economics, Cornell University.
[2] Milling by-products such as wheat bran, etc. are also included.

The feed industry greatly expanded the output of formula feed supplements during the interwar period. Complete feeds were developed for some types of livestock but represented a relatively small part of the total feed business. During this period of agricultural development, a large share of farmers feeding livestock were producing most of their feed grains. They depended upon the mixed feed industry only as a supply of protein supplement. Sometimes these supplements were mixed with the feed grains, but often they were hand fed or self-fed separately.

Following World War II, production patterns on farms began to shift away from the highly diversified pattern common in the interwar period. More farmers became specialized feeders or producers of cash grains. Specialized feeders began using more complete feeds with some species of livestock. Several factors may have contributed to this trend. Many specialized feeders did not have a supply of farm-grown feed grains. Labor cost was a large part of production cost and could be substantially reduced by switching to complete feeds, particularly where bulk-handling techniques were adopted.

Tremendous developments in the area of animal nutrition involving particularly antibiotics, vitamins, and trace minerals have directly affected the feed industry. This know-how enables livestock feeders using these products to get substantially more efficient gains than producers not using them. Under these conditions, the feed manufacturer was not merely providing physical services such as transportation, grinding, and mixing, but was keeping abreast of technology and providing nutritional know-how in mixed feeds.

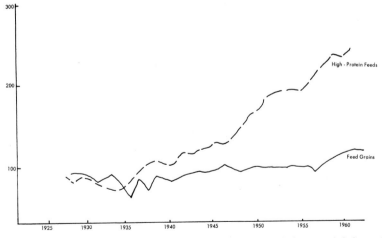

FIG. 11.1—Index of feeding rate for feed grains and the availability of high-protein supplement per animal unit from 1926 to 1960.

It is for this reason that, while inputs in the form of feed grains and other nutritional supplements going into the feed business are homogeneous products bought on a specification basis, outputs in terms of formula feeds coming from this industry are typically highly differentiated. All of the large feed manufacturing companies and some of the relatively smaller manufacturers have highly trained nutrition experts, laboratories, and feeding-trial farms to discover and develop nutritional know-how which is inserted as a part of their branded product.

The physical functions performed by feed manufacturers typically involve significant scale economies. Inputs are typically received in bulk, and processing is carried out in highly automated plants. Recent improvements in transportation facilities, highway systems, and bulk distribution have encouraged wider distribution from centralized manufacturing facilities. The difficulty of securing sufficient sales of differentiated products to make the operation of automated plants efficient explains many of the unusual characteristics of structural development in this industry.

## MARKET STRUCTURE OF THE MIXED FEED INDUSTRY

Market structure involves a classification of some physical and organizational characteristics of buyers and sellers and products in the market. The more important dimensions of market structure include the number and relative size of market participants, the degree of product differentiation in the market, and relative freedom of entry into the market. Primary attention in this industry analysis is directed toward the feed manufacturing industry as the buyer in the input market for feed grains and other products and toward the feed manufacturing industry as a seller of manufactured formula feeds.

### The Input Market

Before it is possible to observe the organization of participants in the input market, it is imperative that the scope of this market be delineated. Market definition is by its nature an arbitrary process. It involves specifying a product group and a geographic or spatial limit of competition. The market for inputs, including feed grains and various milling and industrial by-products, is defined here as being national in scope. While production and availability of many of these products center in the midwestern section of our country, these products are traded on a specification basis and are quoted on open markets. These conditions preclude serious price misalignment in other sections of the country.[3] Since

---

[3] Richard Phillips, *Cost of Procuring, Manufacturing, and Distributing Mixed Feeds in the Midwest*, Agr. Mkg. Serv. Market Res. Rept. 388, U.S.D.A. (Washington, Apr. 1960), pp. 15–20.

TABLE 11.1

PERCENT OF VALUE OF SHIPMENTS ACCOUNTED FOR BY THE LARGEST COMPANIES IN THE
PREPARED ANIMAL FEED INDUSTRY, 1958, COMPARED WITH 1954, 1947, AND 1935

| | | Percent of Value of Shipments Accounted For by | | | | Indexes | |
| Year | Number of Companies | Value of Shipments | Largest 4 | Largest 8 | Largest 20 | Largest 50 | Prim. prod. spec'n | Cover- age |
|---|---|---|---|---|---|---|---|---|
| | | ($1,000) | | | | | | |
| 1958 | 2,016 | 2,942,008 | 22 | 30 | 43 | 56 | .97 | .91 |
| 1954 | 2,037 | 2,702,267 | 21 | 29 | 43 | . . .* | .95 | .90 |
| 1947 | 2,372 | 2,112,241 | 19 | 27 | 40 | . . .* | .95 | .89 |
| 1935 | . . .* | . . .* | 23 | 34 | . . .* | . . .* | . . .* | . . .* |

Source: *Concentration Ratios in Manufacturing Industry—1958,* Part I, Table 2, p. 11,
U.S. Government Printing Office (Washington, 1962).
* Not available.

this input market is national in scope, the measuring of concentration and other structural characteristics will include the feed
manufacturing industry across the nation.

*Market Concentration in the Input Market.* Market concentration
refers to the degree to which the larger participants in the market
control a disproportionate share of market volume. The conventional analytical device for measuring market concentration is the
concentration ratio. This measure may be defined as the share of
the total market volume controlled by a selected number of the
largest firms. Tables 11.1 and 11.2 indicate present levels of concentration in the feed manufacturing industry with comparisons of
concentration levels for the past couple of decades. It is noted that,
while some manufacturing companies are admittedly large in
absolute size, no one firm could be classified as dominant in this
input market across the nation. In no period of time for which

TABLE 11.2

PERCENT OF EMPLOYMENT ACCOUNTED FOR BY THE LARGEST COMPANIES IN THE PREPARED
ANIMAL FEEDS INDUSTRY, 1958, COMPARED WITH 1954, 1951, AND 1935

| | | | Percent of Employment Accounted For by | | | |
| Year | Number of Companies | Number of Employees | Largest 4 | Largest 8 | Largest 20 | Largest 50 |
|---|---|---|---|---|---|---|
| 1958 | 2,016 | 57,313 | 13 | 18 | 29 | 41 |
| 1954 | 2,037 | 58,890 | 13 | 18 | 28 | . . .* |
| 1951 | . . .* | 56,238 | 12 | . . .* | . . .* | . . .* |
| 1935 | . . .* | . . .* | 15 | 21 | . . .* | . . .* |

Source: *Concentration Ratios in Manufacturing Industry—1958,* Part I, Table 3, p. 77,
U.S. Government Printing Office (Washington, 1962).
* Not available.

observations are available do the largest four firms account for more than 23 percent of the total market in terms of value of shipments. The high level of primary product specialization suggests that, while the feed business probably started as a by-product business of the milling industry, by 1947 the important feed firms were very highly specialized. The rather high and increasing coverage index suggests that firms whose primary products are prepared animal feeds do essentially all the feed business. The relatively lower concentration of employment of production workers (Table 11.2) as compared with concentration measured in value of shipments indicates that the larger manufacturers produce more feed per worker than do smaller firms. This observation portrays the adaptability of the feed industry to capital, intensive operation, and automation. These data indicate that statistics gathered on this basis should be fairly accurate and representative of market organization and that the level of concentration is rather low.

***Product Differentiation in the Input Market.*** Product differentiation at this level of the market is almost nonexistent. These products are typically traded on the basis of physical specifications which are measured very accurately by buyers and sellers. The output of one seller is treated very similarly to output of another seller. Standardized government grades have this effect, and the high level of market information on the part of all buyers and sellers tends to diminish the opportunity for extensive product differentiation.

### The Market for Manufactured Formula Feed Products

The scope of the market for manufacturing feeds is certainly much narrower than that of the market for inputs. Market definition at this level of the distribution system is more complicated than in the input market for, while farmers are the final buyers of formula feeds, there is typically a superstructure of distributive institutions in the channel between the feed manufacturer and the farmer. The unit of effective competition between manufacturers in the sale of their output can be restricted to a rather small geographic space because numerous observations are available of small but effectively established feed manufacturing businesses of perhaps not more than a dozen counties. Since farmers, the final buyers, are widely scattered through space, effective programs which serve small groups of farmers' needs may effectively cut them off from competition from other areas.

While large firms may have significant economies of scale in promotion and thereby promote their brands effectively over a wide area, the effective unit of competition is still rather restricted when compared with the scope of the input market due to the

existence of small differentiated firms. The relevant market, therefore, while probably impossible to delineate in a detailed way,
likely includes trade areas smaller than states in most cases. For
this reason it is the nature of organization of market participants
and the degree of product differentiation in the smaller trade areas
that is of particular importance at this point of the analysis.

*The Distributive Channel for Mixed Feeds.* Formula feed products
typically move from manufacturer to farmer through a local dealer
or feed handler. The feed dealers provide a spectrum of services
to farmers in addition to the feed itself which is typically obtained
from the manufacturer. Among the more important of these services may be listed grinding and mixing of farmers feed grains, convenience of location, technical advice on nutritional aspects of
feeding programs, and many types of financing. Costs of these
services in the form of distribution margins may add an additional
increment to price of the final product as large as the costs above
ingredient prices added to cover services performed by the feed
manufacturer. In addition to handling feed products, these dealers
typically have other contacts with farmers. Many feed dealers are
also country elevator operators who buy significant amounts of
grain from farmers and, in addition to selling feed, usually sell
fertilizer and a rather broad spectrum of farm supplies. Feed dealers often handle two manufacturers' lines of feeds but show
considerable reluctance to change from one manufacturer to another. While there are some indications of a trend toward direct
selling from the manufacturer to the farmer, feed dealers represent
an important link in the distribution of feeds at present and in the
foreseeable future.

*The Importance of Cooperatives in the Feed Distribution System.*
Cooperatives have had a significant role in feed manufacturing and
distribution. In 1959, 5,310 local feed outlets were operated by
cooperatives.[4] These organizations manufacture about 90 percent
of the feed which they handle at retail. About 70 percent is manufactured at wholesale mills, and about 20 percent is manufactured
locally. In 1959, almost one-fourth of the industry output was
manufactured by cooperatives. The regional pattern of the share
of the industry output manufactured by cooperative organizations
is as follows: Pacific and North Atlantic, 35–40 percent; North
Central, slightly over 25 percent; Mountain and South Atlantic,
slightly less than 20 percent; and South Central, less than 3 percent.

While some of these wholesale operations are quite large with
distribution in several states, the large part of the market share of

---

[4] Anne L. Gessner, *Integrated Feed Operations Through Farmer Cooperatives, 1959*, Farmer Cooperative Serv., U.S.D.A. (Apr. 1962), p. ii.

TABLE 11.3

PERCENT OF VALUE OF SHIPMENTS OF EACH CLASS OF PRODUCTS ACCOUNTED FOR
BY THE LARGEST COMPANIES, 1958 AND 1954

| SIC Code | Class of Value of Product Shipments | | Percent of Value of Shipments Accounted For by | | | |
|---|---|---|---|---|---|---|
| | | | Largest 4 | Largest 8 | Largest 20 | Largest 50 |
| 2042 | Prepared Animal Feeds: | | | | | |
| | 1958 | 3,076,409 | 22 | 31 | 44 | 58 |
| | 1954 | 2,834,114 | 21 | 29 | 43 | ...* |
| 20421 | Poultry Feeds: | | | | | |
| | 1958 | 1,474,281 | 26 | 37 | 52 | 68 |
| | 1954 | 1,428,707 | 26 | 36 | 52 | ...* |
| 20422 | Livestock Feeds: | | | | | |
| | 1958 | 958,888 | 26 | 36 | 51 | 66 |
| | 1954 | 865,605 | 23 | 33 | 48 | ...* |
| 20423 | Dog and Cat Food: | | | | | |
| | 1958 | 305,360 | 38 | 51 | 70 | 86 |
| | 1954 | 241,505 | 32 | 47 | 64 | ...* |

Source: *Concentration Ratios in Manufacturing Industry—1958,* Part I, Table 4, p. 110 (Washington, 1962).
   * Not available.

cooperatives is handled in small, local operations. Of the 1,054 cooperative mills in 1959, all except 19 had capacities of 30 tons per hour or less.[5] Many of these firms were originally organized as grain elevators and have since diversified into the feed business as the feed industry has grown in importance to farmers. The dominant competitive strategy of these organizations is price competition. Many representatives of cooperative leadership indicate that these units were typically organized specifically to create price competition in an industry which tended toward oligopoly.

*Market Concentration in the Sale of Manufactured Feed.* In viewing the concentration of sellers of mixed feeds, considerable disaggregation is essential. Different sections of the country serve animal populations of varying specialization with respect to species. While the broiler and poultry industries are localized in some sections, beef-hog enterprises tend to be localized in different sections. For this reason, it is of interest to investigate various levels of concentration among manufacturers catering to different parts of this industry. Table 11.3 indicates concentration in terms of value of shipments of the largest companies nationally for manufacturing poultry feeds, livestock feeds, and cat and dog food. These data indicate that, while cat and dog food manufacturers are somewhat more concentrated than poultry and livestock feed manufacturers, the general level of concentration is not significantly different from

---

[5] *Ibid.,* p. 6, Table 3.

that of the combined prepared animal feed complex. Table 11.4 displays data for the North Central region comparing level of concentration in 1954–55 with 1960 for the feed manufacturing industry as well as other related grain products handling industries. It is noted from this table that the feed manufacturing industry displays almost the lowest level of concentration of industries in this grouping.

Since the relevant market for this industry likely includes less trading area than most states, this group of North Central states is probably too aggregated to give an accurate picture of *market* concentration. Table 11.5 shows market concentration measured in value of shipments of the largest four feed manufacturing companies by regions and states for 1958. In this source data are available for 33 states. Market concentration listed on a state basis is typically much higher than the concentration observed on a broader aggregate basis. Twenty-four of the 33 states for which data are available have feed manufacturing industries in which the largest four companies have 50 percent or more of the business. In 16 of the 33 states, the largest four companies do 60 percent or more of the business; and in 6 of the 33 states, the concentration of the largest four is 70 percent or more. Many of these states have rather large numbers of manufacturing plants competing. Nine of the 33 reporting states have 80 or more feed manufacturers reported while 5 of the 33 have more than 100 feed manufacturing firms. It is very likely that if data were available for trade areas within some of these states, market concentration in the effective trade area would be substantially higher than that shown in the data for entire states.

TABLE 11.4

MARKET SHARE OF LARGE FIRMS IN THE GRAIN PROCESSING INDUSTRIES, NORTH CENTRAL REGION, 1954–55 AND 1960

| Type of Processing | No. of Firms | | Percent of Total Volume of Grain Accounted For by | | | | | |
|---|---|---|---|---|---|---|---|---|
| | | | Largest 4 | | Largest 8 | | Largest 20 | |
| | 54–55 | 60 | 54–55 | 60 | 54–55 | 60 | 54–55 | 60 |
| Feed Manufacturing | 132 | 126 | 38.8 | 43.3 | 55.8 | 55.6 | 76.8 | 73.4 |
| Flour Milling | 77 | 59 | 35.8 | 33.6 | 54.3 | 60.5 | 77.7 | 87.1 |
| Oil Seed Processing | 57 | 44 | 42.9 | 41.8 | 66.1 | 66.7 | 86.7 | 91.4 |
| Dry Milling and Cereal Mfg. | 26 | 26 | 58.6 | 59.6 | 80.3 | 85.8 | 99.5 | 99.7 |
| Wet Corn Milling | 9 | 10 | 77.2 | 69.1 | 97.2 | 92.7 | 100.0 | 100.0 |
| Distilling and Alcohol Manufacturing | 9 | 6 | 68.5 | 84.2 | 99.9 | 100.0 | 100.0 | ... |
| Malting and Brewing | 18 | 16 | 59.1 | 62.4 | 86.2 | 86.9 | 100.0 | 100.0 |

Source: Unpublished data assembled by NCM-30 as a part of a regional research project on the market structure of the grain marketing industries.

## TABLE 11.5

PERCENT OF VALUE OF SHIPMENTS ACCOUNTED FOR BY THE FOUR LARGEST
FEED MANUFACTURING COMPANIES, BY DIVISIONS AND STATES, 1958

| Area | Number of Companies | Value of Shipments | Percent of Value of Shipments Accounted For by Largest 4 |
|---|---|---|---|
| | | *($1,000)* | |
| United States, Total | 2,016 | 2,942,008 | 22 |
| New England | 40 | 132,285 | 65 |
| New Hampshire | 5 | 9,075 | ...* |
| Massachusetts | 18 | 31,511 | 71 |
| Middle Atlantic | 234 | 365,648 | 37 |
| New York | 87 | 216,711 | 50 |
| New Jersey | 29 | 39,633 | 63 |
| Pennsylvania | 125 | 109,304 | 35 |
| East North Central | 349 | 567,580 | 29 |
| Ohio | 88 | 161,111 | 52 |
| Indiana | 67 | 92,110 | 61 |
| Illinois | 96 | 250,876 | 43 |
| Michigan | 47 | 14,975 | 48 |
| Wisconsin | 62 | 48,508 | 68 |
| West North Central | 416 | 519,105 | 35 |
| Minnesota | 70 | 81,037 | 56 |
| Iowa | 133 | 184,834 | 46 |
| Missouri | 77 | 138,210 | 57 |
| Nebraska | 89 | 67,224 | 44 |
| South Atlantic | 320 | 485,067 | 35 |
| Delaware | 12 | 62,065 | 80 |
| Maryland | 23 | 38,119 | 64 |
| Virginia | 41 | 56,781 | 64 |
| North Carolina | 111 | 118,621 | 45 |
| South Carolina | 32 | 18,756 | 70 |
| Georgia | 78 | 138,072 | 50 |
| Florida | 37 | 47,938 | 45 |
| East South | 182 | 283,231 | 42 |
| Kentucky | 32 | 27,192 | 72 |
| Tennessee | 61 | 109,800 | 54 |
| Alabama | 50 | 94,235 | 68 |
| Mississippi | 46 | 52,004 | 63 |
| West South Central | 241 | 234,096 | 33 |
| Arkansas | 34 | 43,055 | 52 |
| Louisiana | 22 | 24,838 | 87 |
| Oklahoma | 40 | 31,366 | 53 |
| Texas | 149 | 134,837 | 34 |
| Mountain | 93 | 59,938 | 38 |
| Colorado | 36 | 21,769 | 59 |
| New Mexico | 15 | 5,656 | 75 |
| Pacific | 232 | 295,058 | 30 |
| Washington | 36 | 44,820 | 80 |
| Oregon | 34 | 31,450 | 67 |
| California | 166 | 218,778 | 27 |

Source: *Concentration Ratios in Manufacturing Industry—1958,* Part II,
Table 36, pp. 496–97, U.S. Government Printing Office (Washington, 1962).
* Withheld to avoid disclosing figures for individual companies.

Table 11.6 includes data from a different source concerning market concentration of the feed manufacturing industry in the North Central region. These data are somewhat at variance with census data presented earlier in terms of specialization ratio and level of concentration. These data also show a slightly more rapid trend toward increasing concentration over time than do the census data shown earlier. All data over time, however, indicate a trend toward gradual but steady increases in concentration since 1947. These data also suggest that the level of concentration among the largest sellers is likely quite high in local trading areas.

*Product Differentiation.* Product differentiation implies the degree to which the outputs of alternative sellers receive preferential treatment among buyers. Several features of the feed marketing complex effect the degree of product differentiation in mixed feeds. Where products are typically valued on the basis of readily discernible technical characteristics and are bought and sold on specifications basis, product differentiation tends to be unimportant. That is, similar output of alternative sellers would receive substantially equal reception among buyers. On the other hand, where the technical characteristics of products which give them value are developing very rapidly and are not easily discernible by traders, the opportunity for product differentiation is increased. Where many personal and merchandising services are a part of the total product package, the opportunity for product differentiation is again substantially increased. Product differentiation tends to be more important at the retail end of the distributive channel because buyers at retail typically cannot be market experts in every product they buy. Therefore, they tend to rely on reputations gained by marketing firms and the backlog of satisfactory personal experiences obtained with a particular firm rather than the technical characteristics of the product and its relative price when compared with alternatives. Since livestock feed incorporates technical know-how and rapidly changing nutritional properties at the manufacturing level and is accompanied by many personal and marketing services at the dealer level of the distribution channel, product differentiation has been very important in this industry.

While farmers are typically not nutrition experts, they usually have enough training and/or experience to be aware of the significant developments which have been made in formula feeds in recent years. For this reason, statistics concerning the elaborate and extensive feeding trial programs of feeding manufacturers and the highly trained sales representatives of these firms are significant in influencing a differential reception by farmers of alternative feed brands. This implies that the brand which connotes product development and improved gains is an important influence in

## TABLE 11.6

MARKET SHARE AND DEGREE OF SPECIALIZATION OF LARGE FEED MANUFACTURING FIRMS, NORTH CENTRAL REGION, 1954–55 AND 1960

| Year | Firms | No. of Plants | | Volume of Feed Mfg'd. | Percent of Region | Speciali- zation Ratio | Degree of Vertical Integration | |
| | | Total | Feed mfg. | | | | Acquisition of grain | Disposition of pro. prod. |
| --- | --- | --- | --- | --- | --- | --- | --- | --- |
| 1960 | Largest 4 | 26 | 18 | 24,210 | 43.3 | 52.1 | 3.8 | 51.6 |
| | Largest 8 | 66 | 36 | 69,617 | 55.6 | 22.4 | 11.3 | 35.2 |
| | Largest 20 | 124 | 61 | 91,964 | 73.4 | 19.0 | 9.3 | 33.9 |
| 1954–55 | Largest 4 | 34 | 21 | 54,910 | 38.8 | 31.9 | ...* | ...* |
| | Largest 8 | 48 | 30 | 79,050 | 55.8 | 35.9 | ...* | ...* |
| | Largest 20 | 103 | 56 | 108,852 | 76.8 | 19.2 | ...* | ...* |

Source: Unpublished data assembled by NCM-30 as a part of a regional research project on the market structure of the grain marketing industries.
* Not available.

determining farmer purchases. On the other hand, the parts of a total product package supplied by the local dealer, including convenient location, grinding and hauling services, technical advice, and financial assistance, are also important in influencing farmers' purchases. Research concerning this subject indicates that dealers are typically loyal to manufacturers in that shifts between manufacturers and brands on the part of dealers are uncommon and, further, that farmers display considerable loyalty to dealers.[6] It is extremely difficult to assess the relative importance of manufacturer brand as opposed to dealers' services in explaining the observed loyalty of farmers to their feed dealer.

The feed dealer is an important step in the promotion and differentiation of formula feed products. Likely several elements of competitive strategy go into the choice of manufacturer brand by feed dealers. Feed dealers are extremely conscious of the marketing services provided at this local level of the distribution channel. Surveys of these dealers indicate that they believe their own services are likely more important than manufacturers' brands in keeping customers.[7] On the other hand, they are reluctant to shift lines of feed because, if they lost only a small percent of their customers, it would affect their business volume adversely.

From the perspective of the feed manufacturer, product promotion must have two dimensions. Feed manufacturers are extremely concerned about their image from the farmers' viewpoint and they must also be vitally concerned with their image in the perspective of the feed dealers. For this reason, feed manufacturers are typically involved with rather extensive promotion programs, some of which are aimed at farmers while others are oriented toward improving relationships with feed dealers. Few guidelines are available for allocating promotion budgets of feed manufacturers between these alternative budgets, and the typical situation finds many promotion items in the budget which the manufacturer is reluctant to drop but also which seem very indirectly related to sales.[8]

---

[6] R. L. Kohls, *Farmers' Behavior and Decisions in Purchasing Farm Supplies—Feed, Machinery, Fertilizer,* Res. Bul. 749, Purdue Univ. Agr. Exp. Sta. (Lafayette, Ind., Oct. 1962), pp. 5–9.

[7] Klaus Kalb, "Product Differentiation in the Mixed Feeds Industry," unpublished Ph.D. dissertation, Ohio State Univ. (Columbus, 1964).

[8] From the perspective of the economist, the promotion and advertising associated with product differentiation bring up the old question of whether they are consistent with "efficient marketing." Since advertising and promotion persist in some environmental conditions, some economists have felt a compulsion to rationalize them. They have been rationalized on the bases, among others, that they communicate information concerning product characteristics to final buyers, and because they increase sales and effect scale economies. I do not desire to engage in this exercise. While I do not completely understand the *normative* qualities of promotion and advertising, I suspect they persist for *competitive* reasons.

*Excess Capacity.* Excess capacity refers to the degree to which an industry's production facilities are being utilized. Zero excess capacity implies complete utilization of production facilities. Measurement of excess capacity involves a comparison of actual output with some definition of potential output—excess capacity being that part of the potential not being used. A definition of potential output is usually arbitrary and may involve operation of a plant during a regular eight-hour day or assuming a certain amount of overtime or in several other ways. Since definitions of potential capacity and, therefore, excess capacity often vary within research studies and typically between research studies, it is extremely difficult to develop and compare quantitative measures of excess capacity. However, a few pieces of empirical evidence may be worth noting. Research conducted concerning the grain-handling industries of the North Central region indicated that, during 1954–55, excess capacity in the feed manufacturing industry was 52 percent. This is an average of excess capacity figures for each of the several states. In other grain-handling industries, the average excess capacity in 1954–55 was 43 percent. In 1960, excess capacity in the feed manufacturing industry was 53 percent, with excess capacity in the other grain-handling industries averaging 31 percent. While definitions of excess capacity may be at variance in different states and at different times in these analyses, these comparisons suggest that the feed industry typically has more extensive excess capacity than other grain-handling industries, and this disparity has been greater in the latter period.

*Vertical Integration.* Vertical integration (contract farming) has probably been the most unusual structural development in the mixed feed industry during recent times. Causal factors responsible for this development likely include the need for more elaborate production facilities on farms, the need for standardized and improved cultural practices on farms, the existence of substantial excess capacity in feed manufacturing firms, the inability of manufacturers to substantially increase sales by lowering price (due to the differentiated nature of outputs), and probably many others. Some of the more significant results of this development have been the changing of broiler production and, to a lesser degree, egg production from a diversified farm enterprise to essentially an assembly line operation, with subsequent increases in efficiency of broiler and egg production. Feed manufacturers have taken over some services originally provided by feed dealers and added others, often bypassing dealers in the distributing channel. Sizes of retail accounts have been substantially increased with consequent reduction of distribution costs and probable margins. Uncertainty at the farm level has probably been reduced in affected enterprises.

Vertical integration is not easily defined and in its broad context covers many types of coordinating activities. At a minimum, however, it implies some type of business tie between manufacturers and the final users of feed. It is difficult to determine the extent to which the feed business is affected by these manufacturer-farmer ties. Available data indicate that, in 1959, 18 percent of total industry sales were affected by some type of contract program in the states of Iowa, Illinois, Missouri, Minnesota, Nebraska, and South Dakota.[9] Data shown in Table 11.6 indicate further that the degree of integration is substantially higher among larger manufacturers than smaller manufacturers. While accurate data over time are generally not available, there are indications that vertical integration increased as a portion of total feed business rather rapidly during the 1950's and is currently increasing in this decade, but probably at a slower rate.

One rather detailed analysis suggests that the motive for integration on the part of feed manufacturers is likely not explained by increased profit rates in the contract programs.[10] Results of this study indicate that while some contract programs were profitable, many were not and, in the aggregate, manufacturers sustained an average loss of 87 cents per ton as compared with other feed sales. These data suggest that the presence of excess capacity and the difficulty in obtaining outlets for differentiated products are likely more important explanations for manufacturers' motives toward integration than profit in these programs specifically. For example, the higher plant volume obtained through integrated accounts could be rational if they lowered average production cost for all feed, even though their sale was not as profitable as other types of sale.

Future trends in vertical integration in the feed business are likely to be dependent upon the technical possibilities of developing assembly line type production practices similar to those developed in broiler and egg production for other livestock enterprises. Examples of some early tendencies in this direction may include the "high fixed cost-low labor requirement" slatted floor hog feeding operations. If such cultural practices become useful and efficient in hog and beef feeding operations, integration into this type of business will provide an opportunity for large, well-financed feed companies to get the larger share of the feed business.

---

[9] Richard Phillips, *Feed Industry Financing and Contract Programs in Iowa and Surrounding States,* Spec. Rept. 28, Dept. of Econ. and Soc., Iowa State Univ. (Ames, Apr. 1961), Table A-3, p. 15.
[10] Richard Phillips, *Analysis of Costs and Benefits to Feed Manufacturers From Financing and Contract Programs in the Midwest,* Spec. Rept. 3, Dept. of Econ. and Soc., Iowa State Univ. (Ames, Oct. 1962).

TABLE 11.7
ALLOCATION OF PRODUCTION AND DISTRIBUTION COSTS IN VARIOUS TYPES OF ORGANIZATIONS

| Type of Organization | Percent of Total Production and Distribution Cost* | | | | | | | |
|---|---|---|---|---|---|---|---|---|
| | Ingre-dients | Procure-ment | Produc-tion | Research | Selling | Over-head | Trans-port | Total |
| Premix | 69.89 | .03 | 19.41 | .32 | 3.67 | 4.25 | 2.43 | 100 |
| Concentrate | 68.65 | .21 | 15.85 | .60 | 5.09 | 5.64 | 3.96 | 100 |
| Complete Feed | 67.78 | .37 | 11.12 | 1.07 | 7.23 | 7.14 | 5.29 | 100 |
| Retail-Manufacturer | 72.44 | .39 | 10.39 | .17 | 9.27 | 4.78 | 2.56 | 100 |

Source: Richard Phillips, *Costs of Procuring, Manufacturing and Distributing Mixed Feeds in the Midwest,* Agricultural Marketing Service, Market Research Report 388 U.S.D.A. (Washington, April 1960), Table 35.
* Budgeted for laying mash.

*Manufacturing and Distribution Costs.* Total costs of feed manu-facturers are broken into various functions indicated in Table 11.7. Ingredients represented about 70 percent of total distribution costs in all types of organization. Production was second in impor-tance, ranging from about 10 percent to about 20 percent. It is in-teresting to observe that selling costs increase and production costs decrease as the retail phase of the market channel is approached.

While data concerning the nature and magnitude of scale economies are generally inadequate, there is some evidence that scale economies are important in this industry. In one study it was demonstrated that production (manufacturing), research, selling, overhead, and transportation costs (per ton) decreased as plant volume increased.[11] These observations suggest competitive ad-vantages for larger firms. While this phenomena may exert pres-sure toward consolidation of manufacturing facilities, the bulky nature of feed and its related high transportation costs may pre-clude extensive centralizing of manufacturing facilities.

## COMPETITIVE BEHAVIOR IN THE MIXED FEED INDUSTRY

Competitive behavior may be thought of as a system of incen-tives which acts as a catalyst in effecting the combination of eco-nomic resources and activities. Competitive behavior in this in-dustry may be best described and understood by classifying competi-tors into two organizational types. Large firms with regional or national distribution, highly developed brand names, and extensive research and development programs constitute one part of this dichotomy while a competitive fringe of locally oriented smaller companies make up the other part. As described in the previous section, the major brand companies probably have significantly

[11] Richard Phillips, *Costs of Procuring, Manufacturing . . ., op. cit.,* pp. 27, 35, 47, 55.

more than half of the business in most localities. The competitive fringe, however, has a strong orientation to local needs and a preoccupation with cost reduction and price competition and, therefore, exerts considerable influence on competitive behavior of the industry.

The competitive advantages of the small local firms are essentially in the nature of cost reduction. Output of these firms typically involves less transportation cost, less research and development cost, and less merchandising and promotion cost than the output of other firms. Their organizational nature enables an increased emphasis on direct selling to farmers and, therefore, bypassing feed dealers. While many of these firms have a nutrition specialist on their staff and some laboratory facilities, utilization of these technical inputs is essentially in the nature of quality control and taking advantage of known or developing nutritional know-how rather than research. These small firms rarely have significant advantages in procurement of inputs. However, due to the competitive nature of the markets for most feed inputs, they are not significantly disadvantaged relative to larger national companies.

Major brand companies have some competitive instruments not generally available to firms in a competitive fringe. The extensive regional or national distribution of output from the large firms creates the possibility of geographic price discrimination. Larger companies typically have the potential of much more extensive financing due to their access to national money markets and larger internal sources (retained earnings). Larger firms are in a position to take advantage of scale economies in any competitive dimensions in which they may be significant. For example, there are some indications that promotion and advertising are more efficient on a regional or national basis than on a local basis. In automated plants, there are some opportunities to take advantage of technical scale economies. There are also indications that scale economies may be significant in feeding program development, particularly where new cultural practices may be important. In the introduction of cultural practices such as cage layer operations or slatted floor hog feeder operations, large firms are able to develop efficient facility designs and accumulate experience in associated feeding practices more efficiently than small companies. The size and organizational structure of larger companies enables greater emphasis on research and development as compared to smaller companies.

Rather well-developed patterns of competitive strategy have developed from the differential competitive position of large major brand companies as compared to small, local companies. The large companies have combined their superiority in the areas of research and development and promotion and advertising to develop an emphasis on nonprice competition. They have combined their advantages in the design of new facilities and development of advanced cultural practices with their advantages in availability of financing to create an emphasis on vertical integration. These two competitive strategies have been prominent in the competitive behavior of this industry over the past decade. It is generally unknown to what extent regional price discrimination has been practiced although it may have been important.

On the other hand, firms in the competitive fringe have used their cost advantages to move into price competition. They have resisted the rather general urge to increase promotion and advertising. There are indications that, while the promotion-development-advertising budgets as a percent of sales of the major brand companies have rapidly increased over the past decade, similar cost items for some smaller firms have actually decreased as a portion of total sales. The product mix of the small firms typically contains a higher proportion of feed to technical know-how with respect to animal nutrition. The increasing size of farms and increases in the extent of training in animal nutrition on the part of farmers themselves may have facilitated the growth of these small firms which compete pricewise. Direct selling, a phenomenon of considerable interest to the trade, has been essentially a strategy of nonmajor brand companies.

Problems concerning "unfair trade practices" have not been a dominant feature of the competitive behavior in this industry. Numerous cases of misrepresentation are available in the literature involving promotion and labeling problems. This matter, however, has been kept under fairly close surveillance by the Federal Trade Commission, Food and Drug Administration, and state control agencies. In view of the rather tight regulations concerning labeling, many of the misrepresentation problems could result from the inherent difficulties of quality control which result from rather wide variations in the nutrient content of feed grains and other input products.

## MARKET PERFORMANCE IN THE MIXED FEED INDUSTRY

The evaluation of market performance involves a rather overall or general view of economic activity accruing from the particular market structure which is catalyzed by particular patterns of competitive behavior. The primary objective is to determine to what extent these economic results from a particular industry are consistent with broader and more general economic goals. Criteria for performance evaluation center around costs and services performed but must include some dimensions of progressiveness in an environment characterized by change over time.

The major services performed by the feed industry include the assembly of many types of products most of which are farm grown; the manufacture of hundreds of different types of specialized animal feeds; the distribution of these feeds to farmers who are scattered throughout the country; the development of a considerable research effort oriented to the basic science of nutrition as well as the applied areas of feeding programs and cultural practices; the dissemination of information to farmers through various types of fieldman organizations; and the financing of a significant quantity of productive enterprises on farms. Attention is now directed to the quality of these products created and services performed.

Animal feed products are certainly made available in sufficient variations and specializations. Major feed companies and most small companies list literally hundreds of variations of ingredient and drug constituents of feed. In addition, many of these companies are able and quite willing to manufacture feed to specifications of individual farmers where volume is sufficient to make this specialized operation feasible. While there is substantial variation in the nutritional constituents of inputs going into this industry, the nature of competition and government surveillance essentially assures that products manufactured by this industry are rather closely standardized to the ingredients listed on the labels. There seem to be no significant institutional barriers to the adoption of new and improved product variations. On the contrary, perhaps the most significant aspect of performance in this industry is the substantial product development which is carried on.

This industry not only adopts innovations developing from the abundant state and federally supported nutrition research, but also conducts substantial research internally. The results of this emphasis on product development move through to the farmer rather quickly creating increased productivity on the farm. Farmers have indicated that information disseminated as a part of promotion programs of feed companies is often more up-to-date and useful than nutritional information available from other sources. While the quality of products produced by an industry is difficult to evaluate for lack of usable standards, it seems reasonable to conclude that this industry is characterized by good performance in product quality, the availability of appropriate quality variations, and a high degree of progressiveness concerning the improvement of product quality over time.

When attention is directed toward the costs of obtaining these products, the important question becomes, Are there unnecessary costs which result from characteristics of structure or the competitive behavior within this industry? One form of unnecessary cost could result from exploitative pricing patterns. The structure of the feed manufacturing industry which consists of hundreds of firms in most trading areas and the homogeneous nature of input products essentially preclude serious exploitative pricing in the input markets. In the market for the outputs of the feed manufacturing industry, the importance of product differentiation and the relatively high concentration in some trade areas create the possibility of exploitative pricing. In this market, however, the presence of an important and aggressive fringe of small but price-competitive manufacturers substantially reduces this possibility. While the organizational nature of several of the large feed manufacturers present the opportunity for geographic price discrimination, very little of this activity has reached the courts. While there are doubtless exceptions in particular areas, in general, exploitative pricing has not been a problem in this industry. Analysis of profit rates shows no tendency toward chronic "excess profits."

Other types of unnecessary costs which may be important in relatively highly concentrated industries or in industries which have several firms of a large absolute size are excessive selling costs. Some of the firms in this industry have increased selling and promotional costs rather rapidly during the past decade. While there is little question that these costs are increasing, there may be substantial basis for questioning the extent to which they are unnecessary. In an industry which has a substantial number of firms which are motivated to compete essentially with price, rapid product development may occur only if the large firms capable of conducting necessary research are able to obtain product differentiation advantages in their output market. If the competitive positions of firms engaging in price competition as opposed to firms engaging in nonprice competition are altered in the future, unnecessary selling costs may become a more serious problem than they seem to be at present.

Excess capacity, which seems to be rather extensive in this industry, may represent a type of unnecessary cost. While empirical analysis of excess capacity is presently inadequate, it is likely that excess capacity is more commonplace among the firms making up the price competitive fringe than among the larger firms. There is some basis for speculation, consistent with experience with small business in other industries, that excess capacity may be a rather inherent feature of a small business competitive fringe.

In general, market performance in this industry (composed of a few very large firms engaged in nonprice competition and containing many small firms which are motivated toward price competition) seems to be rather good. It is also likely that this competitive fringe is an important condition for the maintenance of this good market performance.

## A Look to the Future

What may be expected in terms of structure or behavior in this industry in the decades ahead? There seem to be no strong trends in structural or behavioral characteristics of this industry useful for making simple projections. There are indications that the number of distribution points or feed dealers may decline in the future. On the other hand, the feed dealer is an important part of the distribution system of the large national feed manufacturers. There are no indications that this will be less true in the future.

This industry is presently rather sensitive to the needs at the farm level and it is therefore likely that changes in the organization and behavior in this industry will be rather closely related to changes on the farm. As farms become larger and farm managers better trained, there is some indication that the need for extra services at a cost may be reduced. The need for educational programs and the importance of major brands may therefore diminish. On the other hand, as new cultural practices come into importance, particularly those requiring extensive capital investment on the farm and sophisticated specialized know-how, the importance of large companies may increase. While it seems likely at this point to expect the market share of the larger firms to continue a slow increase, the competitive fringe of small manufacturers will continue to exist and continue to be an important influence upon market behavior and performance.

## SELECTED REFERENCES

Askew, W. R., and Brensike, V. J., *The Mixed-Feeds Industry*, Mkg. Res. Rept. 38, U.S.D.A. (Washington, May 1953).

*The Changing Feed Mixing Industry*, Market Res. Rept. 506, E.R.S., U.S.D.A. (Washington, Oct. 1961).

Farrell, K. R., *Grain Marketing Statistics for the North Central States*, N. Cen. Grain Mkg. Res. Com., published at Mo. Agr. Exp. Sta. (Columbia, June 1958).

Fletcher, L. B., *Market Organization of the Grain Industries in the North Central Region*, N. Cen. Grain Mkg. Res. Com. publication (Oct. 15, 1963).

Gessner, Anne L., *Integrated Feed Operations Through Farmer Cooperatives, 1959*, Gen. Rept. 100, Farmer Cooperative Serv., U.S.D.A. (Washington, Apr. 1962).

Kalb, Klaus, *Product Differentiation in the Mixed Feeds Industry*, unpublished Ph.D. thesis, Ohio State Univ. (Columbus, 1964).

Kohls, R. L., *Farmers' Behavior and Decisions in Purchasing Farm Supplies, Feed, Machinery, Fertilizer*, Res. Bul. 749, Ind. Agr. Exp. Sta. (Lafayette, Oct. 1962).

Phillips, Richard, *Feed Industry Financing and Contract Programs in Iowa and Surrounding States,* Iowa Agr. Exp. Sta. Spec. Rept. 28 (Ames, Apr. 1961).

——, *Analysis of Costs and Benefits to Feed Manufacturers From Financing and Contract Programs in the Midwest,* Iowa Agr. Exp. Sta., Spec. Rept. 30 (Ames, Oct. 1962).

——, *Costs of Procuring, Manufacturing, and Distributing Mixed Feeds in the Midwest,* Mkg. Res. Rept. 338, U.S.D.A. (Washington, Apr. 1960).

Roy, E. P., *Contract Farming, USA* (Danville, Ill.: The Interstate Printers and Publishers, Inc., 1963).

# THE COTTON INDUSTRY

**12**

## MARK L. FOWLER[1]

IN MOST YEARS since 1929, government programs have played an important role in production, marketing, and pricing of cotton. The major role of public policy in the cotton industry has been that of a vehicle for improvement of actual or alleged unsatisfactory market performance. It has usually been assumed that poor performance stems primarily from "excessive" or "destructive" competition flowing from the industry's atomistic structure.

Remedy has been sought mainly through restrictions on strategic elements of market conduct and direct regulation of certain aspects of performance. Major decisions relating to one or more key components of enterprise profit have been shifted from the individual firm level to the government level. With respect to these aspects of enterprise behavior, the structure of the industry has been transformed from conceptual pure competition to conceptual monopoly.

Conventionally, market structure analysis has a strong public policy orientation. Hence a market structure study of the cotton industry must perforce be concerned to a significant degree with an analysis and appraisal of past, present, and potential cotton policies. The fundamental question at issue is what type of government programs will tend to be an effective remedy for unsatisfactory performance in the industry given its organizational and economic structure.

In order to set the stage for dealing with the question at issue, a couple of points need to be clarified regarding the scope of the analysis. Since public policy has operated primarily at the farm level or in the market for raw cotton, the analysis is restricted mainly to the cotton producing industry. But the concept of the industry employed is one that considers not only a group of com-

---

[1] Associate Professor and Chairman of the Marketing Section, Department of Agricultural Economics and Sociology, Texas A & M University.

peting sellers but extends forward to take into account the nature of the demand for the product.

Thus the concept of the industry employed here is the traditional one that combines suppliers on the one hand and demanders on the other hand in a way that permits the construction, at least conceptually, of industry or aggregate demand and supply functions for raw cotton. In this sense, our concept corresponds to Bain's definition of a market "as including all the sellers in any individual industry, and all the buyers to whom (in common) they sell."[2] However, Bain goes on to point out that when he speaks of the structure of an industry he is emphasizing market structure. In this context, then, we are concerned with the competitive structure of the market for raw cotton.

The second point is concerned with the content of what is called market structure analysis. The currently received doctrine of market structure analysis focuses on the concepts of market structure, conduct, and performance, and the interrelationships among them. According to Clodius and Mueller, "the direction of causation is assumed to run from structure through conduct to performance."[3] Thus, the basic assumption of the market structure model is that market structure determines in some more or less predictable manner the competitive behavior of firms in the market, and that the policies pursued by firms and their interaction generate the totality of economic results that flow from the industry as an aggregate of competing firms, i.e., market performance.

In the literature on market structure analysis, the concept of market structure has become more and more narrowly defined to refer only to organizational characteristics. The characteristics usually emphasized are (1) the number and size distribution of buyers and sellers, i.e., buyer and seller concentration, (2) the degree of product homogeneity or, conversely, of product differentiation, and (3) conditions of entry.[4] Within this context, the power of market structure and conduct to explain performance is severely restricted, as pointed out by Bain when he said that "market structure and conduct clearly represent only a small fraction of the total determinants of market performance."[5]

Consequently, restricting our study of the cotton industry to the organizational characteristics specified by this narrow definition of market structure would seriously weaken the usefulness of the

---

[2] Joe S. Bain, *Industrial Organization* (New York: John Wiley & Sons, Inc., 1959), p. 7.

[3] Robert L. Clodius and Willard F. Mueller, "Market Structure Analysis as an Orientation for Research in Agricultural Economics," *Journal of Farm Economics*, Vol. XLIII (Aug. 1961), p. 516.

[4] *Ibid.*, and Bain, *op. cit.*

[5] Bain, *op. cit.*, p. 44.

analysis in providing guidelines for cotton policy. The point to be made is that effective cotton policy measures depend not only on socially derived performance norms, policy goals, and the organizational structure of the industry, but they depend also on the economic structure of the industry embodied in the demand and supply characteristics for raw cotton in both the short and long run.

## RELATIVE IMPORTANCE OF THE INDUSTRY

Cotton is the most important cash crop in American agriculture. It ranks first among all farm commodities as a source of cash receipts to farmers in ten states. Nationwide, sales of cotton and cottonseed provided cash receipts to farmers of $2.9 billion in 1963. This represented 7.8 percent of cash receipts from all farm commodities and was exceeded only by cattle and calves, hogs, and dairy products.[6] In 1963, there were 639,144 effective cotton allotment farms, and the number of farmers with an interest in the allotments—owners, operators, share tenants, and sharecroppers—was estimated to be 833,275.[7]

But the industry's importance is not confined to its producers. The domestic textile industry depends on cotton for about 55 percent by weight of its raw fiber requirements, although this percentage has been dropping steadily for some time. It is becoming increasingly difficult to distinguish clearly between the cotton segment and other branches of the textile industry, but it is estimated that in 1961 the cotton segment accounted for approximately 542,000 employees and proprietors.[8] In 1958, cotton broad woven fabric mills had shipments valued at $2.7 billion. In addition, much of the activity of the four census industries classified as yarn mills (except wool), thread mills, narrow fabric mills, and finishing plants (cotton) was devoted to cotton and had combined shipments of $2.0 billion.[9]

In terms of consumption in final uses on a cotton equivalent basis, it is estimated that, in 1962, cotton accounted for about 60 percent of the total domestic fiber market in apparel uses, 45 percent of the market in household uses, and 22 percent of the market

---

[6] *Farm Income, State Estimates, 1949–1963*, FIS–195 Supplement, E.R.S., U.S.D.A. (Washington, Aug. 1964).

[7] *Tabulations for Upland Cotton Allotments Showing Summaries by States and Size Groups by Farms and Acreages*, Policy and Program Appraisal Div., Agr. Stabilization and Conservation Serv., U.S.D.A. (Washington, July 1963).

[8] Dabney S. Wellford, *Measurements of the U.S. Cotton Industry*, National Cotton Council of America (May 1963), p. 2. The estimate is obtained by multiplying total textile mill products industry employees and proprietors by cotton's percentage of total fiber consumption by mills, 62.1 percent.

[9] "Industry Statistics," *Census of Manufactures*, U.S. Dept. of Commerce, Bur. of the Census, Vol. II (Washington, 1958).

in industrial uses. Cotton was estimated to account for 44 percent of the total market in all final uses.[10]

In addition, thousands of individuals and firms are involved in supplying cotton growers with goods and services used in production. Others are engaged in providing the many services in marketing raw cotton and in marketing and processing cottonseed. Many of these individuals and firms derive all or a major portion of their income from cotton. The quantity of cotton produced and consumed, price and profit levels and variations therein, and government policy affecting them are of vital importance to all the people engaged in these enterprises.[11]

Cotton is also an important export commodity and source of foreign exchange. During the 5-year period 1955–59, the value of cotton exports averaged $667,551,000 per year and accounted for 17 percent of the value of all agricultural exports.[12] During this period the United States accounted for about one-third of total world exports of raw cotton.

## HISTORY

Cotton has played an important role in the growth and development of U.S. agriculture and industry almost from the birth of the Republic. The invention of the cotton gin by Eli Whitney in 1793 removed a major obstacle to, and paved the way for, large-scale production of cotton. In 1793, cotton production in the United States totaled only 10,000 bales of which 4,000 bales were exported (Table 12.1). From this modest beginning, cotton production increased rapidly and more or less continuously until the outbreak of World War I, with the notable interruption as a consequence of the Civil War. Cotton quickly became the largest commercial crop in the South and was the mainstay of its entire economy.[13] During the 5-year period 1910–14, production ranged from 11.6 million to 16.1 million bales.

Production of cotton exceeded domestic mill demand almost from the beginning and exports usually accounted for the great bulk of the annual crop. Cotton early became the largest single

---

[10] *Cotton Counts Its Customers,* Natl. Cotton Council of Amer. (Aug. 1963). The estimates on end uses do not cover exports of fabric and yarn but do include imported fabrics and yarn. Materials consumed are measured in terms of cotton equivalents. Some relatively minor end uses are not covered.

[11] For estimates of the number of people whose livelihoods are closely related to cotton, see Wellford, *op. cit.,* pp. 2–4; also see Fig. 12.1 and text discussion.

[12] *U.S. Foreign Agricultural Trade by Commodities, Calendar Year 1962, A Supplement to the Monthly Foreign Agricultural Trade of the United States,* E.R.S., U.S.D.A. (Washington, June 1963), pp. 2–3.

[13] Everett E. Edwards, "American Agriculture—The First 300 Years," *Farmers in a Changing World,* Yearbook of Agriculture (1940), p. 209.

TABLE 12.1
COTTON PRODUCTION, MILL CONSUMPTION AND EXPORTS, SELECTED YEARS, 1790–1960*

| Year Beginning August 1 | Production | Mill Consumption | Exports |
|---|---|---|---|
| | *(1,000 bales)* * | *(1,000 bales)*† | *(1,000 bales)*† |
| 1790 | 3 | 11 | ... |
| 1793 | 10 | ... | 4 |
| 1800 | 73 | 19 | 32 |
| 1810 | 178 | 36 | 124 |
| 1820 | 335 | 100 | 250 |
| 1830 | 732 | 130 | 554 |
| 1840 | 1,348 | 245 | 1,060 |
| 1850 | 2,136 | 423 | 1,854 |
| 1860 | 3,841 | 842 | 615 |
| 1870 | 4,352 | 1,027 | 2,896 |
| 1880 | 6,606 | 1,860 | 4,409 |
| 1890 | 8,653 | 2,604 | 5,859 |
| 1900 | 10,124 | 3,604 | 6,743 |
| 1910 | 11,609 | 4,498 | 8,027 |
| 1920 | 13,429 | 4,893 | 5,973 |
| 1930 | 13,932 | 5,263 | 7,133 |
| 1940 | 12,566 | 9,722 | 1,174 |
| 1950 | 10,014 | 10,509 | 4,280 |
| 1960 | 14,272 | 8,279 | 6,857 |

Source: 1790–1920: *Statistics on Cotton and Related Data*, B.A.E., U.S.D.A., Statistical Bulletin No. 99, Table 1 (June 1951).
1930–1960: *Statistics on Cotton and Related Data, 1925–1962*, E.R.S., U.S.D.A., Statistical Bulletin 329, Table 1 (April 1963).
* Mill consumption plus exports may not equal production because of (1) imports of raw cotton and (2) variations in carryover stocks of raw cotton.
† Bales of 500 pounds gross weight, except consumption which is in running bales.

export of the United States. In 1809, it represented 23 percent of the value of all exports and, by 1860, 61 percent.[14] In 1910–14, exports ranged from 8.0 million to 11.1 million bales, accounting for well over one-half of the annual crop.

In the United States, as in England, the cotton textile industry was in the vanguard of the shift in manufacturing from the home to the factory. The first successful cotton spinning mill in the United States was established in 1790. The industry developed slowly during the next several years, but a series of events began in 1807 that provided the stimulus to greatly increased activity in cotton textile manufacturing, and the stage was set for a rapid expansion and the establishment of the industry on a factory basis. In 1807, Congress passed the Embargo Act which prohibited American ships from sailing from American ports to those of foreign countries. This was followed in 1809 by the Non-Intercourse Act which prohibited commercial relations with England and France

[14] *Ibid.*

and the War of 1812 which brought all foreign trade to a virtual standstill.

The effect of these developments was to restrict the flow of raw cotton from the United States to England and the return flow of British-made textiles into the domestic market. As a result, prices of cotton cloth in the United States increased some fourfold, while prices of raw cotton declined by more than 50 percent. This sharply increased margin made the manufacturing of cotton cloth in the United States highly profitable, and the number of spindles increased from 8,000 in 1807 to 87,000 in 1810, and 130,000 in 1815.[15]

Another development also occurred during this period which had profound and lasting effects on the industry. Francis Cabot Lowell, after intensive study of textile machinery and manufacturing in England, developed a power loom. In 1813, he and his associates established the first integrated mill in the world by combining power spinning and power weaving under one roof.

General economic growth and development in the United States and technological innovations in textile machinery combined to provide a favorable economic climate for domestic cotton manufacture, and the industry continued to expand steadily and rapidly. The total number of spindles reached 5.2 million in 1860 and mill consumption was 842,000 bales. In spite of the disruptive influences of the Civil War, the number of spindles rose to 7.1 million in 1870 and consumption exceeded 1,000,000 bales of cotton for the first time.

The industry continued to grow and, by 1910, the total number of spindles reached 28.6 million. As capacity grew and competition became more intense, mill margins and profits began to fall in the first decade of the 1900's. However, sharply increased demand growing out of the outbreak of World War I stimulated new growth in the industry. The total number of spindles increased to 35.9 million by 1920, and consumption was averaging over 6 million bales per year.

There has been no discernible trend in total U.S. cotton production since World War I, although wide year-to-year variations have occurred because of governmental programs and fluctuating yields. However, there has been a substantial decrease in acreage harvested that has been offset by sharply rising yields. New and improved production practices involving pesticides, varieties, fertilization, irrigation, mechanization, and others have been adopted. Cotton production has shifted from land less adaptable to land

---

[15] This account of development in the textile industry up to 1920 is based primarily on H. E. Mickl, *The Textile Industries: An Economic Analysis* (Washington: The Textile Foundation, 1938), especially Chap. 6, "Cotton Textiles—History of the Industry," pp. 65–79.

more adaptable to mechanization, and from production under rain-fall conditions to production using irrigation. These shifts have occurred both within and between the major producing areas. Generally, there has been a shift from the older producing areas in the Southeast to the newer areas in the West. As a result of all these developments, the United States is now producing roughly the same quantity of cotton as it did in the 1920's but utilizing only about one-third as many acres.

Abstracting from short-term variations, total disappearance of U.S. cotton has remained at about the same level since World War I. However, there has been a pronounced shift in the relative im-portance of the domestic and export markets. During the 1920's, U.S. exports of cotton averaged 7.4 million bales annually and ac-counted for 54 percent of disappearance. In the decade of the 1950's however, exports averaged 4.7 million bales per year and accounted for only 38 percent of disappearance.

The relative importance of U.S. cotton in world markets has also declined substantially. In the 1920's, U.S. exports accounted for about 60 percent of total world exports and 46 percent of total foreign mill consumption of cotton from all sources. In the 1950's, the United States accounted for only about one-third of world ex-ports of cotton and about 16 percent of total foreign mill consump-tion. The deterioration of the position of U.S. cotton in world markets over this long period has been influenced mainly by the world-wide depression in the 1930's, nationalistic policies of eco-nomic self-sufficiency on the part of many foreign countries in the 1930's and since World War II, and domestic supply control and price support programs.

In the domestic market, economic conditions in the cotton textile industry were generally unfavorable throughout the inter-war period. Profits of cotton manufacturers dropped sharply after World War I and remained depressed until prosperity returned with the outbreak of World War II.

Active spindles reached a peak of 36.3 million in 1923 and then began a steady and continuing decline. By 1940, active spindles totaled 23.6 million. However, except for annual varia-tions, mill consumption remained at roughly the same level through-out the interwar period. Productive capacity was maintained by increased hours of spindle operation (double shifts) and increased efficiency as reflected in increased output per man-hour.[16]

One of the most important developments in the interwar period from the viewpoint of the cotton industry was the emer-

---

[16] For an account of conditions in the industry during the interwar period see Jules Backman and M. R. Gainsbrugh, *Economics of the Cotton Textile In-dustry* (New York: Natl. Ind. Conf. Bd., 1946).

gence of man-made fibers as a major competitor. Mill consumption of rayon and acetate increased from only 0.3 percent of all textile fibers in 1920 to 10.0 percent in 1939. This represented an increase from 23,000 cotton equivalent bales to 857,000 bales.[17]

Since World War II the role of cotton in the domestic textile industry has shifted significantly. There has been a rapid expansion in production and utilization of man-made fibers, and it is becoming increasingly difficult to distinguish clearly between the cotton segment and other branches of the industry. New and improved man-made fibers and other materials have replaced or supplemented cotton in a wide range of products and uses. Per capita consumption of cotton is less than it was in the 1920's and 1930's, and cotton now accounts for only about 55 percent of the total domestic fiber market compared to over 80 percent in the years prior to World War II.

Nevertheless, total domestic mill consumption is running well above the level maintained during the interwar years, primarily because of a rapidly growing population. Total mill consumption averaged about 8.5 million bales per year during the period 1956–60 compared to about 7.0 million bales per year in 1935–39. Parenthetically, however, there is little or no evidence of an upward trend in total domestic mill consumption when only the postwar years are analyzed. The growth in population is being offset by a decline in per capita consumption.

## MARKET STRUCTURE

### The Supply Side

*Number and Size.* The cotton producing industry is characterized by an organizational structure closely approximating the economist's limiting concept of pure competition. There are many producers, and the size distribution is such that no one of them can affect market price perceptibly by variations in his own output.

In addition to large numbers, the industry is characterized by a large proportion of farms that produce only a small quantity of cotton. Cotton was harvested on more than one-half million farms in the United States in 1959. Sixty-five percent of the farms harvested 15 acres or less of cotton and accounted for only 16 percent of harvested acres and 15 percent of total production. On the other hand, only a little over 6 percent of the farms harvested 100 acres or more of cotton and accounted for 47 percent of total acres and 52 percent of total production (Table 12.2). 

Of the 502,008 farms that harvested cotton in 1959, only

---

[17] *Statistics on Cotton and Related Data, 1920–1956*, A.M.S., U.S.D.A., Stat. Bul. 99 (revised Feb. 1957).

TABLE 12.2

COTTON: DISTRIBUTION OF FARMS REPORTING, ACRES AND BALES HARVESTED,
BY ACRES HARVESTED PER FARM, 1959*

| Acres Harvested Per Farm | Farms Reporting | | Acres Harvested | | Bales Harvested | |
|---|---|---|---|---|---|---|
| | (percent) | (cumula- tive) | (percent) | (cumula- tive) | (percent) | (cumula- tive) |
| Under 5 | 18.8 | 18.8 | 2.0 | 2.0 | 1.7 | 1.7 |
| 5 to 9 | 25.9 | 44.7 | 6.0 | 8.0 | 5.3 | 7.0 |
| 10 to 14 | 16.7 | 61.4 | 6.6 | 14.6 | 6.2 | 13.2 |
| 15 | 3.2 | 64.6 | 1.6 | 16.3 | 1.5 | 14.7 |
| 16 to 24 | 11.5 | 76.1 | 7.6 | 23.8 | 7.2 | 21.9 |
| 25 to 49 | 10.8 | 86.9 | 12.7 | 36.5 | 11.4 | 33.3 |
| 50 to 99 | 6.8 | 93.7 | 16.1 | 52.6 | 14.4 | 47.7 |
| 100 to 199 | 4.2 | 97.9 | 19.8 | 72.4 | 18.7 | 66.4 |
| 200 to 299 | 1.2 | 99.1 | 10.8 | 83.2 | 10.4 | 76.8 |
| 300 to 499 | .6 | 99.7 | 8.2 | 91.4 | 9.5 | 86.3 |
| 500 or More | 0.3 | 100 | 9.3 | 100 | 13.7 | 100 |
| Total Numbers† | 502,008 | | 14,571,291 | | 13,840,044 | |

Source: "General Reports," *U.S. Census of Agriculture, 1959,* Vol. II, Chap-
ter 7, U.S. Department of Commerce, Bureau of the Census.
* Data all estimates based on a sample of farms.
† Totals for 14 states.

241,849, or less than 50 percent, were classified as commercial cotton farms. Sixty-two percent of these commercial farms had gross
farm sales of $5,000 or less and accounted for only 15 percent of cot-
ton sales by all commercial cotton farms. At the other extreme,
about 5.5 percent of these farms had gross sales of $40,000 or more
and accounted for 46 percent of cotton sales (Table 12.3).

In 1963, 35 percent of all original cotton allotments were for
less than 5 acres, 59 percent were for less than 10 acres, and 69 percent were for less than 15 acres (Table 12.4).

TABLE 12.3

COMMERCIAL COTTON FARMS: DISTRIBUTION OF FARMS, COTTON SALES, AND
COTTON SALES AS A PERCENT OF ALL SALES BY ECONOMIC CLASS OF FARM, 1959

| Economic Class | Number of Farms | Percent of Farms | Percent of Cotton Sales | Cotton Sales as Percent of Total Sales |
|---|---|---|---|---|
| Total | 241,849 | 100.0 | 100.0 | 75 |
| $40,000 and Over | 13,171 | 5.4 | 45.7 | 73 |
| $20,000 to $39,000 | 15,984 | 6.6 | 16.1 | 74 |
| $10,000 to $19,000 | 24,473 | 10.1 | 12.5 | 73 |
| $ 5,000 to $ 9,999 | 37,961 | 15.7 | 10.3 | 76 |
| $ 2,500 to $ 4,999 | 67,058 | 27.7 | 10.2 | 82 |
| $50 to $2,499 | 83,202 | 34.4 | 5.2 | 86 |

Source: *U.S. Census of Agriculture, 1959,* Vol. II, Chapter 12, Table 72, U.S.
Department of Commerce, Bureau of the Census.

TABLE 12.4

UPLAND COTTON:* DISTRIBUTION OF ORIGINAL AND EFFECTIVE COTTON ALLOTMENTS
BY SIZE OF ALLOTMENT, 1961 AND 1963

| | 1961 | | 1963 | |
| --- | --- | --- | --- | --- |
| Acres | Original allotment | Effective allotment | Original allotment | Effective allotment |
| 0.1–4.9 | 356,795 | 242,269 | 269,857 | 192,415 |
| 5.0–10.0 | 226,046 | 181,780 | 185,237 | 143,149 |
| 10.1–14.9 | 85,737 | 74,839 | 80,258 | 68,690 |
| 15.0–29.9 | 124,432 | 118,008 | 112,611 | 102,322 |
| 30.0–49.9 | 57,414 | 58,461 | 54,133 | 53,546 |
| 50.0–99.9 | 48,920 | 52,708 | 45,325 | 48,621 |
| 100.0–199.9 | 21,486 | 23,622 | 19,199 | 21,318 |
| 200.0–499.9 | 8,253 | 8,947 | 6,852 | 7,797 |
| 500.0 & Over | 1,472 | 1,623 | 1,182 | 1,286 |
| Totals | | | | |
| Farms | 930,555 | 762,257 | 774,654 | 639,144 |
| Acres | 18,451,501 | 18,415,909 | 16,239,518 | 16,209,324 |

Source: Cotton Division (1961) and Policy and Program Appraisal Division
(1963), Agricultural Stabilization and Conservation Service, U.S.D.A.
* All American cotton is upland cotton, except for small quantities of American-Egyptian,
Sea Island, and Sealand cotton.

*Nature of Product.* Strictly speaking, cotton is not of course a
homogeneous product. However, it is a standardized product in
the sense that it is sold on reasonably well-defined and objective
quality standards. It is also a manufacturing raw material for
which there is considerable degree of technical substitutability between contiguous qualities over a wide range of end uses. For
practical purposes, these factors permit us to treat cotton as a
homogeneous product in aggregate analysis without serious loss
in generality.

*Entry and Exit.* It has usually been assumed that entry is relatively
easy so that new producers can enter the industry quickly in the
event of favorable price conditions. However, a sizable initial investment is required to establish a unit of economical size under
present conditions and this will undoubtedly make entry more difficult in the future.

Much has been said to the effect that rather long periods of
depressed prices and incomes have been required to induce removal of redundant resources from cotton production. But this depends crucially on income prospects in alternative crop and livestock enterprises as well as opportunities in the nonfarm sector.
Moreover, the question of exit must be considered in the light of
available evidence that farmers have been and are moving out of
cotton growing in substantial numbers even under the rather favorable price levels prevailing in recent years.

TABLE 12.5
COTTON: DISTRIBUTION OF FARMS REPORTING BY BALES HARVESTED, 1954 AND 1959*

| Bales Harvested Per Farm | 1954 Number | 1954 Percent | 1959 Number | 1959 Percent | Percentage Change |
|---|---|---|---|---|---|
| Under 25 | 779,567 | 90.3 | 407,385 | 80.1 | −47.7 |
| 25 to 49 | 45,106 | 5.2 | 48,010 | 9.4 | 6.4 |
| 50 to 99 | 20,440 | 2.5 | 26,459 | 5.2 | 29.4 |
| 100 to 499 | 16,120 | 1.9 | 24,083 | 4.7 | 49.4 |
| 500 to 999 | 1,236 | 0.1 | 744 | 0.2 | 36.0 |
| Total Numbers | 863,016 | 100 | 508,502 | 100 | −41.1 |

Source: "General Report," *U.S. Census of Agriculture, 1959,* Vol. II, Chapter 7, U.S. Department of Commerce, Bureau of the Census.
* Data all estimates based on reports for only a sample of farms.

According to the Census of Agriculture, the number of farms harvesting cotton declined from 863,016 in 1954 to 508,502 in 1959, a decline of 41 percent (Table 12.5). The number of farms harvesting less than 25 bales declined 48 percent, while the number in all other volume classes shown in Table 12.5 increased.

The fact that farms are withdrawing from cotton growing and that those leaving are mainly the small-scale farms is also illustrated by a comparison of original and effective cotton allotment farms for 1961 and 1963 (Table 12.4). In each acreage class the number of allotment farms was smaller in 1963 than in 1961 for both original and effective allotments. In both years the number of effective allotments of 30 acres or less was substantially smaller than the number of original allotments of 30 acres or less. On the other hand, the number of effective allotments of 50 acres or more exceeded the number of original allotments of 50 acres or more.

*Elasticity of Aggregate Supply.* For the nation as a whole and for the precontrol (1933) period, estimates of the short-run price elasticity of supply (acreage) are of the order of about .25[18] Blakley and Nerlove have reported estimates of .41 and .67, respectively, for the long-run elasticity.[19] These estimates are based on analyses of time series data, and prices of production alternatives were not included in the analyses.

Because of acreage controls in most years since 1933, meaningful estimates of supply response based on time series analyses are not available. However, recent estimates of regional supply func-

---

[18] Marc Nerlove, "Estimates of the Elasticities of Supply of Selected Agricultural Commodities," *Journal of Farm Economics,* Vol. XXXVIII (May 1956), pp. 496–509; and Robert M. Walsh, "Response to Price in Production of Cotton and Cottonseed," *Journal of Farm Economics,* Vol. XXVI (May 1944), pp. 359–72.

[19] Leo V. Blakley, *Quantitative Relationships in the Cotton Economy With Implications for Economic Policy,* Okla. Agr. Exp. Sta. Tech. Bul. T-95 (Stillwater, May 1962); and Nerlove, *Ibid.*

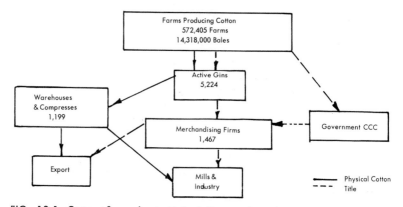

FIG. 12.1—Cotton flow chart, United States, for 1961. (Source: Farms—U.S.D.A., Agr. Stabilization and Conservation Serv., reported by Dabney; S. Wellford, **Measurements of the U.S. Cotton Industry**, Natl. Cotton Council of Amer., May 1963, p. 28; Bales—**Cotton Production in the United States,** crop of 1961, U.S. Dept. of Commerce, Bur. of the Census, p. 2; Active gins—**ibid.**, p. 4; Warehouses and compresses—Natl. Cotton Compress and Cotton Warehouse Assn., reported in Dabney, p. 36; Merchandising firms—listings in **Davison's Textile Blue Book** under "Index to Main Offices of All Cotton Firms in U.S.," 1961, reported in Dabney, p. 35. The **Blue Book** counts each cotton merchandising firm as a unit, regardless of the other business activities in which it may be engaged and regardless of whether it operates in one or in many locations. The **Census of Business** counts as an establishment each location in which one or more persons are employed on a payroll basis, but excludes those engaged principally in ginning or other business activities and unincorporated businesses having no paid employees. The **Census of Business** reported 955 cotton merchandising establishments in 1958.)

tions for cotton based on aggregation of optimum adjustments on individual farms yield elasticities that appear to be consistent with those derived from time series data when account is taken of differences in length of run, geographical area, and the fact that prices of production alternatives are included in the analyses.[20]

These studies also indicate that it would be profitable for farmers to expand acreage and production sharply at prices substantially below current support prices for cotton with prices of production alternatives at present levels.

---

[20] Gerald W. Dean, Stanley S. Johnson, and Harold O. Carter, "Supply Functions for Cotton in Imperial Valley, California," *Agricultural Economics Research,* Vol. XV (Jan. 1963), pp. 1–14; James S. Plaxico, "Cotton in an Efficient Southern Agriculture," paper presented at the Beltwide Cotton Prod. Mech. Conf., Memphis, Tenn., Jan. 11–12, 1962; and Charles V. Moore and Trimble R. Hedges, *Economics of On-Farm Irrigation Water Availability and Costs, and Related Farm Adjustments,* 3. *Some Aggregative Aspects of Farmer Demand for Irrigation Water and Production Response on the San Joaquin Valley Eastside,* Calif. Agr. Exp. Sta., Giannini Foundation Res. Rept. 261 (Mar. 1963).

## The Raw Cotton Marketing Sector

The raw cotton merchandising system is the essential link between cotton growers on the supply side and manufacturers of cotton textile products on the demand side. A wide variety of middlemen and services are required to move American cotton from farm to mill, either domestic or foreign. In 1961, there were over 5,000 active gins, approximately 1,200 warehouses and compresses, and almost 1,500 merchandising firms (Figure 12.1). In addition, thousands of firms are involved in insuring, transporting, financing, and risk-taking in the movement of the crop from farm to mill. Practically all cotton in the United States is ginned locally before it is sold by the farmer. From the gin, the physical cotton usually moves to warehouses, many of which have compresses, where it is concentrated and stored. From compresses and warehouses it flows by rail or truck to domestic mills or to ocean ports for export to foreign countries.

Most cotton is sold by farmers in local markets or placed in the government loan. The primary function of these farmers' markets is to provide a ready outlet for cotton in odd lots consisting of a varying number of bales of mixed quality. Local markets vary widely in terms of organization, number and kind of buyers, physical facilities and services performed, and practices followed by merchandising agencies.

A study by the Southern Regional Cotton Marketing Research Committee of operations of local cotton marketing agencies in four major producing areas in the 1949–50 season found that the following types of agencies operated in some or all of the four areas studied:[21]

1. Ginner buyers, who purchase cotton from their farmer patrons and sell to other local buyers or central market merchants.
2. Independent country buyers, who purchase cotton from growers or other local buyers and sell to other local buyers or central market agencies.
3. Local market shippers, who buy mixed lots of cotton from producers and other local agencies and sell to domestic or foreign mills in even-running lots.
4. Salaried buyers, who purchase cotton from producers or other local merchandising firms for central market merchants or for mills.
5. Brokers, who do not take ownership of cotton but sell for producers and other local agencies.
6. Commission buyers, who purchase cotton in the local market for other merchandising firms or mills for a commission.

---

[21] William A. Faught et al., The Operations of Local Cotton Marketing Agencies, Four Major Cotton Producing Regions, 1949–50 season, Southern Cooperative Ser., Bul. 40 (Aug. 1954).

Because of the relatively short active marketing period in local markets, many of the local market operators combine their cotton merchandising operations with other enterprises. In recent years much of the cotton in many areas bypasses the local cotton buyers when farmers place the cotton under loan to the Commodity Credit Corporation. If the farmer does not redeem the cotton by repaying the loan by a specified date, title passes directly to the Commodity Credit Corporation. For this reason, together with substantially reduced production in many areas, increased direct mill buying in some areas, and the increased importance of relatively large cotton marketing cooperative associations in some areas, the number of local market operators has declined and many of those remaining in business have experienced a substantial reduction in volume of cotton handled.

The degree to which prices to growers in local markets reflect central market differentials for grade and staple length varies widely from market to market. The Southern Regional Cotton Marketing Research Committee also made a study of 24 local markets during the three seasons of 1951–52 through 1953–54.[22] In general, this study showed that where growers had and used quality information in the sale of their cotton, local market prices reflected rather fully and accurately central market differentials for grade and staple for individual lots on the day of sale. When growers did not have quality information, or when they did not use it in the sale of their cotton, local prices reflected little of the central market differentials. The size of the market also appeared to influence the extent to which local prices reflected central market quality differentials. However, week-to-week variations in average prices received by growers were more closely related to week-to-week variations in central market evaluations of average grade and staple length. This was true in many markets where local market prices did not reflect central market quality evaluations for individual lots sold on a single day.

Merchandising firms operating in local markets usually sell to central market merchants or shippers, or they represent central market merchants, mills, or cooperative marketing associations. A primary function of the central market merchants or shippers is to buy and assemble the individual bales and small, mixed lots of cotton offered for sale in the thousands of local markets and to pool this cotton into even-running lots of the same grade, staple length, other quality characteristics for sale to domestic mills or in the export market.

[22] William A. Faught et al., Cotton Price Relationships in Farmers' Local Markets, Southern Cooperative Ser., Bul. 51 (June 1957).

A recent study showed that cotton shippers obtained their cotton from the sources indicated below:[23]

### SOURCES OF COTTON SOLD BY SHIPPERS IN INDICATED YEARS

| Source of Cotton | 1960–61 (percent) | 1956–57 (percent) | 1952–53 (percent) |
|---|---|---|---|
| Farmer | 35.6 | 40.3 | 13.3 |
| Ginner | 6.9 | 7.9 | 51.6 |
| Other Merchant or Firm | 5.7 | 8.0 | 14.6 |
| U.S. Government Program | 35.4 | 19.6 | 5.7 |
| Country Buyer | 16.4 | 24.2 | 14.8 |

This tabulation shows that between 1952–53 and 1960–61 farmers and the Commodity Credit Corporation have become more important sources of cotton for shippers, while ginners and other merchants have become less important. The proportion of cotton obtained by shippers from country buyers remained roughly the same, although it was a more important source in the 1956–57 season than in either 1952–53 or 1960–61.

The same study found that the cotton consumers, i.e., the mill spinners, obtained their cotton from the following sources for the indicated years:

### PERCENT OF COTTON PURCHASED BY MILLS FROM INDICATED SOURCES

| Source | 1960–61 | 1956–57 | 1952–53 |
|---|---|---|---|
| Merchant | 84 | 85 | 91 |
| CCC | 7 | 3 | . . .* |
| Farmer | 3 | 3 | 1 |
| Ginner | 6 | 9 | 8 |

* Less than .2 percent

This tabulation shows that the bulk of the cotton purchased by mills is obtained from central market merchants (shippers). The most notable change in recent years has been an increase in the proportion of cotton obtained by mills from the Commodity Credit Corporation and the farmers, with a corresponding decrease in

---

[23] *Changes in Cotton's Movement From the Farm to Mill,* Res. Rept. 60, Cotton Econ. Res., Univ. of Tex. (Austin, 1961). For a detailed description of the characteristics of central cotton markets, their role as a source of price information, and the marketing activities of central market firms, see R. C. Soxman and Shelby H. Holder, Jr., *Official Spot Cotton Quotations, Where and How Quoted,* Mkg. Res. Rept. 547, U.S.D.A. (Washington, June 1962).

the importance of the merchant and the ginner as sources of raw cotton.

The increasing importance of the Commodity Credit Corporation as a source of cotton by both merchants and mills is the result of price supports above market levels maintained by the non-recourse loan program. When market prices press on the support level, farmers place a large proportion of the crop in the government loan, either directly or through their cooperative organizations. If the loan is not repaid by some later, specified date, title of the cotton passes to the CCC and is disposed of into trade channels in accordance with provisions of a number of government programs. Also, the role of government in cotton marketing was increased greatly in 1959–60 and 1960–61 because of the Choice A and Choice B programs (see Footnote 41). Practically all of the cotton produced by Choice A growers was sold to the CCC.

The structural characteristics of the central spot, or merchants, markets and the markets in which they sell, i.e., mill markets, closely approximate those of pure competition. All transactions are made on the basis of designated grade, staple length, and other quality characteristics, including in recent years specifications regarding a number of fiber properties measured by instruments—particularly fineness and strength. There is a large number of buyers and sellers, none of which is large enough to influence price by the quantity it sells or buys, although a relatively small number of shippers are alleged to handle a sizeable portion of each crop.

### The Demand Side

The demand for cotton is a demand for a manufacturing raw material. In recent years, aside from annual fluctuations, the domestic textile industry has accounted for about 60 percent of total disappearance (domestic mill consumption plus exports) of American cotton, while the remainder has been exported for use in foreign mills. The structures of these two segments of the total market and the policy issues associated with them differ markedly and must, therefore, be treated separately.

*Domestic Demand.* There is some debate about the structure of the cotton segment of the domestic textile industry on the selling side.[24] There is considerable concentration in some major textile product

---

[24] For contrasting views about the structure of and competitive behavior in the cotton textile industry, see Solomon Barkin, "The Regional Significance of the Integration Movement in the Southern Textile Industry," *The Southern Economic Journal*, Vol. XV, No. 4 (Apr. 1949), pp. 395–411; and Jesse W. Markham, "Integration in the Textile Industry," *Harvard Business Review*, Vol. XXVIII, No. 1 (Jan. 1950), pp. 74–88.

lines.[25] Since the end of World War II there has been an increase in the size of the productive unit, and integration has modified somewhat the behavior of prices and output as compared with prewar experience and the competitive norm. Product differentiation, branding, and sales promotion have become much more widespread and important in recent years. Entry may have become somewhat more difficult because of increased size of productive units.

But regardless of the conclusion about the structure of the textile industry on the selling side, it seems safe to conclude that the industry still closely approximates the theoretical model of pure competition on the buying side, i.e., in the market for raw cotton. The *1959 Census of Manufactures* reported 495 broad woven fabric mills, 488 narrow fabric mills, 355 yarn mills (except wool), and 86 thread mills. The corresponding number of companies reported in each of these industries was 325 in broad woven fabrics, 352 in narrow fabrics, 268 in yarn mills, and 70 in thread mills.[26] Apparently, none of these firms is sufficiently large in terms of the absolute and relative quantity of raw cotton consumed to affect prices perceptibly by variations in its rate of purchases. Hence the supply curve for raw cotton facing the individual firm is horizontal at the market price, i.e., perfectly elastic.

The degree of concentration within each of four major segments of the cotton textile industry is shown in Table 12.6. Actually, in 1958, cotton weaving mills accounted for about 73 percent of total raw cotton consumption, and yarn mills, except wool, accounted for another 23 percent of the total.[27]

Between 1954 and 1958, concentration in the cotton broad woven fabrics industry increased sharply. In 1958, the four largest manufacturers of cotton broad woven fabrics accounted for 25 percent of total industry shipments while, in 1954, they accounted for only 15 percent of the total. The eight largest companies accounted for 40 percent of total shipments in 1958 but only 29 percent in 1954. The twenty largest companies increased their

---

[25] For a recent detailed analysis of the market structure of the cotton textile industry *as a group of competing sellers,* see Irwin M. Stelzer, "The Cotton Textile Industry," in Walter Adams (ed.), *The Structure of American Industry,* 3rd ed. (New York: Macmillan, 1961), pp. 42–73. These comments are based on that analysis.

[26] "Industry Statistics," *U.S. Census of Manufactures, 1958,* Vol. II, U.S. Dept. of Commerce, Bur. of the Census.

[27] "Industry Statistics," *U.S. Census of Manufactures, 1958,* Vol. II, Part I, U.S. Dept. of Commerce, Bur. of the Census, pp. 221–28. This classification in the text is based on the new SIC system, while the industry classifications in Table 12.6 are based on the SIC system used prior to 1957. However, cotton weaving mills correspond closely to cotton broad woven fabric mills, and the yarn mills (except wool) industry is composed chiefly of yarn mills, cotton system.

TABLE 12.6

PERCENT OF VALUE OF SHIPMENTS ACCOUNTED FOR BY THE 4, 8, AND 20 LARGEST COMPANIES
IN SELECTED TEXTILE MILL PRODUCTS INDUSTRIES, 1947, 1954, AND 1958

| Industry* | Companies† (number) | Value of Shipments‡ (thousands of dollars) | Concentration Ratio: Percent of Total Shipments Accounted For by§ | | | Primary Product Specialization Ratio‖ |
|---|---|---|---|---|---|---|
| | | | 4 largest companies | 8 largest companies | 20 largest companies | |
| Thread Mills | | | | | | |
| 1958 | 70 | 165,906 | 68 | 79 | 92 | .90 |
| 1954 | 84 | 183,746 | 66 | 78 | 92 | .88 |
| 1947 | 83 | 154,269 | 65 | 78 | 90 | .85 |
| Yarn Mills, Cotton System | | | | | | |
| 1958 | 263 | 1,145,238 | 24 | 36 | 54 | (NA) |
| 1954 | 278 | 1,030,627 | 26 | 40 | 56 | .95 |
| 1947 | ...# | 1,162,607 | ...# | ...# | ...# | ...# |
| Cotton Broad Woven Fabric | | | | | | |
| 1958 | 321 | 2,719,432 | 25 | 40 | 59 | .94 |
| 1954 | 413 | 2,789,621 | 15 | 29 | 49 | .94 |
| 1947 | ...# | 2,912,651 | ...# | ...# | ...# | ...# |
| Narrow Fabric Mills | | | | | | |
| 1958 | 455 | 289,110 | 16 | 26 | 41 | .94 |
| 1954 | 489 | 250,162 | 13 | 21 | 37 | .96 |
| 1947 | 445 | 215,194 | 17 | 25 | 41 | .95 |

Source: *Concentration Ratios in Manufacturing Industry, 1958*—Part I. Report prepared by the Bureau of the Census for the Subcommittee on Antitrust and Monopoly of the Committee on the Judiciary, U.S. Senate, 87th Cong., 2nd Sess.

* These industry descriptions are based on the Standard Industrial Classification system which was used through 1957 and may differ from those appearing in the *1958 Census of Manufactures*.

† The determination of company affiliation of establishments is based on census reports and publicly available records. Value of shipment totals for establishments have been summarized into company totals in each manufacturing industry. "Largest" companies are determined by each company's value of shipments in the specified industry.

‡ Includes, for all manufacturing establishments classified in the industry, not only (a) their value of products "primary" to the industry, but also (b) their value of "secondary" products, which are primary to other industries, and (c) their "miscellaneous receipts" such as receipts for contract and commission work on materials owned by others, scrap and salable refuse, etc. Excludes sales of products bought and sold in same condition. The 1954 and 1957 figures for some industries reflect minor revisions of previously published census data.

§ The percentage consists of the sum of the value of shipments of the largest 4 companies (or 8 or 20), divided by the total value of shipments of the industry.

‖ The "primary product specialization ratio" measures the extent to which plants classified in the industry specialize in making products regarded as primary to the industry; that is, value of shipments of primary products of plants in the industry is expressed as a ratio of the total shipments of all products made by these establishments (excluding miscellaneous receipts, such as receipts for contract and commission on materials owned by others, scrap and salable refuse, repair, etc.). The 1954 and 1947 ratios for some industries reflect minor revisions of previously published census data.

# Comparable data are not available because of significant changes in the 1947 classification of plants or products in the industry.

share of total industry shipments from 49 percent in 1954 to 59 percent in 1958.

There has been little change in concentration within the other three segments during the postwar period. The four largest manufacturers of cotton yarn accounted for 26 percent of total industry shipments in 1954 and 24 percent in 1958; the eight largest firms accounted for 40 percent of the total in 1954 and 36 percent in 1958; and the twenty largest companies accounted for 56 and 54 percent of total industry shipments in 1954 and 1958, respectively. In 1958, the four, eight, and twenty largest manufacturers of narrow fabrics accounted for 16 percent, 26 percent, and 41 percent of total industry shipments, respectively. This was practically unchanged from the corresponding concentration ratios in 1947, but up slightly from those in 1954.

The thread industry is highly concentrated, although this is the least important of the four segments of the industry in terms of value of shipments. In 1958, the four largest manufacturers of thread accounted for 68 percent of total industry shipments; the eight largest companies accounted for 79 percent of the total; and the twenty largest companies accounted for 92 percent of the total.

A notable structural change that has an important effect on the competitive behavior of textile manufacturing firms as purchasers of raw cotton is the trend toward diversification in many companies in terms of fibers used and products produced. For example, Burlington Industries, which was formerly engaged exclusively in the manufacture of rayon textiles, now manufactures yarns and fabrics made from man-made fibers, cotton and wool, and numerous blends of man-made and natural fibers. The extent of product and fiber diversification in this company is indicated in a recent analysis of conditions in the textile industry. "Most of the larger companies have come a long way from the old idea of a one fabric, one mill type of operation. . . . Take Burlington Industries, for example, where sales are divided into apparel fabric, 65%; household fabrics, 25%; and industrial fabrics, 10%. About 45% of sales are in products composed principally of man-made fibers, while cotton accounts for 35% and wool, 20%."[28]

A second example involves a formerly all-cotton company that has just recently switched to the manufacture of rayon-cotton blends. Mr. J. B. Kyser of of the Graniteville Company in a recent paper said, in part, that "Graniteville Company has used cotton for 118 years. During that time our company . . . never used any other fiber until a few months ago. We began using some rayon in a blend of one-eighth rayon and seven-eighths cotton. That percentage has increased over the months until we are now using half rayon and half cotton at one of our plants."[29]

A critical characteristic of the demand for cotton is that it is quite inelastic in the short run. The policy implications of this

[28] Harvey B. Storch, "Can the Textile Industry Maintain Its 1962 Improvement?" *The Magazine of Wall Street and Business Analyst* (June 1, 1963).

[29] J. B. Kyser, "Why Textile Mills Are Replacing Cotton With Synthetics," *Proceedings of the Twenty-fourth American Cotton Congress*, Dallas, Tex., July 12, 1963, p. 39.

relationship have been emphasized many times and require no further elaboration here. Suffice it to say that this has been one of the fundamental theoretical bases for output restriction and price enhancing programs for cotton and other farm commodities since the 1920's. If demand were elastic, gross farm value would increase in response to an expansion in output rather than decline.

Econometric studies have provided estimates of the short-run price elasticity of domestic mill demand ranging from −.23 derived by Lowenstein and Simon to −.86 derived by Blakley.[30] In a recent study, final domestic cotton consumption data were used instead of mill consumption and the price elasticity was estimated to be only −.14.[31] Estimates of the income elasticity of demand have centered on about .9, and estimates of the elasticity of mill consumption of cotton with respect to man-made fiber production are of the order of −.1, i.e., a 10 percent change in production of man-made fibers has been associated with a 1 percent change in mill consumption of cotton in the opposite direction with other factors included in the analyses held constant.

Our quantitative knowledge about the nature of demand is restricted largely to the short run. For many questions about government policy, however, we need to know something about long-run demand relations. Although some attempts have been made to estimate the long-run price elasticity of demand, we simply do not have adequate knowledge about this important economic attribute of the cotton industry.

The distinction between short-run and long-run elasticities and the important role of time in the adjustment process goes back at least to Marshall. He pointed out that

> . . . allowance must be made for changes in fashion, and taste and habit, for the opening out of new uses of a commodity, for the discovery or improvement or cheapening of other things that can be applied to the same uses with it. In all these cases there is great difficulty in allowing for the time that elapses between the economic cause and its effect. For time is required to enable a rise in the price of a commodity to exert its full influence on consumption. Time is

[30] Frank Lowenstein and Martin S. Simon, "Analysis of Factors That Affect Mill Consumption of Cotton in the United States," *Agricultural Economics Research*, Vol. VI, No. 4 (Oct. 1954), pp. 101–10; and Leo V. Blakley, *Quantitative Relationships in the Cotton Economy With Implications for Economic Policy*, Okla. Agr. Exp. Sta., Tech. Bul. T-95 (May 1962). Also see Frank Lowenstein, "Factors Affecting the Domestic Mill Consumption of Cotton," *Agricultural Economic Research*, Vol. IV, No. 2 (Apr. 1952), pp. 44–51; and James T. Bonnen and William A. Cromarty, "The Structure of Agriculture," in Earl A. Heady *et al.* (eds.), *Agricultural Adjustment Problems in a Growing Economy* (Ames: Iowa State College Press, 1958), p. 112.

[31] James R. Donald, Frank Lowenstein, and Martin S. Simon, *The Demand for Textile Fibers in the United States*, E.R.S., U.S.D.A., Tech. Bul. 1301 (Nov. 1963), pp. 56–69.

required for consumers to become familiar with substitutes that can be used instead of it, and perhaps for producers to get into the habit of producing them in sufficient quantities. Time may be also wanted for the growth of habits of familiarity with the new commodities and the discovery of methods of economizing them.[32]

These observations by Marshall suggest that demand is probably more elastic in the long run than in the short run and they have particular relevance for cotton programs. However, there are two closely related but nevertheless distinct concepts involved. The first concept has to do with shifts in the short-run demand function in response to changes in variables that are not influenced perceptibly by the price of cotton. Examples are population, real disposable national income per capita, advances in technology that provide new and/or improved satisfactory substitutes from the consumer view or that change technical substitution rates at the manufacturing level.

The second concept involves shifts in the level and/or slope of the short-run demand function for cotton which is caused by a change in the relative price for cotton when this new price is maintained for a period of time sufficient for desired adjustments to be made to the new price level. In this case, changes in the level of shift variables and their effect on the demand function enter only to the extent that the change is caused by a change in the price of cotton. It appears that only a price-induced shift is properly a component of the long-run price elasticity of demand.

Undoubtedly, the demand for cotton has shifted over time in response to both types of influences. In any event, it seems clear that the domestic mill demand for cotton has shifted downward during the postwar period and has become more elastic (or less inelastic) in the intermediate and longer run. In this connection, I would view about five years as constituting the intermediate run.

Diversification by textile manufacturing firms and the development and extensive production of blended fabrics have added a new dimension to the competitive environment in the fiber market. Presumably, substitution has been made easier and, therefore, competition between cotton and other fibers, especially man-made fibers, has become more intense. It seems reasonable to assume that the textile industry's purchase curve for cotton (i.e., the demand curve facing raw cotton producers) has been lowered (i.e., shifted to the left) and become more elastic, or less inelastic, with respect to price.

A further comment by Mr. Kyser is relevant to this point: "We have a new mill that is going into production this month. Gentle-

---

[32] Alfred Marshall, *Principles of Economics*, 8th ed., The Macmillan Co., (New York, 1950), p. 110.

men, we are going to use whatever fiber or fibers we can to make money in that plant and in all our plants. We want to use cotton. If cotton is priced competitively, we will use cotton. If it is not, we will use some other fibers."[33] This would also appear to be the import of the following conclusion drawn by another analyst discussing the current governmental pricing policy for cotton: "Continued prosperity of several of the large companies depends on improvement in the cotton [price] situation. *On the other hand, when this problem is solved, it means trouble for rayon producers, cotton's chief competitors* (italics in the original)."[34]

**Export Demand.**[35] The export market for raw cotton has been, and still is, of major importance to the U.S. cotton economy. Since World War II, however, dramatic changes of far-reaching importance have occurred in the structure and organization of the export market for raw cotton and the institutional environment within which market forces operate.

As a reflection of these developments in the export market, sources of supply and centers of mill demand have become more decentralized; world exports of raw cotton have failed to keep pace with the rapid expansion of foreign production and consumption in the postwar period; foreign mill consumption has increased at a slower rate than has production of man-made fibers; and the relative importance of the United States in foreign cotton markets has declined substantially.

The demand for exports from the United States is defined to be the difference between total foreign mill demand for all growths of cotton and the total supply of cotton from all foreign countries, each in a schedule or functional sense. Since there are many countries that either produce or consume raw cotton, or both, the total foreign demand and supply functions are aggregates of demand and supply functions of individual countries.

Analytically, the export demand is given by

$$Q_e = \sum_{j=1}^{m} Q_{dj} - \sum_{k=1}^{n} Q_{sk} \tag{1}$$

where $Q_e$ is the demand for exports from the United States as a function of the export price $(P_e)$, $Q_{dj}$ is the demand for mill consumption of all growths of cotton in country $j$ as a function of local price $(P_{dj})$, and $Q_{sk}$ is the supply of all cotton in country $k$ with

---

[33] Kyser, *op. cit.*

[34] Storch, *op. cit.*

[35] This section is based on Mark L. Fowler, *Export Demand for United States Cotton: Implications of Structural Changes in the World Cotton Economy*, Okla. Agr. Exp. Sta. Bul. B-616 (Stillwater, Dec. 1963).

respect to local price. It is assumed that local prices confronting demanders and suppliers in foreign countries are functions of the U.S. export price, i.e., $P_{dj} = f_j (P_e)$ and $P_{sk} = f_k (P_e)$.

Elasticity of export demand with respect to export price derived from the export demand function is given by

$$
E_e = \sum_{j=1}^{m} E_{dj} \frac{Q_{dj}}{Q_e} \lambda_{dj} - \sum_{k=1}^{n} E_{sk} \frac{Q_{sk}}{Q_e} \lambda_{sk} \qquad (2)
$$

where $E_e$ is the elasticity of demand for U.S. exports with respect to the export price, $E_{dj}$ is the elasticity of demand for all cotton in country $j$ with respect to local price; $E_{sk}$ is the elasticity of supply in country $k$ with respect to local price; $Q_{dj}$ is the quantity of all cotton demanded in country $j$; $Q_{sk}$ is the quantity supplied by country $k$, $E_{sk}$ is the elasticity of supply in country $k$; $\lambda_{dj}$ and $\lambda_{sk}$ are the elasticities of local prices expressed in U.S. currency with respect to the U.S. export price.

In this framework, the *structure* of the export market refers to the organizational characteristics of the market treating the individual countries as suppliers and demanders as counterparts of individual firms in the usual analysis of market structure where the primary unit for analysis is an industry of competing firms in a single country. Two aspects of the structure of the export market appear potentially important. The first aspect is the number and size distribution of (1) producers, (2) consumers, (3) importers, and (4) exporters. The second aspect is the degree of product differentiation among the various producing countries, i.e., the substitutability of various growths and qualities of cotton in mills facing given demands for cotton products.

In recent years, major decisions relating to one or more strategic determinants of cotton production, mill consumption, and the magnitude and direction of raw cotton trade flows in international commerce have been transferred from the individual firm to the national level in many countries.[36] National governments have adopted measures to reduce their dependence on imports for both manufactured cotton goods and the raw fiber. Production and exports have been pushed vigorously in many countries. Increased cotton production in foreign exporting countries frequently is the principal means by which underdeveloped countries can increase their foreign exchange earnings. Increased cotton manufacturing

---

[36] For an outline of foreign governmental regulations that have been in effect since 1957, see *Government Regulations on Cotton,* Internatl. Cotton Advisory Com., Doc. 12, XVII (June 1958); Doc. 16, XVIII (May 1959); Doc. 10, XIX (May 1960); and Doc. 9, XXII (April–May 1963).

and production for use in domestic mills is an important method of reducing foreign exchange requirements.

Thus, the international market for raw cotton has come to be characterized by import and export quotas, export taxes and subsidies, currency exchange controls (including multiple exchange rates), and other trade barriers and impediments. These aspects of national policies serve to partially insulate production, consumption, and trade from the full effects of changes in the world price level, or the U.S. export price. Within this competitive context, national governments may seek to exploit any monopolistic or monopsonistic powers that they possess and may adopt a wide range of market policies—external, internal, or both—in pursuit of national goals.

Within the framework outlined above, these policies and regulations are considered to be strategic aspects of *market conduct*. In this sense, "market conduct refers to the patterns of behavior which enterprises [countries] follow in adapting or adjusting to markets in which they sell (or buy)."[37] Elements of conduct (government policies) that influence the level and elasticity of demand for U.S. exports are (1) those that influence the level or elasticity of demand or supply in a given country with respect to price in that country, (2) those that influence directly the level or elasticity of local prices with respect to the U.S. export price, or (3) those that affect through nonprice measures the volume of production, consumption, or trade.

Hence, the structure of the export market and policies of foreign countries (conduct) are important determinants of the level and elasticity of demand for U.S. exports. Since most of the usual regulations and policies of foreign governments tend to insulate internal developments from external price movements, they also tend to reduce the elasticity of demand for U.S. exports. Moreover, policies and regulations of foreign governments may be and often are changed in response to changes in U.S. policies in much the same manner as firms are assumed to respond in oligopolistic industries. These actions and reactions tend to reduce further the elasticity of demand for U.S. exports.

These considerations suggest that the elasticity of demand for U.S. exports with respect to the U.S. export price may be inelastic in the short run. This would appear to be the case especially at prices moderately below current world prices. Although the price elasticity of export demand may be severely low in the short run, there are several reasons for believing that export demand may be quite elastic over a period of several years duration. First, the U.S.

---

[37] Bain, *op. cit.,* p. 9.

export price effectively establishes the general level of world prices. Second, it seems clear that the level of cotton prices has an important influence on foreign cotton production and consumption, given time for desired adjustments to price levels in spite of extensive activities of foreign governments affecting cotton production and consumption. Third, the United States in recent years has accounted for only about one-third of total world exports of raw cotton.

But, in addition to the *level* of U.S. export and world prices, a major factor affecting the gap between foreign consumption and production of cotton—over time—is the method used in pricing U.S. cotton for export. The U.S. export price is established by the government. Generally, it is known well in advance of the planting season for both U.S. producers and foreign growers (and governments) whose production will be in competition with U.S. cotton in world markets. Consequently, the United States supports the world price structure, and other exporting countries produce all they can or care to at predetermined, known prices. They can export all they produce at or slightly below the U.S. supported price level, while U.S. exports make up the difference between total foreign demand and production at the support level. Thus, the United States assumes the role of "residual supplier" in export markets. Fluctuations in foreign demand and supply are reflected in variations in U.S. exports and carry-over stocks, while foreign countries export all available supplies at stable, known, and protected prices.

If the U.S. cotton industry were released from the pernicious shackles of "residual supplier" in world markets, and foreign production subjected to some of the risks and uncertainties of export markets long assumed exclusively by the United States, there is every reason to expect that U.S. exports—the gap between foreign consumption and production—would be much more responsive to the general level and changes in the U.S. export price.

The difficulties involved in estimating and interpreting long-run elasticities are numerous and well known. However, the author has derived estimates of the elasticity of export demand applying to about a 5-year adjustment period varying from —1.1 to —1.8 for the interwar period, and from —1.1 to —2.5 for the mid-1950's.[38] Brandow derived an estimate of —3.66 for the price elasticity of export demand for cotton.[39] But, his estimate applies to a longer ad-

[38] Marquis Lyndon Fowler, "An Economic-Statistical Analysis of the Foreign Demand for American Cotton," unpublished Ph.D. dissertation, Univ. of Calif. (Berkeley, 1961).

[39] G. E. Brandow, *Interrelations Among Demands for Farm Products and Implications for Control of Market Supply*, Bul. 680, Penn. Agr. Exp. Sta. (Aug. 1961), p. 56.

justment period (1954–56 to 1965) than does the author's and he
cautions that "the quantity exported . . . rises perhaps too rapidly
at prices below 23 cents [farm level]."[40]

## GOVERNMENT PROGRAMS AND PERFORMANCE—THE POSTWAR PERIOD

Two undesirable aspects of market performance have been attributed to the organizational and economic structure of the cotton industry outlined in the preceding pages, and their solution
has been sought through government programs to restrict competition and control performance. One is short-term instability in
prices and returns to producers. The second is long-term depressed returns to resources compared to returns in other employ-
ments (especially in the nonfarm sector), i.e., chronic oversupply or
excess capacity.

Highly variable prices and returns to producers in the short
run are a consequence of (1) low short-run price elasticities of aggregate demand and supply, (2) unplanned year-to-year variations
in aggregate supply because of weather, insects, disease, and other
uncontrollable factors, and (3) year-to-year shifts in short-run aggregate demand mainly because of instability in the export component stemming primarily from unplanned variations in export
availabilities in competing exporting countries.

Prolonged depressed returns to resources can be traced mainly
to inelastic demand and supply coupled with supply shifting to the
right more rapidly than demand under the force of technological
advance, together with a competitive structure and a substantial
degree of asset fixity for some specialized resources. If demand and
supply shifted at equal rates there would be no long-term income
problem for efficient units of economic size. If demand were elastic,
increased supply would not result in depressed returns. Even with
inelastic demand, excess resources would shift out of the industry
quickly in response to low prices and returns as a consequence of
technologically induced shifts in supply if profitable alternatives
for resource employment existed either in other segments of agriculture or in the nonfarm sector.

Due to these two undesirable aspects of market performance,
the federal government has had in operation, in process of revision,
or on a standby basis a series of price and income support and production control programs since 1929. Presumably, the main objective has been the stabilization and enhancement of grower returns. Operationally, the objective has been sought primarily

---

[40] *Ibid.*, p. 64.

through the indirect means of supporting market prices at levels higher than would have prevailed under the free play of economic forces.

Since the passage of the Agricultural Adjustment Act of 1938, primary reliance has been on guaranteed minimum prices supported through nonrecourse loans, with acreage allotments and marketing quotas to help hold production in line with demand at the price support level. In the postwar period, the price support and acreage restriction programs have been supplemented in two important ways. One has been the use of a series of special governmental programs to finance and otherwise encourage exports, and the other has been the two-price or export subsidy program that was in effect from 1956 to 1964. Other programs such as the Soil Bank and the A and B Choice Program have played important but temporary roles.[41]

These programs have meant higher and more stable prices and returns to growers in the short run. But the programs have also made it difficult for cotton growers—and, at times, policy makers—to grasp and appreciate the implications of the industry's competitive characteristics to their own long-term interests. Apparently, the relationship between the rapid growth of substitutes in demand and competing production in foreign countries and domestic program measures are either not well understood or not appreciated. Control in the cotton industry is becoming increasingly difficult. And, in spite of short-term benefits to growers, the impact of the programs on the longer-term interest of growers and other groups has not all been on the positive side.

Three features of industry performance under the program will be examined: (1) production efficiency, (2) returns to resources, and (3) ability to meet competition.

---

[41] The Agricultural Act of 1958 provided for two levels of price support for cotton for the 1959 and 1960 crop years. For those producers electing Choice A, price supports would be made available at a level specified by the Secretary of Agriculture through a purchase program. Choice A producers had to plant within their regular acreage allotment. Choice A support prices were 34.1 and 32.4 cents per pound basis middling one-inch in 1959 and 1960, respectively. Producers electing Choice B could plant up to 40 percent in excess of their regular acreage allotments but received price supports at 15 percent of parity below the Choice A level. Support prices for Choice B cotton were 28.4 and 26.6 cents per pound basis middling one-inch in 1959 and 1960, respectively. Prices were supported by nonrecourse loans. Sales of cotton by the Commodity Credit Corporation for unrestricted use were authorized at not less than 110 percent of the current level of price support for Choice B cotton. This resulted in lower prices at designated spot markets and to the mills. The average price per pound at designated spot markets basis middling one-inch was 34.47 in 1958 before the program was initiated; 31.93 in 1959; 30.96 in 1960; and 33.67 in 1961 after the termination of the program.

## Production Efficiency[42]

Major changes have occurred in practices and techniques used in cotton production during the postwar period. The composition of the input mix has changed markedly. Inputs purchased from nonfarm sources have been substituted for land and labor. Mechanization and irrigation have increased sharply. More and better fertilizers, pesticides, and other chemicals are being used. Between 1947–49 and 1959–61, yield per acre increased one-half, acreage decreased one-third, and total man-hours used in cotton production decreased almost three-fifths while total production has remained at about the same level.

As a result of these developments, the efficiency of cotton production, as measured by inputs per bale, increased 19 percent between 1947–49 and 1959–61 on a national basis. However, prices paid for items used in cotton production increased 31 percent, and the total cost per bale increased 6 percent. Nevertheless, changes in production practices and increases in physical efficiency undoubtedly shifted the supply curve to the right. Prices for direct inputs increased only 14 percent during the period, while prices for land increased 123 percent, and prices for items included in overhead increased 47 percent. Direct costs per bale decreased 8 percent.

In summary, there has been a rapid substitution of capital in its various forms for land and labor, and yields have increased sharply. When this condition is related to an essentially static market, severe adjustment problems are created for land and labor. If it were coupled with a free market it would put strong downward pressure on prices and incomes in the short run because short-run price elasticities of aggregate demand and supply are quite low.

### Returns to Resources

Data on commercial cotton farms covered in the U.S.D.A. Economic Research Service, Farm Costs and Returns (F.C.R. Series) indicate that returns to resources on many commercial cotton farms were relatively low even in a period when prices were supported at relatively high levels and an aggressive and expensive program was operating to maintain exports. During the 1957–59 period, returns to operator and family labor on commercial cotton farms, after allowing for 4.1 percent return on owned capital, averaged 44 cents per hour on small-scale farms in the Mississippi Delta, 50 cents per hour in the Southern Piedmont, and 56 cents per hour in the Black Prairie of Texas. Net income, i.e., income before deducting a re-

---

[42] This section is based on I. R. Starbird and W. H. Brown, *Changes in Costs and Efficiency of Cotton Production: A Preliminary Report,* E.R.S., U.S.D.A. (Nov. 1962). See also *Changes in Farm Production and Efficiency: A Summary Report,* U.S.D.A., Stat. Bul. 233 (revised July 1963).

turn for owned capital, averaged only $1,667 for small-scale farms in the Mississippi Delta, $2,194 in the Southern Piedmont, and $2,927 in the Black Prairie of Texas (Table 12.7).

Masucci has estimated that in order to achieve parity returns to capital and labor on commercial cotton farms in 1961, gross income would have had to increase by 85 percent, 74 percent, and 39 percent, respectively, on farms in the Southern Piedmont, small-scale farms in the Mississippi Delta, and the Black Prairie of Texas. On the other hand, incomes on cotton farms in the irrigated High Plains region of Texas and the San Joaquin Valley of California were above parity returns based on the assumed rates of return to capital and labor.[43]

## Production, Prices, and Markets

The carry-over of cotton in the United States was 13.0 million bales on August 1, 1939 and remained above 10.0 million bales through 1945. Below-average production, sustained domestic mill demand, and increased exports in 1945 and 1946 combined to reduce the carry-over to about 2.5 million bales on August 1, 1947.

However, a sharp increase in production in the 1947–49 period resulting from rising acreage and yields, together with declining domestic mill consumption, resulted in an increase in the carry-over to about 6.8 million bales on August 1, 1950. Again, however, the growth in stocks was halted and reversed, this time by a marked upsurge in demand for domestic mill consumption and exports growing out of the Korean conflict coupled with a sharp drop in production in 1950. The carry-over was reduced to 2.3 million bales on August 1, 1951.

The short crop in the United States in 1950 in the face of sharp increases in domestic and export demand led to a serious shortage of supplies throughout the world in the 1950–51 season. United States farm prices advanced sharply to about 40.0 cents in 1950 and prices were reported to be much higher in many foreign markets. These highly profitable prices and the abandonment of acreage controls in the United States provided a strong stimulus for expansion of acreage at home and abroad.

Following the Korean episode, the carry-over of cotton in this country was only 2.3 million bales (Aug. 1, 1951). But large crops in the United States coupled with declining domestic and export demand caused stocks to increase each year from the low point in

---

[43] Robert H. Masucci, "Income Parity Standards for Agriculture," *Agricultural Economics Research*, Vol. XIV, No. 4 (Oct. 1962), pp. 121–33. Returns are estimated at 1959 production adjusted for normal yield and abandonment: returns to capital estimated at 5 percent, hired labor at $1.25 per hour, and operator and family labor at $2.32 per hour.

TABLE 12.7

SELECTED CHARACTERISTICS OF U.S.D.A. COMMERCIAL COTTON FARMS

| Type of Cotton Farm and Location | Total Farm Capital Per Farm 1957–59 | Cotton Acres Harvested Per Farm 1957–59 | Speciali- zation Ratio* 1957–59 | Returns Per $100 Invested† 1956–60 | Increase in Gross Income To Achieve Parity Income 1961 | Return to Operator and Family Labor‡ 1957–59 | Net Income§ 1957–59 |
|---|---|---|---|---|---|---|---|
| | (dollars) | (acres) | (percent) | (dollars) | (percent) | (dollars) | (dollars) |
| Southern Piedmont | 20,670 | 21.7 | 61 | 4.01 | 84.7 | .50 | 2,194 |
| Mississippi Delta | | | | | | | |
| Small | 12,890 | 15.0 | 72 | 5.63 | 73.5 | .44‡ | 1,667 |
| Large scale | 196,740 | 219.0 | 67 | 8.93 | 15.0 | 11,060‖ | 20,268 |
| Texas | | | | | | | |
| Black Prairie | 37,670 | 55.2 | 55 | 2.72 | 38.9 | .56‡ | 2,927 |
| High Plains (nonirrigated) | 53,500 | 112.8 | 72 | 9.66 | 21.2 | 2.35‡ | 7,503 |
| High Plains (irrigated) | 103,040 | 147.3 | 83 | 11.80 | −5.5 | 3.83‡ | 14,227 |
| San Joaquin Valley, Calif. (irrigated) | | | | | | | |
| Cotton, specialty crop | 250,000 | 123.0 | 45 | 16.78 | 10.5 | 21,104‖ | 32,877 |
| Cotton, general crop (med.) | 254,920 | 133.0 | 74 | 8.79 | −3.2 | 15,844‖ | 27,517 |
| Cotton, general crop (large) | 865,990 | 426.0 | 76 | 8.77 | −8.4 | 45,452‖ | 85,025 |

Source: *Farm Costs and Returns*, Economic Research Service, Agricultural Information Bulletin No. 230 (Revised August 1963), except Column 5.
* Ratio of cash receipts from cotton and cotton seed to total cash receipts.
† With operator and family labor calculated at wage rates paid for hired labor.
‡ Return per hour after allowing for 4.1 percent return on capital.
§ Before deducting a return to owned capital.
‖ Total return after allowing for 4.1 percent return on capital.

1951 until they reached the record high of 14.5 million bales on August 1, 1956. Although acreage controls were reimposed in 1954, the reduced acreage was largely offset by record yields in both 1954 and 1955.

Exports declined from 5.7 million bales in 1951 to only 2.3 million bales in 1955. This occurred at the same time that foreign mill consumption was growing steadily from 19.4 million bales in 1951 to 27.8 million in 1955. But foreign mills turned to other sources of supply because, among other things, U.S. cotton prices were being supported well above competitive levels for comparable foreign growths. Since the U.S. support price tended to establish the world price level, foreign exporters could move all their cotton at prices just below the U.S. price. This apparently was at a level that provided a strong stimulus to expansion of production in foreign countries, although other important factors were involved. Foreign production increased from 20.6 million bales in 1951 to 28.0 million in 1955.

Faced with the possibility of the complete loss of the export market, the U.S. government instituted an export subsidy program in an attempt to reestablish and maintain a fair historical share of the world market for U.S. cotton. Under this program, U.S. cotton has been sold for export at prices substantially below the domestic price. The export subsidy, or two-price program, was first carried out on a limited basis in 1955 under permissive authority of the Agricultural Act of 1949. The program was expanded under the mandatory provision of Section 203, Title II of the Agricultural Act of 1956, which directed the Commodity Credit Corporation (CCC) to make cotton available for export at prices not in excess of prices of comparable growths being offered by other exporting countries. This program has continued in one form or another until August 1, 1964. Export prices have ranged from about 6.0 to 8.5 cents below domestic prices.

Exports increased sharply and averaged 6.1 million bales per year during the five years from 1956 to 1960, compared with 3.3 million per year during the three-year period 1953–55.

Increased exports and below-average production, due in part to the Soil Bank programs and acreage controls, brought about a reduction in the carry-over from 14.5 million bales in 1956 to 7.2 million on August 1, 1961. However, in each of the last four years, production has been larger and the volume of exports smaller than in 1960. As a result, the carry-over has increased each year since 1961. It was expected to reach about 14 million bales on August 1, 1965, the second highest on record.

Throughout the period, the competitive position of cotton in the domestic market has continued to deteriorate. Domestic mills operated at a $30.00 to $42.50 per bale raw material cost disadvantage compared with foreign mills between 1956 and 1964 and have faced increasingly intense competition from foreign manufactured cotton goods in both their domestic and foreign markets.

In the calendar year 1955, before the two-price plan was well under way, the raw cotton equivalent of U.S. exports of manufactured cotton products was 547,000 bales, while imports amounted to 181,200 bales, for a net export balance of 365,800 bales. In 1960, exports were down to 485,600 bales and imports had increased to 525,500 equivalent bales. This was the first time on record that imports of manufactured cotton products exceeded exports. Imports reached a record high of 644,600 bales in the calendar year 1962, but then receded slightly in 1963 and amounted to 625,600 bales in 1964. Exports of manufactured cotton products declined to 432,900 equivalent bales in 1963, the smallest since 1940. They were up slightly to 443,700 bales in 1964.

Thus, from 1955, before the two-price plan was initiated, to 1964 our foreign trade in cotton textiles went from a net export balance of 365,000 bales to a net import balance of 181,900 bales, slightly below the 201,000-bale import balance in 1963. This represents a loss in the domestic mill market of more than one-half million bales per year between 1955 and 1964.

Perhaps of even greater importance to cotton growers is the competitive loss of cotton to man-made fibers in domestic mills. There are many reasons for this, but the level at which cotton prices have been supported relative to the prices of its man-made fiber competitors unquestionably has been an important factor. The situation was improved somewhat in 1959 and 1960 by the Choice A and B Program provided for in the Agricultural Act of 1958. The price of cotton to mills was reduced by roughly 3 cents per pound (see Footnote 41). The program was terminated in 1961, however, and the support price was set at 33.04 cents per pound for middling one-inch at average location. Price to mills returned to approximately its former level and remained there until April 1964.

The extent to which cotton was losing markets is well summarized in a recent statement prepared by the National Cotton Council, "Summary of Cotton's Current Market Situation," September 6, 1963.

> Cotton's competitive situation on the domestic market can be illustrated most effectively by examining fiber consumption on the cotton spinning system. All of the cotton, seven-eighths of the rayon staple and half of the non-cellulosic staple (Dacron, nylon, etc.) used in the U.S. go through this system, and here is where our competition is at its closest.

From December 1960 to June 1963, consumption of rayon staple on the cotton system rose 85 percent.

On the cotton system, from December 1960 to June 1963, consumption of non-cellulosic fibers was up by an almost unbelievable 172 percent.

Across this period of 2½ years, on the cotton system alone, cotton sustained a competitive loss of about 940,000 bales in annual rate to rayon and the non-cellulosics combined, and the losses appear to be accelerating. Other losses have occurred outside the cotton system to man-made fibers and other products. The total competitive loss amounted to about 1,520,000 bales in the same period.

Up to 1960, cotton had been increasing its share of the fiber consumed in many important apparel end uses. These gains had been off-setting losses in other uses, holding our share of the total market about even. But from 1960 to 1962, there were no net gains to off-set losses. And losses have occurred even in markets like towels, work trousers and men's underwear that have traditionally been almost 100 percent cotton.

What has been the net result of the changing economic, institutional, and technological forces on markets for U.S. cotton? The most important forces appear to be (1) the increasingly intense competition from man-made fibers across an ever-widening range of end-use products in both the domestic and foreign markets and (2) the phenomenal increase in cotton and man-made fiber production in foreign countries.

Domestic mill consumption of cotton per capita is now less than it was in the 1920's and 1930's, and cotton now accounts for 55 percent of the total domestic fiber market compared to over 80 percent in the years prior to World War II. In other words, total consumption has not only failed to maintain its share in the expanding total domestic market for all fibers resulting from increasing real per capita incomes and standards of living, but is now failing to keep pace with the increase in population. So far, however, population has increased faster than per capita consumption has declined, and total mill consumption increased from an average of 7.0 million bales per year in 1935–39 to about 8.5 million bales in the first half of the 1960's. However, there is little evidence of any increase in total consumption in the post-World War II years.

At the same time, domestic production (and consumption) of man-made fibers has been increasing tremendously from 3.4 million cotton equivalent bales in 1947–49 to 8.8 million in 1963. Their share of the fiber market has increased from less than 20 percent to about 45 percent during the same period. Much of the relative increase was in the noncelluloses.

In foreign countries, there has been a pronounced upward

trend in both aggregate mill consumption and production of cotton but, because production has increased at a somewhat faster rate than has consumption, the gap between foreign consumption and production has narrowed. As a result, exports from the United States have followed a generally downward trend. While it is true that the average volume of exports in the last five or six years has been at about the level of the 1930's, clearly this has been made possible only because of an aggressive export subsidy program and special governmental programs to finance exports. The essential point is that, even with these costly export programs, the United States has not and is not sharing in the tremendous growth in total mill consumption of cotton in foreign countries that increased from 25.2 million bales in 1950 to 40.6 million in 1964.

## IMPLICATIONS FOR POLICY ALTERNATIVES

The cotton industry is characterized by two main problems that stem from the structural attributes of the industry summarized above. The first problem is marked short-run instability in prices and incomes in the absence of government programs. The second problem is chronic excess capacity due to productivity increasing faster than demand. With high price supports and ineffective output controls, excess capacity is reflected in burdensome government stocks. In the absence of government programs it is reflected in prolonged depressed prices and returns.

Remedy for these problems has been sought mainly by supporting prices above competitive levels through nonrecourse loans with acreage controls and marketing quotas to help hold production in line with demand at the support price. Temporary measures have been used to check the buildup in surplus stocks and aid in their disposal. Exports have been encouraged by special financing arrangements and a two-price or export subsidy program operated continuously from 1956 to 1964.

These programs have meant higher and more stable prices and returns in the short run by effectively limiting quantity sold on given inelastic aggregate demand. But even in the short run, a high price support and/or restrictive output policy is a clearly ineffective remedy for the low incomes of the large proportion of cotton producers characterized by inadequate resources and managerial abilities. Moreover, prolonged operation of the programs may not have been in the best interest of producers or allied industry groups. It is quite likely that aggregate demand is elastic over a few years' time.

Those responsible for the continuation of the programs failed to recognize or refused to appreciate two important attributes of the demand for cotton. First, the demand for cotton is a demand for an industrial raw material. This means that the focal point of *price competition* is at the spinning mill. Second, both domestic and export demands are serially related. This means that extended limitations of sales (or high price) will lower the demand schedule in subsequent periods.

Production and utilization of substitute products and production of cotton in foreign countries has been stimulated. The export subsidy program ignored the fact that demands in domestic and export markets are not independent. Raw cotton is prevented from entering the United States in significant volume in response to high domestic price but manufactured cotton goods are not. These imports, which result in part from the export subsidy, are an effective depressant on domestic mill demand.

Extended operation of high price and output restriction programs in the cotton industry has also brought heavy injury to other economic groups whose employment and incomes depend heavily on the quantity of cotton produced, merchandised, and utilized. These damages may have been disproportionate to any short-term net benefits accruing to producers.

For the reasons enumerated, a high-price low-output policy is self-defeating in the cotton industry. Contributing to the weakness of such controls is their inherent instability. Many decisions remain within the discretion of individual producers. They are still conscious of their role as atomistic competitors. Research results and extension services are institutionalized and free to the producer. Fixed costs are relatively high and land, family labor, and specialized equipment are relatively immobile in the short run. These conditions coupled with rapid technological advance create a chronic situation of supply pressing against a static or declining demand. The result is a severe adjustment problem for land and labor utilized in cotton production. There is continuous downward pressure on acreage allotments. Control becomes more and more difficult.

A free market approach for the cotton industry would not be satisfactory, at least in the short run. Two of the industry's most pressing problems would be solved. Cotton would become competitive in price with its substitutes. The harmful effects of the present programs on nonproducer groups would be mitigated. But the problem of excessive short-term instability would reappear, and prices and net returns to producers would drop sharply in the short run. Free entry and restricted economic alternatives for resource employment in producing other agricultural commodities or in the nonfarm sector may combine to keep prices and returns depressed for an extended period, even with elastic long-run de-mand. *Economics aside, prices and returns would probably drop to levels that would be politically unacceptable.*

If this is a reasonable assessment of the situation, the implica-tion is that some form of price protection to growers and output restriction will be required for some time, although the level of price support might well be reduced gradually from the present level. However, *if* markets are to be maintained or expanded, and *if* further reductions are to be avoided in the statutory minimum national acreage allotment of 16 million acres, U.S. cotton must be priced competitively to domestic mills and on the export market.

But if prices (or returns) to growers are to be supported above the market level, and if cotton is to be made available to domestic mills and for export at competitive prices, some politically ac-ceptable and economically feasible means must be devised to bridge the gap. Some version of compensatory payment plan (direct pay-ments to producers) or a trade incentive plan (payments to handlers) could accomplish these objectives. Some restrictions on output would be required for some time in order to hold treasury costs within acceptable levels. Costs may be relatively high at first, but not necessarily out of line with past program costs. They could be made to decline gradually in response to increased offtake and re-ductions in costs of production. These programs have no particular advantage or disadvantage compared to past programs in solving the income problem of the small-scale producer.

In summary, it appears that political and economic realities preclude a free market approach in the next few years. On the other hand, the economic vitality of *all* segments of the cotton economy demands a competitive, one-price system for cotton. Over the long pull, it may be possible to close the gap by reducing costs of production and expanding markets. In the meantime, however, the working out of a politically acceptable program to close the gap between an income support price to growers and a competitive market price in domestic and export markets represents the major challenge to the economic and political statesmanship of the various groups struggling with cotton policy.[44]

---

[44] The Agricultural Act of 1964 (P.L. 88–297) which became effective on Apr. 11, 1964 embodies these principles. Prices to domestic mills were reduced sharply by a payment of 6.5 cents per pound, compared to the export subsidy of 8.5 cents per pound. They were reduced further by about 2.5 cents per pound and the export differential was eliminated on Aug. 1, 1964. At that time, the support price to growers was reduced from 32.47 cents to 30 cents per pound and the payment rate for both domestic mill consumption and export was set at 6.5 cents per pound. However, the problem of "residual supplier" was left un-changed. The program is effective through the 1965 marketing year, i.e., it ex-pires on July 31, 1966.

The major purpose of this legislation was to increase domestic mill consumption of cotton by eliminating the two-price feature of the then existing program and reducing the price of cotton to domestic mills to make it competitive with substitute fibers, principally rayon. A secondary objective was to reduce production and carry-over stocks by means of the domestic allotment provisions in the program.

Although domestic mill consumption in 1964–65 is expected to be up substantially from the 1963–64 level as a result of lower cotton prices to mills, there is growing concern and criticism of the program. Exports are down and stocks are up. Costs of the program are running almost double what had been estimated. There appears to be general agreement among all segments of the industry, the Congress, and the Administration that the cotton situation is serious and that early enactment of new legislation is of major importance. Thus far, however, controversy over the broad type of program needed, as well as the specific provisions to be written into a new program, has effectively blocked agreement on new legislation.

# 13

# THE FARM MACHINERY INDUSTRY[1]

## W. G. PHILLIPS[2]

FARM MACHINERY PRODUCERS are classified as either full-line or short-line firms. According to the *Census of Manufactures*, there were 1469 establishments producing farm machinery in the United States in the late 1950's.[3] Only seven firms, however, were full-line producers, producing a wide range of machinery for normal farm needs at different seasons and in all major areas of the country. A full line typically includes machines for soil preparation, seeding, cultivating, harvesting, haying, and preparation for market, with a variety in each type to accommodate different crops and different terrains. Dominating the full line is the tractor, technically integrated with the line of machinery, serving as it does for carrying mounted implements, for supplying directly transmitted power to moving parts of machines, and simply for tractive power. Firms which produce no tractor and a limited number of machines for special crops or areas are known as short-line firms.

The industry is one of the country's oldest. Most of the largest producers date back, either directly or through merger, more than 100 years. The International Harvester Company, the world's largest producer, resulted from the merger of the five largest producers of harvesting machinery in 1902, the oldest of which was the McCormick Company, established in 1831. The merger brought under a single control 90 percent of the trade in grain binders and 80 percent of the trade in mowers in the United States.

---

[1] The author expresses appreciation to the University of Toronto Press for permission to use extensively material from: W. G. Phillips, *The Agricultural Implement Industry*. (Toronto: University of Toronto Press, 1956).

[2] Professor and Head of the Department of Economics and Sociology, University of Windsor, Canada.

[3] *Statistical Abstract of the U.S.* (Washington, 1963), p. 780.

The transition to a full-line firm had been accomplished by 1919 through the further acquisition of a number of tillage machinery producers and through the development of tractor production in the company's own plants. Between 1906 and 1927, Harvester was faced with an almost unbroken series of investigations and suits by both state and federal governments, inspired by the company's dominating position in harvesting machinery. These resulted in the enforced sale of some plants and implement lines, and the elimination of a large number of duplicating dealerships, but left the basic structure of the company intact. International produces farm machinery in a number of other countries and has diversified its production at home, particularly into trucks, which now account for about 45 percent of total output.

Deere and Company, whose domestic farm machinery sales exceeded those of Harvester for the first time in the late fifties, began in 1837 as a plow producer. By 1900, the company had expanded to become the largest manufacturer of plows and tillage machinery in the United States and shortly thereafter launched a program of merger and internal expansion to produce a full line. This was completed in 1918 with the acquisition of the Waterloo Engine Company and the "Waterloo Boy" tractor, the prototype of all Deere tractors until 1960.

Massey-Ferguson, third among the full-line firms, is the result of a large-scale merger of Canadian firms in 1891, the subsequent acquisition of established plants in the United States, and an amalgamation with the operating companies controlled by Harry G. Ferguson in 1953. Massey-Ferguson is a Canadian firm, a fact of little economic significance since neither the United States nor Canada imposes any tariff on farm machines. It is the most "international" in the industry—more than half of its sales being made outside the United States and Canada.

The Allis-Chalmers Company, reversing the usual sequence, produced a farm tractor for many years before it produced implements. In 1928, the company began acquiring established firms manufacturing both tillage and harvesting implements, and, by 1931, it was producing a full line.

Fifth in today's industry is the White Motor Company, a newcomer to farm machinery through the acquisition of three marginal enterprises since 1960—Oliver Farm Equipment, Cockshutt Farm Equipment, and Minneapolis-Moline, then a part of Motec Industries.

Ford Motor Company ranks sixth. Ford first produced the Fordson tractor in 1917, and immediately displaced International Harvester as the country's largest producer. No implements were produced for the Fordson, however, a weakness which International exploited through developing closer integration of its own tractor and implements. In 1924, Harvester introduced the power-take-off for its tractor, and three years later it resumed sales leadership. Ford then left the field, returning in 1939 under an arrangement to use the Ferguson systems of hydraulic control with its own lightweight tractor. This was discontinued in 1947, after which Ford began producing machines for use with its tractor in its own plants.

The seventh of the full-line producers is the J. I. Case Company, whose antecedents date to 1837, and which attained full-line status in the late 1920's.

## MARKET STRUCTURE

### Full-Line Production and Market Shares

The advantages of full-line production of farm machinery are found at both the production and distribution levels. The seasonal nature of most farm implement production results in some discontinuous use of plant unless this can be offset through rotation of production on a seasonal basis. Production of tractors, the *sine qua non* of the full line, is largely nonseasonal, providing year-round plant activity. Moreover, the prestige factor in a full line of machines may mean higher sales across the board, resulting in increased scale economies in their production. The leading incentives to full-line production, however, appear always to have been on the level of distribution. A full line means the ability to give a dealer full-time employment, an important factor in the competition for good dealers. Short-line firms producing no tractor are impeded in this competition. As Conant says, "The demand and cost structures of an implement retail store and selling organization are such that, to be profitable, it must include a line of tractors."[4]

It should be noted that small firms in this industry do have some advantages over large firms. Their lower overhead provides flexibility which frequently enables them to produce profitably the smaller runs of specialized machines which larger firms would find unprofitable. This will be discussed further under entry conditions.

As for market shares, Michael Conant's study estimated an increasing proportion of total farm machinery sales made by the full-line firms.[5] This is shown in Table 13.1. Though these are estimated shares and are subject to a considerable margin of error because domestic sales data are not normally published by the

---

[4] Michael Conant, "Competition in the Farm-Machinery Industry," *Journal of Business of the University of Chicago* (Chicago, Jan. 1953), p. 32.
[5] *Ibid.*, p. 27.

TABLE 13.1

ESTIMATED SHARE IN DOMESTIC FARM MACHINERY SALES BY FULL-LINE PRODUCERS, 1922–1948

| Firm | 1922 | 1929 | 1937 | 1948 |
|---|---|---|---|---|
| | | (percent) | | |
| Total, full-line firms | 64.6 | 54.7 | 72.6 | 73.6 |
| International Harvester Co. | 44.0 | 28.3 | 32.7 | 22.8 |
| Deere and Co. | 11.6 | 11.9 | 18.5 | 15.3 |
| J. I. Case Co. | 9.0 | 3.8 | 4.8 | 7.0 |
| Allis-Chalmers Mfg. Co. | | 1.8 | 8.1 | 6.8 |
| Oliver Corp. | | 4.7 | 4.8 | 4.2 |
| Minneapolis-Moline Co. | | 2.5 | 2.7 | 3.6 |
| Massey-Harris Co. | | 1.7 | 1.0 | 3.8 |
| Dearborn Motors Corp. | | | | 10.1 |

Source: See Michael Conant, "Competition in the Farm Machinery Industry," *Journal of Business of the University of Chicago* (Chicago, January 1953), p. 27.

firms, it is nevertheless clear that the share of the full-line producers increased between 1922 and 1948.

Data since 1948 give reason to believe that this advance has halted and may even have reversed. Recent Census Bureau material showing the portion of total shipments of the eight largest companies in tractor production and farm machinery production (here presumed to be the eight full-line producers shown in the table for 1948) shows a decline to 71.2 percent in 1954 and to 69.3 percent in 1958.[6] This may have resulted from the influx of specialty producers in the industry since the war, increasing the number of farm machinery companies from 955 in 1947 to 1288 in 1958, and tractor companies from 86 to 109. The relevant concentration ratios are shown in Table 13.2.

The steady, though slow, increase in the *number* of full-line producers, also evident in Table 13.1, appears likewise to have reversed. Following a series of lean years in the fifties, Oliver Corporation and Minneapolis-Moline[7] were taken over by the White Motor Company.[8] White also absorbed the next largest of the full-line companies (not shown in Table 13.1), Cockshutt Farm Equipment, a Canadian company. Thus nine full-line companies in 1948 had become seven by the early sixties. Over the total span from 1922 to 1960, it is seen that in high-sales years such as the twenties and the forties new full-line firms have been formed,

---

[6] *Concentration Ratios in Manufacturing Industry, 1958,* Bur. of the Census, report prepared for the Senate Committee on the Judiciary, Part I (Washington, 1962), p. 33. Hereafter cited as *Bureau of the Census Report, 1962.*

[7] Minneapolis-Moline had by then become part of Motec Industries, from which the M-M line of implements was acquired by White Motor.

[8] *Forbes* (Apr. 1, 1963), pp. 32–33.

W. G. PHILLIPS

TABLE 13.2

<small>CONCENTRATION RATIOS IN THE TRACTOR AND FARM MACHINERY INDUSTRIES,
1947, 1954, AND 1958</small>

| Industry | Year | Number of Companies | Value of Shipments | Percent of Value of Shipments Accounted For by | | | |
|---|---|---|---|---|---|---|---|
| | | | | 4 largest co's. | 8 largest co's. | 20 largest co's. | 50 largest co's. |
| | | | *($ 000)* | | | | |
| Tractors | 1958 | 109 | 1,576,085 | 69 | 90 | 98 | 99 |
| | 1954 | 141 | 1,177,974 | 74 | 90 | 97 | ... |
| | 1947 | 86 | 890,841 | 67 | 88 | 97 | ... |
| Farm Machinery | 1958 | 1,288 | 1,467,836 | 38 | 47 | 59 | 71 |
| | 1954 | 1,145 | 1,095,685 | 38 | 51 | 64 | ... |
| (tractors) | 1947 | 955 | 889,037 | 36 | 47 | 58 | ... |

Source: *Concentration Ratios in Manufacturing Industry, 1958,* Bureau of the Census (Report prepared for the Senate Committee on the Judiciary), Part I (Washington, 1962), p. 33.

while in low-sales years such as the thirties and the fifties the numbers have either remained steady or decreased.

One of the remarkable things about this industry is, in fact, the instability of market shares. The estimated share of the International Harvester Company continued the decline which began early in this century, being cut by about half between 1922 and 1948. Other firms' shares, as seen in Table 13.1, were erratic. Similar variations characterized individual product lines. Between 1954 and 1958, the share of the eight largest firms in total shipments increased sharply in planting, seeding, and fertilizing machinery, but declined in harvesting machinery and in haying machinery as well as in total.[9] Between 1937 and 1958, while the total share of the four largest firms remained approximately steady, it dropped significantly in disk harrows (drawn), grain drills, cornpickers, mowers, and corn and cotton-type cultivators, both drawn and mounted.[10]

### The Nature of Product Differentiation

Variations in the fortunes of individual firms in this industry have been largely attributable to technological competition in the development and improvement of products. This will be discussed as an aspect of conduct and performance, but some note might be taken of the nature of product differentiation within the industry. The large-scale consolidations of the late 19th and early 20th

[9] *Bureau of the Census Report, 1962, op. cit.,* Part I, p. 148.
[10] *Ibid.,* Part II, p. 490. The 1937 figures are based on the 1937 TNEC Rept. 27, p. 466.

centuries[11] coincided with a period of stabilization in the industry's markets and in its products. Geographic expansion ceased, and products themselves settled down into standardized patterns, symbolized by the twine binder, the hinged-bar mower, and various horse-drawn tillage and planting implements. The early mergers were intended partly to remove competition in highly standardized products (the International Harvester merger of 1902), and partly to achieve some seasonal stability through combining the production of both harvesting and tillage machinery (Harvester's subsequent acquisitions).

Product standardization was disrupted when the farm tractor appeared around 1910 and its production became centralized in the farm machinery industry. The tractor forced the redesigning of entire lines, both to integrate them with the tractor and to provide added strength to withstand the sustained pull of gasoline power. This process led to chaotic conditions in which product differentiation was frequently overemphasized either in an attempt to mislead farmers, most of whom were still mechanically untutored, or to force tie-in sales of equipment once the tractor had been sold. The spread in the use of the power-take-off after 1924, the gradually increasing level of technical sophistication among buyers, and the pressure of official investigation by such public bodies as the Federal Trade Commission in the thirties[12] directed efforts once again to ways and means of standardization.

Since World War II, these efforts have been intensified, largely through the intermediacy of the American Society of Agricultural Engineers and the Farm Equipment Institute. The latter, which is the trade association of the industry, seems constantly mindful of the industry's vulnerable position as a supplier of producer's goods exclusively to agriculture, and it scrupulously confines itself to activities of universal acceptability. The Institute's program, now widely accepted in the industry, involves standardization in basic design to permit the interchangeability of one make or model of implement with a tractor of different make or model and also involves standardization in component parts, intended to reduce the variety of parts necessary to service farm equipment.[13]

The return to standardization has been accompanied by a resurgence of competition in those aspects of product design not affected by the standardization measures. Complaints, in fact, are

---

[11] See the chronological chart of mergers in the industry in W. G. Phillips, *op. cit.*, 1956, p. 12.

[12] See, for example, *Report on the Agricultural Implements Industry*, Federal Trade Commission (Washington, 1938).

[13] *Report of Ontario Farm Machinery Investigation Committee*, Ontario Dept. of Agr. (Toronto, 1963), pp. 48 ff.

frequently heard that the process of differentiation is carried to excess and more often has the effect of simply impeding price competition rather than contributing genuinely to farm productivity. While doubtless many of the so-called improvements are of the "frill" variety (and thus expendable), the complaint has only a restricted validity. There are no annual model change-overs in this industry and product design is a continual process. The full-line companies are acutely conscious of the industry's great historical contribution to farm productivity. This awareness and the fact that price competition suffers under certain limitations in a market where the selling season is limited to, at most, a few months per year seem together to have inspired an unusual emphasis on constant product improvement over and above the major techno-logical breakthroughs which have periodically characterized the industry. Patents have lost the extreme importance which they had in the 19th century,[14] and improvements are copied as soon as their benefit to the innovator has become apparent.[15]

### Conditions of Entry

J. S. Bain treats product differentiation as one of the leading barriers to new entry. In his study covering 20 industries,[16] Bain distinguishes between "large and complex" farm machines and "small and simple" ones—firms producing the former being gen-erally full-line firms, and the latter, the host of short-line firms of various sizes in the industry. Bain finds that the importance of entry barriers differs between the two groups. Examining three types of barriers—those arising from scale economies, product dif-ferentiation, and absolute costs—Bain finds

1. Scale economies in farm machinery production are "moderately important," judging by the proportion of the total market capac-ity of a single category (e.g., harvesting machinery) which a specialized plant at minimum optimum scale would supply.[17] For tractors, the minimum optimal scale is higher but the bar-rier is nevertheless classified as moderately important. Scale economies, however, "are felt to be distinctly less important in

---

[14] See Phillips, op. cit., pp. 5 ff; Simon N. Whitney points out that, of the 1233 patents held by International Harvester in 1946, 1193 had been released to other farm machinery producers. See his *Antitrust Policies, American Experience in Twenty Industries* (New York, 1958), p. 244.

[15] Recent examples of such improvements are: increase in the speed of plant-ers; increased capacity of beet harvesters; introduction of the four-row potato planter; dual grain tanks, on either side of the combine, to equalize the load on the drive wheels.

[16] Joe S. Bain, *Barriers to New Competition* (Cambridge: Harvard Univ. Press, 1956).

[17] *Ibid.*, p. 81.

the manufacture of relatively 'small and simple' farm machinery."[18]

2. Product differentiation as a barrier to entry is estimated to be "quite small" in simple implements and local specialties, and "large" in tractors and large, complex machines. In simple implements and local specialties, the new entrant's disadvantage is seen centered in product reputation and the existence of established dealer systems; in the latter case, it centers in brand allegiance based on product reputation and customer service as well as in established dealer systems.[19]

3. For both types of production, absolute cost differences are not found to be important as a barrier to entry.[20]

In the aggregate, Bain found entry barriers "very high" in the case of tractors; "substantial" in the case of large, complex machines; and "moderate to low" in the case of small, simple machines.[21] The classification conforms to industry experience. Note has been taken of the large influx of small producers since 1947 and of the advantage of such producers in terms of adaptability to small-scale production for local demand.[22] Such demand provides opportunity for ingenuity in product design which a small firm could scarcely enjoy in the national market. In tractors, new entrants have been rare; no new tractor has entered the market on a national scale since before World War II. Of the two new full-line firms—Ford and White Motor—the first one had already had extensive experience in the market,[23] and the second made its entry through absorption of three existing full-line producers.

Moreover, as seen above, Bain includes the channels of distribution as a type of product differentiation.[24] Again, the difference between producers of large, complex and of small, simple machines is noted. Bain found the general consensus to be that customer attachments to dealer systems "are important in determining or maintaining an apportionment of business among firms. . . ."[25] Generally speaking, however, the small short-line firms do not appear to have had undue difficulty finding adequate outlets through dealers of full-line firms. Some short-line firms such

[18] *Ibid.*, p. 233.
[19] *Ibid.*, Table XI, pp. 127 ff.
[20] *Ibid.*, pp. 148–49.
[21] *Ibid.*, Table XV, p. 170.
[22] Whitney, *op. cit.*, p. 239, cites as examples of such demand a mower for one of the many types of alfalfa, or a plow for one of the many distinct types of terrain and soil in the country.
[23] Phillips, *op. cit.*, pp. 27 ff.
[24] Bain, *op. cit.*, p. 313.
[25] *Ibid.*, p. 314.

as New Idea (haying equipment, fertilizer equipment, spreaders) and New Holland (a variety of hay harvesting equipment) have established themselves over large territories through producing a quality product and relying in varying degrees on dealers enfranchised by the full-line companies, usually not in direct competition. Single-line firms producing such items as grain loaders, tractor-operated post-hole diggers, or baled hay loaders have a similar viability. A study in Iowa in 1961 showed that only 13.6 percent of dealers handled full-line implements exclusively, whereas 70.4 percent sold both full- and short-line makes and 16.0 percent only short-line makes.[26] Clearly, a new full-line producer, seeking to establish a national distributive system, would have much greater difficulty than his short-line, local-selling counterpart.[27]

## The Supply Side: Costs of Production

Costs of production are an important structural element bearing upon market conduct since these condition price policy and in turn affect the nature of competition. In the farm machinery industry, the so-called overhead costs are particularly significant. Not only do these tend to be relatively high in the full-line firm because of the nature of production of tractors, combines, and other complex machines, but variations in annual output and sales entail comparable variations in the portion of annual overhead costs attributable to each unit of output. In years of high output, this will be low, and vice versa. Where variations in annual output are great, as has been the historical case in farm machinery, full unit costs of production may be expected to rise in years of low production, with an obvious bearing on price policy.

The most striking illustrations of this characteristic of the industry are those which the Federal Trade Commission drew from the experience of the thirties. Table 13.3 shows the Commission's figures for the average factory costs of producing representative implements in the low-sales year of 1932 and the higher sales year of

---

[26] R. J. Jessen *et al.*, *Accessibility and Availability of Farm Machinery in Iowa*, Res. Rept. prepared for J. I. Case Co. by the Stat. Lab. and Ind. Sci. Res. Inst., Iowa State College (Ames, 1951). Cited by Simon Whitney, *op. cit.*, p. 243. Whitney also cites, *ibid.*, a study made by Dun and Bradstreet for another manufacturer, showing 97 percent of its dealers in 1947–49 buying competing implements in substantial amounts.

[27] The difficulty is not insuperable. The Allis-Chalmers Co., which produced farm tractors as early as 1915, succeeded in adding to these a line of farm implements through acquisition of existing firms. By the early thirties, it was a small full-line producer, after which it "edged" its way into the national market through a policy of contracting with many dealers who were already handling the lines of other manufacturers.

TABLE 13.3

Costs of Production of Farm Machinery, 1932 and 1937

|  | Row-Crop Tractors | | Eight-Foot Binders | | Threshers | |
|---|---|---|---|---|---|---|
|  | 1932 | 1937 | 1932 | 1937 | 1932 | 1936 |
| Material | 382.85 | 273.67 | 84.42 | 76.44 | 361.02 | 360.73 |
| Direct Labor | 34.84 | 58.24 | 17.00 | 21.20 | 84.19 | 96.41 |
| Overhead | 486.00 | 91.59 | 53.30 | 31.62 | 343.16 | 193.22 |
| Total Factory Cost | $903.69 | 423.50 | 154.72 | 129.26 | 788.37 | 650.36 |

Source: Federal Trade Commission.

1936 (or 1937).[28] In each case, lower overhead accounted for lower unit costs in the high-production year. Summing up, the Commission found that the increased production between 1932 and 1936 accounted for a drop of as much as 40 percent in unit production costs.

The significance of Table 13.3 should be carefully qualified as was done in Footnote 28. The extent to which present-day cost behavior is similar to that of the thirties is difficult to judge. No output variations comparable to those of the thirties have occurred since the war, nor has there been any public inquiry of comparable magnitude to that of the Federal Trade Commission in the midthirties. It seems likely, however, that cost conditions have not changed appreciably. Overhead is still high relative to the volume of production in most farm machinery plants, and annual output changes must result in an uneven cost burden from year to year.

---

[28] *Report on the Manufacture and Distribution of Farm Implements,* Federal Trade Commission (Washington, 1948). The Commission was guarded in its interpretation of these figures. It said: "In presenting these figures, the Commission disclaims any belief that they should be regarded as costs per unit appropriate to have served as guides for price policy or even as a basis for computations of profits and disbursements of dividends. Indeed, such uses of this type of computation would be seriously misleading. So long as volume does not fluctuate greatly, it is often convenient to determine the amount of fixed charges which must be borne by each unit of product, and which therefore may be regarded as a part of unit costs, by dividing the total of fixed charges by the number of units produced. In a depression, however, when volume of production is low, such a procedure increases inordinately the amount of the apparent fixed charge per unit. . . . Awareness of these difficulties has produced various accounting techniques designed to present more realistically the cost aspect of fixed charges under conditions of fluctuating production.

"Nevertheless, the change in average expenditures per unit with changes in volume is significant as an indication of the importance of inequalities in the rate of production and as a rough measure of the distortions which fluctuations in volume are likely to create in the income of a corporation if they are not foreseen and provided for. Moreover, since enterprises are seldom wholly free from the tendency to base sales policies partly upon costs which include fixed charges thus computed, the computations may help explain corporate policies."

TABLE 13.4

COMPARISON OF PRODUCTION OF SELECTED FARM MACHINES WITH PRODUCTION OF
CHEVROLET AND FORD AUTOMOBILES IN THE U.S.A., 1960

| | Total 1960 Farm Machinery Production | Farm Machinery Production as a Percent of 1960 Automobile Production | |
| --- | --- | --- | --- |
| | | Chevrolet* | Ford† |
| | *(units)* | | |
| Wheel Tractors | 146,499 | 7.8% | 8.6% |
| Crawler Tractors | 38,416 | 2.1 | 2.3 |
| (Ag. and Non-Ag.) | | | |
| Combines | 28,615 | 1.5 | 1.7 |
| Corn Pickers | 40,014 | 2.1 | 2.3 |
| Hay Balers | 47,298 | 2.5 | 2.8 |
| Forage Harvesters | 23,217 | 1.3 | 1.4 |

Sources: U.S. Bureau of the Census, U.S. Department of Commerce; *Automotive Industries Magazine.*
* Includes 1,614,312 Chevrolets; 259,276 Corvairs. Total 1,873,588.
† Includes 1,004,305 Fords; 505,428 Falcons; 198,031 Comets. Total 1,707,764.

In any case, the experience of the thirties seems to have fostered a consciousness of the weight and the inflexibility of overhead which conditioned price policies in the industry then and probably still does, though to a decreasing extent. This will be discussed as an aspect of price policy. At a recent investigation of farm machinery prices, Deere and Company presented data to emphasize the smallness of farm machinery output in comparison with automobiles. This is shown in Table 13.4.[29] Deere pointed out that the relatively greater problem of farm machinery overhead implied in the table is aggravated in its case by the company's producing some 8700 different machines and attachments. "We are in a constant dilemma," said the company, "between trying to reduce costs by producing a greater volume of standard machines on one hand, and responding to constant pressure from farmers on the other hand to adapt these basic machines to local needs."[30]

Deere also presented cost data in percentages which have been adapted in Table 13.5 to show how the significance of overhead as a percentage of selling price changed between the lower sales year of 1956 ($313 millions) and the higher sales year of 1959 ($551 millions). The adaptation is necessarily somewhat crude because of the absence of precise definition of cost categories, particularly that of labor. Nevertheless, an appreciable drop in the relative significance is seen in each case between the low and higher sales years.

[29] *Minutes of Proceedings and Evidence Respecting Prices of Farm Machinery,* No. 10, Standing Com. on Agr. and Colonization, Canada, House of Commons, 24th Parlt., 4th Sess., 1960–61, p. 775. Hereafter cited as *Standing Committee on Agriculture and Colonization.*
[30] *Ibid.,* p. 768.

TABLE 13.5
Costs of Selected Farm Machines, Deere and Company, Moline, Illinois,
1956 and 1959
(expressed as percentages of net selling price, f.o.b. factory)

|          | Combine | | Tractor | | Spreader | |
|----------|---------|--------|---------|--------|----------|--------|
|          | 1956    | 1959   | 1956    | 1959   | 1956     | 1959   |
| Material | 41.7    | 41.9   | 39.1    | 38.1   | 42.7     | 43.8   |
| Labor*   | 18.2    | 17.1   | 19.0    | 15.1   | 16.1     | 14.4   |
| Overhead† | 14.0   | 10.4   | 15.8    | 10.4   | 14.6     | 8.3    |

Source: *Standing Committee on Agriculture and Colonization*, No. 10, pp. 831 ff.
* Weekly-paid plant labor. Some of this would likely be indirect labor and thus more properly classifiable as overhead.
† Includes salaried plant labor, depreciation, plant maintenance materials, power, light, heat, taxes (excluding income), insurance, research and development, etc.

## Interfirm Cost Differentials

Because of the importance of overhead, differences in cost levels among firms are often related to differences in volume produced. Of two companies equal in other respects, the higher volume firm will likely have lower average total costs because overheads per unit are lower. Moreover, higher volume facilitates the use of specialized year-round plants for specific machine types, lowering the average variable costs over a broad range of output. Particularly in the large, complex machines with national markets, therefore, large firms have definite cost advantages.

In illustration of this, Conant[31] points out that the largest plants in the industry have consistently recorded the lowest average costs per unit of output. This was the case in 1911, when the International Harvester Company, with the largest binder plants in the industry, was found by the Bureau of Corporations to have the lowest factory costs plus general expense of producing binders. A similar finding for International Harvester, Deere, and Allis-Chalmers, the three largest firms, was made by the Federal Trade Commission in 1938.[32] Specialization through volume is illustrated in the White Motor Company's acquisition of three firms between 1960 and 1963 resulting in the consolidation into five plants of the work previously done in 12. Facilities of Cockshutt Farm Equipment were specialized entirely in combines production, and former tractor production of that company discontinued; those of Oliver Farm Equipment were specialized in tillage machinery and tractors. White's acquisitions included the existing distributive systems of the merged firms. Thus the Oliver Company's tractor plant, which

---

[31] Conant, *op. cit.*, p. 31.
[32] *Report on the Agricultural Implements Industry, op. cit.*, pp. 1040 ff.

TABLE 13.6

PAYROLL PER EMPLOYEE, BY NUMBER OF EMPLOYEES, 1958

| | Firms Employing | | | | | | | | Over |
| | 1–4 | 5–9 | 10–19 | 20–49 | 50–99 | 100–249 | 250–499 | 500–999 | 1000 |
|---|---|---|---|---|---|---|---|---|---|
| Payroll Per Employee | 3330 | 3990 | 4200 | 4330 | 4430 | 4590 | 4780 | 5240 | 5560 |

Source: *Bureau of the Census Report,* Part I (1962), p. 259.

previously ran six months a year and then virtually shut down, was reported after merger running full speed for six months and at 70 to 80 percent of capacity the other six months.[33]

As in White's case, so throughout the industry, the cost position of individual firms owes much to historical development. During the industry's merger period, acquired firms frequently possessed backgrounds of experience and market success in individual products which could not be duplicated. Market superiority so acquired has usually been retained and increased. International's position, for example, though it has declined overall since 1902, remains stronger in harvesting than in tillage machinery. In other cases, aggressive developmental and marketing policies have conveyed at least temporary advantages in volume and consequently in cost. Massey-Ferguson introduced the self-propelled combine in 1939. The war and postwar shortages retarded other firms in overtaking Massey's lead and, by 1949, this company sold 50 percent of the North American total. By 1960, competition had reduced this to 30 percent. Again, different levels of wages paid affect relative costs. Smaller firms, frequently located in rural areas, had a smaller payroll per employee than larger firms in 1958 (Table 13.6). Thus, even allowing for lower productivity in smaller firms, labor costs could be competitive with larger firms.[34]

These various influences supplement that exerted by management capability in determining interfirm cost differentials. One rough measure of the extent of these differentials is in the income-statement cost of goods sold. As an average percentage of total sales over the period 1959 through 1962, this was 73.7 percent for Deere and Company, 80.4 percent for International Harvester, and 91.8 percent for J. I. Case (for 1961 and 1962 only). The overall cost differentials suggested in these figures are not, of course, spread uniformly among products. It would be exceedingly difficult to

---

[33] *Forbes, op. cit.,* pp. 32–33.

[34] Small firms in the industry do not seem content to rely on lower wage payments for survival. In 1958, firms employing 1 to 50, averaged $5300 in capital expenditures per employee; firms employing more than 50 averaged $4500. *Bureau of the Census Report,* Part I (1962), p. 259.

illustrate interfirm cost differentials by products.[35] Indeed, even within the industry it is only by virtue of a kind of accepted lore that cost leaders in particular products are pin-pointed. Rapid technological change and the unpredictable success of single-line firms make it a tenuous lore, the significance of which is perhaps not so much in its objective reality as in the fact of its acceptance. In an oligopolistic milieu where price decisions are dominated by considerations of possible retaliatory action from lower cost rivals, a general conviction that no individual firm has cost advantages across-the-board may reduce the amount of interdependence in pricing and, in particular, will reduce the likelihood of price leadership.

## The Demand Side: Cyclical Responses

On the demand side, the outstanding feature of market structure is the high sensitivity of farm machinery sales to farm income and their low sensitivity to price. This characteristic is attributable to the durability of farm machinery, enhanced by a number of special characteristics of the market which the author has expanded elsewhere.[36] It is illustrated in Figures 13.1 and 13.2 for the 40-year span from 1920 to 1960, containing a major depression (early thirties), two recessions (early twenties and middle fifties), and three sharp upswings (late twenties, 1937, and 1951). Using simple index numbers, these show that the significant changes in farm income over the period have been accompanied by relatively greater changes in farm machinery production and sales. Price levels remained remarkably steady between 1920 and 1940 in spite of wide variations in income and sales. The post-World War II period has been marked by a steady uptrend in price and by less pronounced income changes, but the presence of income sensitivity is still evident.

This hyper-response of machinery sales to farm incomes was an early destabilizing factor in the farm machinery industry, contributing to the formation of a somewhat fatalistic "seven lean years" philosophy which has accounted for much of the diversification into other product lines,[37] and has had a distinct bearing on

---

[35] George R. Slater, "The Relative Market Power of Farm Machinery Manufacturers," *Journal of Farm Economics*, Vol. XLII (1960), p. 1253. "It is difficult for one firm to obtain cost advantages over a wide range of the industry's products because (1) the largest proportion of finished product costs are purchased components and parts from common suppliers, (2) wage rates are similar among firms, and (3) information and knowledge used by the various manufacturers flow through such channels as common suppliers, the press, and the employment of competitors' technical and management personnel."

[36] Phillips, *op. cit.*, pp. 96 ff.

[37] Deere, the last to diversify, produces industrial machinery and farm fertilizers; Massey-Ferguson, industrial machinery and office equipment; Allis-Chalmers, industrial and electrical machinery.

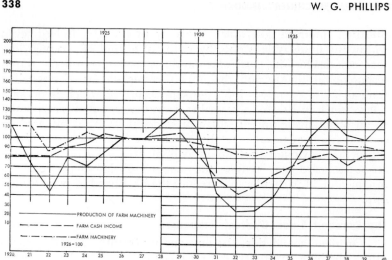

FIG. 13.1—Index of farm machinery prices, production, and farm cash
income in the United States from 1920 to 1940.

price policy. Industry experience has bred a firm conviction that
price reductions, especially in low income periods, would have but
little effect on sales and on unit costs. As expressed in 1960 by
Deere and Company:

> It is sometimes said that our industry could make the same or higher
> profits by reducing prices, thereby gaining greater sales volume and
> lower unit costs. This is a tempting idea. Unfortunately, it is an
> illusion when applied to our industry. For it to work for the in-
> dustry, decreasing prices would have to result in a very much larger
> total market for farm machinery. For it to work for any one com-
> pany, all other companies in the industry would have to maintain
> their present prices. The end result of such action would be little
> or no profits with business failures resulting in fewer manufacturers
> in the industry. The conclusion is distasteful but nonetheless realis-
> tic.[38]

## MARKET CONDUCT

### Long-Term Price Behavior

This section is concerned with competition—the price and
nonprice varieties. The price level of farm machinery has been
more stable over the past four decades than prices of most durable
goods. Between 1926 and 1929, for example, prices of farm machinery actually declined slightly while those of metals and metal
products in general showed a slight increase. Between 1929 and

---

[38] *Standing Committee on Agriculture and Colonization, op. cit.*, No. 10,
p. 771.

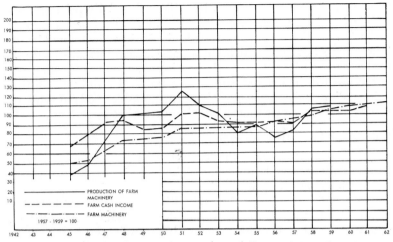

FIG. 13.2—Index of farm machinery prices, sales, and gross farm income in the United States from 1945 to 1962.

1933, metal and metal products prices fell some 20 percent, and farm machinery about 9 percent. Again, during the decade of the fifties, the prices of the former rose 40 percent, and farm machinery 31 percent.[39]

The persistence of relatively more rigid prices for farm machinery reflects four structural characteristics already observed: a few firms dominating the market, high sensitivity of sales to income, low sensitivity of sales to price, and rigid overhead costs. The small number of firms provides a necessary first condition for price rigidity. Because of high income elasticity, fluctuations of farm income have been projected onto the operations of the farm machinery industry in magnified form, resulting in alternating periods of very high and very low output. The profits which have been made by the industry in high output years have resulted primarily from decreased unit overhead costs in those years and only secondarily from increased prices. Likewise, losses have resulted during years of low output, not because of falling prices but because of vastly increased overhead per unit. Any hope which the industry may entertain of stabilizing output and costs from period to period through cyclical price adjustment appears to be thwarted by the extreme sensitivity of the market to farm income changes and its low sensitivity to changes in machinery prices.

A further influence on long-term price policy has been political in nature. As an oligopolistic supplier of capital goods exclusively to agriculture, the industry attracts the attention of sincere re-

[39] *Statistical Abstract of the United States, op. cit.*

formers and political opportunists alike. Especially prior to 1940, public inquiries were made into virtually every aspect of the industry's operation by governments in the United States and Canada. These have been directed both at individual firms and at the industry as a whole. The result has been an unusually high consciousness within the industry of the political ramifications of its price policy, and a proneness to accept unstable levels of sales and profits as a lesser evil than a widely fluctuating price level.

### Individual Price Determination

The question of how the level of prices is determined is complex and difficult, and only some of the more important aspects will be touched. Retail prices paid by buyers consist of production costs (including administrative and selling costs) plus manufacturer's profit, plus transportation costs, plus dealer's commission. Of these, profit is the most flexible element. The profit rate is seldom the same for any two machines in a company's line; according to Kaplan et al., International "has various profit objectives for different machines, depending upon such factors as the competitive situation, the intricacy or originality of design, and the estimate of economic worth to the customer. Weight is also given to full-line advantages in marketing for items that cannot themselves carry the full mark-up."[40] Among representative implements introduced by International Harvester in 1956, profit as a percentage of total unit costs was found to vary from a loss of 2 percent to a profit of 21 percent.[41] Profit, in fact, is not generally seen as a markup consciously applied to costs but rather as an amount determined by the difference between the cost of the product and the amount for which it can be sold, this price depending on the prices at which other producers are selling a similar product.[42]

The discussion of pricing which follows addresses itself to two questions.[43] First is that of the establishment of an initial list price on a product being newly added to an existing line. What influences the amount of profit included in the price selected by such a

---

[40] A. D. H. Kaplan, Joel B. Dirlam, and Robert F. Lanzillotti, *Pricing in Big Business* (Washington: Brookings Institute, 1958), p. 73.

[41] *Ibid.*

[42] Cf. the following from the brief of the Massey-Ferguson Co. to the Com. on Agr. and Colonization, 1961: "We wish to make it unmistakably clear that, in pricing, we are guided overwhelmingly by considerations of the market. We must be sensitive to preferences of our farmer-customers . . . and we must be competitive. The emphasis we place on demand in pricing our products is no denial of the importance of costs in our business; but this importance is in terms of internal adjustments of our operations. Costs must be met over a period of years; otherwise the manufacturer goes out of business. This is the major significance of costs."

[43] The following discussion is based directly on Phillips, *op. cit.*, pp. 124 ff.

firm? Discussion of this question, it is felt, illustrates some aspects of the role of profit in pricing which are seen only with difficulty if price decisions on established products alone are considered. Secondly, the question of the initiation of *changes* in the level of existing prices is considered. This involves the question of price leadership.

**Pricing a New Product.** Two related considerations normally affect decisions regarding additions to the line of machines produced. They are the importance of the product to the firm's "full line" and the costs of producing it; these being related, of course, to the volume which the firm expects to sell.

Ever since the full-line replaced the single-line firm as the typical unit in the industry, production of a complete line of machines and implements has been the object of all firms. One reason, already noted, has been the necessity of supplying a line complete and varied enough to retain retail dealers on a permanent basis throughout the year. In addition, considerable significance is attached by producers to the prestige which adheres to a full line, and which may suffer if a particular machine is missing. The history of the industry contains many instances where, production being considered unfeasible, selling arrangements have been entered into with other firms in order to round out a particular firm's line of products.

Suppose that on the basis of these considerations a firm desires to add a new machine, say a tractor, to its line of products. Having designed the machine and calculated material and direct labor costs, it adds the overhead markup for the current production period, plus administrative and selling costs. Suppose, further, that the full costs so obtained are as high as, or higher than, the prices then being charged by competitors for tractors of about the same size and power, so that even the smallest profit markup would mean charging a price higher than competitors.

In such a case, several questions must be answered before a final decision to produce the machine can be made. Sustained conversations with executives in the machinery industry suggest that the following would be the principal of such questions. What is the cause of the higher costs? Do they reflect high unit overhead and, if so, can this be reduced through a stricter check on inefficiencies in the manufacturing process?

On the other hand, do the higher costs reflect the fact that more quality (in materials, workmanship, design, or even in the number of "extras" included) is being built into this machine than into those of competitors? If this is the case, a decision must be made concerning a reduction in quality. Such a reduction itself would probably entail extra costs of redesigning so that a prior decision must be made as to whether the company should, through extra sales effort, try to persuade buyers to take higher quality even at the higher price. Finally, a decision which one company reported might result after a special market and cost analysis had been made was that the machine might simply be placed on the market at a price equal to that of its competitors, and sales estimates increased on the assumption of farmers' preference for higher quality at the given price. In this case, of course, the increased sales estimate would result in lower estimated full costs through a downward adjustment of the overhead rate.

If consideration of none of the foregoing factors yields a solution, and the firm finds itself unable to even build a machine comparable to the competitor's to sell at his price, then the only remaining question is whether the machine should be added to the line at all. The answer to this must depend on the best estimates of the firm regarding this machine's probable effect on total sales, either through its enhancement of the prestige of the line of implements or through its long-term effect in attracting and retaining for the company better dealers than it otherwise might have. The result may be that the machine is added to the line and sold below its full cost, since its general contribution is considered to outweigh the loss involved in its production and sale.

Executives of individual firms show less assurance when discussing the policy they would follow if, assuming similar circumstances, their estimated costs are found to be below the prices of competitors by an exceptionally wide margin. Such a firm would be potentially the price leader in that product, assuming that if it set its price lower than current competitors' prices, they would be forced to follow. A decision would have to be made concerning whether to charge a price as high as competitors were charging, realizing a relatively large profit per unit of sale, or to price below them taking a smaller unit profit on a larger volume.

A whole complex of factors would necessarily enter such a decision, but principally it would hinge on the firm's estimate of competitors' ability to meet the lower price and the possibilities of retaliation from them in other machines. If it were known that all other firms could, and would, lower their prices accordingly so that each would gain only a small increase in sales (industry demand being inelastic), the lower price would less probably be chosen. If it were known that some other firms had it in their power to retaliate by lowering prices on machines in which they possessed the advantage in costs, then it is highly improbable that the lower price would be chosen. Finally, there is the possibility that, if the spread between the firm's low costs and the prices which competitors are charging is very substantial, ethical considerations alone may inhibit the firm from charging a price as high as theirs, regardless of the results.

*Initiating Changes in Price.* For a number of decades ending with the late 1930's, the International Harvester Company was the recognized price leader in the farm machinery industry. Conditions in the industry favored this situation. From the invention of the twine binder in the late nineteenth century to the widespread adoption of the combine, harvesting machinery was fairly standardized. Similarly, until tractor-mounted and tractor-activated tillage and planting machines replaced those of the horsedrawn variety, these too had become standardized in appearance and design. Under these conditions, reasonable proximity of prices of competing machines was imposed by competition. International Harvester, moreover, dominated the industry in almost all respects: in research and engineering advances, in tractor and harvesting machinery production, and in production of a number of tillage machines.

The exact nature of International's early price leadership is difficult to determine. From evidence obtained by the Federal Trade Commission in 1937 and 1938, it appears to have been of the dominant-firm variety; yet, considering that in some lines, International never did have a dominant position, it seems either that, to some extent, competitors followed suit through fear of retaliation or that International, by reason of its superior resources, its generally progressive policies, and its mature judgment (the wisdom born of some 20 years in court), was accepted by the industry as best fitted to make the decisions concerning the time and extent of price changes for the industry. In other words, Harvester's early price leadership probably contained elements of both the dominant firm and the competitive barometric variety.[44] Moreover, Harvester's price leadership was on occasion successfully challenged, as when Ford slashed the prices of farm tractors in the 1920's[45] and Harvester was forced to follow.

At the end of 1938, International's position appears to have been still intact. Following the publication of the Federal Trade Commission's *Report on the Agricultural Implements Industry* in 1938, International immediately announced a voluntary reduction in prices of a large number of implements and also the elimination within the company of every trade practice criticized by the Commission. This announcement gratified the Commission, which

---

[44] See George J. Stigler, "The Kinky Oligopoly Demand Curve and Rigid Prices," *Journal of Political Economy*, Vol. LV, No. 5 (1947), pp. 444–46; and Jesse W. Markham, "The Nature and Significance of Price Leadership," *American Economic Review*, Vol. XLI, No. 5 (1951), pp. 891 ff.

[45] Phillips, *op. cit.*, p. 29.

later took credit for its part in the achievement.[46] Other producers immediately followed Harvester's lead, as a result of which the general level of implement prices was 2 percent lower in 1939 than in 1938. The effects of the decrease even appear to have spread into Canada where the price index also declined slightly in 1939.

Shortly after the end of the war, during which prices were controlled, the beginnings of a change became evident. Controls were lifted in 1946. Some increases were put into effect late that year; but, early in 1947, International Harvester announced its intention of making substantial reductions in the prices of about half its line of tractors, motor trucks, and industrial power equipment. Company officials emphasized that the proposed reductions had not resulted from buyer sales resistance or competitive factors, but were undertaken because "the company realizes it has a social responsibility to consumers" and because the business outlook made it possible for the company to move toward the goal of lower prices.[47] These reductions were made in an environment of extremely heavy demand and at a time of acute shortage of materials and finished goods in the industry, and of acceptance throughout the industry of new union contracts providing for substantial wage increases for the ensuing year. Under the circumstances, the reduction must be seen as a sequel to its 1938 reduction, an attempt to demonstrate good faith and to overcome, as far as possible, the last traces of the stigma of monopoly and of well-publicized court proceedings. It could hardly have been thought to be permanent.

Whatever the motive for the 1947 reduction, it marked the first serious break in Harvester's traditional role as price leader. Other companies did not follow suit and, in fact, within a few months prices had begun to edge upward in the beginning of a lengthy climb. Whatever element of the barometric had inhered in Harvester's earlier leadership appears to have dwindled rapidly after the 1947 experience. Moreover, the company's relative position in the industry suffered in the early postwar years as a result of the rapid advances made by Deere and Company and Massey-Ferguson. As for the pattern of price changes, the last 15 years have shown a lack of uniformity. The position of recognized price leader appears to have been vacated by International, but no other firm has yet succeeded in occupying the position in any conclusive way.

Some of the reasons for this and for believing that it may continue might be suggested. As already noted, the historical development and the multi-product nature of the industry have resulted in

---

[46] *Report on the Manufacture and Distribution of Farm Implements, op. cit.,* p. 1.

[47] *Ibid.,* p. 74.

cost advantages being typically spread unevenly among the firms. This appears to be still a significant factor in interfirm cost differentials and its presence reduces the likelihood of there emerging a price leader of the dominant-firm variety. Moreover, the advent of power-driven and tractor-mounted machinery made differentiation a real possibility and, with it, a tendency within the industry to attach less importance to price differentials, at least to the extent that these could be shown to reflect product differences. Competition in product design may be said to have partly replaced competition in price, although it is questionable whether the tendency reflects a desire for a competitive advantage over rivals or a less creditable desire to render price competition partially inoperative.

The decline of price leadership in the industry seems to have been further enhanced by a widespread incidence of secret price cutting in the depressed market of the middle fifties. This has had the effect of decreasing the significance attached to list prices, since these tend to be set on the basis of the best expectations concerning farm income, in the knowledge that in-season price cuts can be effectively made simply by announcing a bonus to dealers on the price of a particular machine, without any change in the list price proper. In such a case, the dealer is free to offer a higher trade-in allowance or to keep the bonus if he sells at full price. This particular method of price adjustment appears to have been widely used in the industry after 1952 when the postwar boom came to a halt. A similar influence is exerted by the increasing importance of trade-in allowances on larger machines.[48] Finally, the complete absence of tariff protection in this industry and the increasing import competition have probably contributed to the reduced role of price leadership. Though still not large, imports increased from about 4 percent of domestic sales in the early fifties to around 8 percent in the early sixties.

To sum up, the postwar years have seen the reduction or elimination of some of the noncompetitive elements in farm machinery pricing, while others, such as product differentiation, have become more prominent. On balance, however, the factors mentioned, and especially the more evenly divided strength of the industry's large firms, appear to have exerted a stimulating effect

---

[48] Cf. the following from the *Report of Canadian Cooperative Implements Limited, 1960:* "It will no doubt be a surprise to many to know that, in the years from 1952 to 1959, we paid member customers approximately $2,600,000 more for their trades than we were able to sell them for. And it will be a further surprise to know that a total of more than $750,000 was allowed to customers by way of discounts for cash. . . . One example which we received of the allowance for a used machine which illustrates the extremes to which dealers will go to sell a new machine is that one dealer offered $35 for an old hay rake while another dealer offered $250 for the same rake."

on price competition. Price increases are frequently put into effect on single lines of machines, or a small number, rather than across-the-board. Pricing of farm machinery is a continuous process involving constant comparison of prices of hundreds of different items, demands for which are in varying degrees complementary, with prices charged by competitors. Decisions to revise prices seem to be based primarily on comparisons among the products themselves and on buyers' reactions to existing price differentials. It is evident that the role which costs play in pricing is really that of setting a floor, below which individual prices should not be allowed to fall without special efforts to determine whether the product should be dropped from the line. Moreover, the rate of profit on individual machines is not regarded as a true indication of their respective contributions to the company's total profit. Insofar as a machine contributes prestige to the line simply by its presence, or enables the company to market through better channels, its general contribution may be considerable even though it shows only a small accounting profit or even a loss.

### Nonprice Competition

During the years of price leadership in the industry, competition of the nonprice variety was often quite vigorous. This took principally two forms: competition in distribution and competition in credit extension. In these areas too, some significant modifications have become evident in recent years.

*Distribution.* The scattered nature of the farm machinery market imposed an early need for decentralization in distribution, in answer to which the branch system developed. Companies maintain branches at important regional centers at which stocks of implements are kept. Branches normally keep accounts with retail dealers in their respective territories and supervise dealer activities in sales, servicing, and the general conduct of business. The branch largely eliminated the independent wholesaler, since it enabled companies to maintain closer contact with the far-flung agricultural market than an independent wholesaler system could have done. It might be noted, however, that the rise of specialty manufacturers since the war has, to some extent, brought the wholesaler back into the picture.

At the retail level, the early practice in the industry was to ship on consignment to agents. This practice had given way by the middle twenties to the use of purchase agreements under which it was intended that the dealer should buy machines outright. In this capacity, the dealer might be expected to become an independent businessman, free to make his own decisions and to compete as best he saw fit. This has not actually been so. As for competition, it took the form principally of excessive numbers of retail outlets, clusters of which became pinpointed over the agricultural market. Whatever excess distributive capacity may have been inevitable by reason of local crop uncertainties was duplicated many times by the tendency to cluster and by the practice by manufacturers of generally insisting on exclusive dealing at the retail level. Its most extreme manifestation was the frequency of the so-called "curbstone" dealer—the dealer with little or no capital, with little real interest in the company he was representing, capable only of accepting products on consignment or on liberal credit, finding a place for them among the junk heaps that frequently littered the premises, and hoping that a buyer might appear.

The consequent high cost of distribution has been much criticized within the industry and without. Yet individual companies have remained loathe to undertake vigorous pruning of their dealers, choosing to be represented in every area of the market on the principle that losses from local crop failures will be balanced by profits in other areas, the average of the total market being more easily predicted than the average of one area. What modification has come about, therefore, has resulted from external pressures rather than from conscious efforts or policy in the industry. Such pressures have included the increased financial requirements of dealers, the technical expertise needed for servicing complex machinery, and the smaller numbers and increasing size of farms. According to the National Retail Farm Equipment Association, the average net worth of farm machinery dealers increased from about $25,000 in 1940 to $96,000 in 1958. Between 1952 and 1962 the number of farms in the United States decreased some 29 percent while the average acreage of farms increased by about 40 percent.

It has always been difficult to say accurately how many farm machinery dealers there are in the United States. According to the dealers' association, however, the number has declined sharply since the war, specifically from 27,500 to about 18,000 between 1940 and the late fifties.[49] The reduction has been accompanied by a general increase in the caliber and financial status of dealers—in their technical versatility and their ability to assist farmers in making economic decisions regarding purchase. They must maintain facilities for service and for handling repair parts as well as trade-ins and used machines. Dealers, moreover, are being encouraged by the companies to fortify themselves by handling supplementary lines such as small crawler tractors for construction work and so on. Despite these trends, there is still a question whether changes at

---

[49] Figures from the National Retail Farm Equipment Association. See W. G. Phillips, "Changing Structure of Markets for Farm Machinery," *Journal of Farm Economics*, Vol. XL, No. 5 (Dec. 1958), p. 1175.

the dealer level have been sufficient to eliminate excessive distributive capacity.

A final aspect of distribution concerns cooperative selling.[50] Cooperative retailing of farm machinery has developed along three lines. At the end of World War II, Cockshutt Farm Equipment Company made an arrangement with the National Farm Machinery Cooperative, Incorporated (U.S.A.), under which it turned out a portion of its output bearing a distinctive color and the "Co-op" name. This was sold directly to regional cooperatives in the United States, which in turn sold it to farmers through their own outlets, ostensibly as cooperative machinery. This arrangement enjoyed conspicuous success during the tight market conditions until about 1954, after which it waned steadily under the onslaught of keener competition. Secondly, some, though not all of the other full-line firms as well as a number of the short-line specialty firms, sell their machinery to local cooperatives in certain areas. Finally, cooperatives themselves have, to a limited extent, gone into farm machinery production.

Cooperative selling is still very small in the total market. In view of the undoubted economies which it can mean for a buyer, and the vigorous efforts of the organized cooperatives to make it work, its limited success calls for some explanation. Over and above a not inconsiderable reluctance on the part of some major manufacturers to do business with cooperatives, their difficulties reflect the peculiarities of the market itself. There are, for example, the problems of credit, servicing and trade-ins, for which the co-ops have been well equipped. Many in the farm machinery industry suggest, rather ruefully, that the industry has for so long "pampered" the farmer in these respects that he now expects greater patronization from machinery sellers than from any others. It does seem true that farmers do not buy machinery as they buy other commodities. They have become accustomed to having their machinery sold to them. Thus some sales practices which have long since been abandoned in the selling of other goods have come to be considered "essentials" in the sale of farm machinery. The savings normally associated with cooperative sale are consequently extremely elusive in the sale of farm machinery. It seems, in fact, that a long-standing mode of thought among farmers would have to be changed before large-scale success could come to the implement-selling cooperatives.

*Credit Extension.* A second phase of nonprice competition has been credit extension. The special credit needs of the farm machinery market offered an early opportunity for firms seeking higher sales

---

[50] This discussion of cooperative selling is based directly on *ibid.*, pp. 1181–82. See also *The Agricultural Implements Industry, op. cit.*, pp. 140 ff.

without lower prices. The Bureau of Corporations pointed out in 1913:

> The granting of long terms of credit was originally developed in the harvesting machinery industry on account of the general inability of farmers to purchase expensive machines, like binders, for cash; *but it has been continued to a certain extent at least, as a specific means of getting trade by those firms which had ample financial resources.* Moreover, it has been extended by them to other lines of farm implements of a less expensive character in which the custom was not developed until a comparatively recent time.[51]

In the buoyant market of the late twenties, credit became the chief competitive instrument in the market, characterized by extremely low down payments, exceedingly easy terms, and an almost indiscriminate acceptance of risks. This financial fling ended abruptly in 1929, after which the necessity of heavy write-offs of receivables goaded the industry belatedly into greater credit stringency which lasted throughout the thirties. For eight or nine years following the war, farm income was high enough, country bank credit available enough, and memory of former experience probably vivid enough, that the industry avoided any significant involvement.

By the middle fifties, the situation was changing. In the lean market after 1952, country banks became less accommodating, and many dealers were unable to finance inventories of expensive machines. Companies faced the possibility of a significant number of dealer failures which could have had serious competitive effects. Arrangements to finance such dealers only created new demands for further accommodation and for the extension of company-sponsored finance to the retail level. As one banker later remarked:

> Naturally, the salesmen wanted to lengthen terms and shorten down payments to stimulate sales. Maybe terms were extended beyond that which the independent banker understood. Lack of sale was attributed to ineffective financing, and the trend started moving back toward the manufacturer handling the whole package.[52]

The result of this reentry into credit in the fifties was the creation by most of the full-line companies of subsidiary credit companies which have now assumed the entire credit-granting function of the parent concerns. Their extremely heavy credit commitment may be seen in an example from one full-line firm, which was typical

---

[51] *Report on the International Harvester Company*, Bureau of Corporations (1913), p. 20, emphasis added.
[52] Address by Paul M. Winch, Vice-President, The Citizens and Southern National Bank, Atlanta, Ga., May 22, 1958.

of the late fifties and early sixties. The example points strongly
to the fact that very little real difference exists between the consignment arrangements of an earlier time and the purchase agreements
of today.

Financing of dealers by the manufacturing company covers
not only their purchases of new machines and repair parts, but
also used machines taken in trade and installment paper advanced
by buyers. Inventory financing is usually done without any interest
charge or additional cost and without requiring a down payment.
On a shipment of new machines to a dealer, for example, no payment would be required for a year (except in case of sale) and, on
half the delivery, no payment would be required for 21 months.
The company would finance trade-ins without interest or down payments for four months, after which the loan might be extended at 6
percent. Should the dealer sell the first trade-in, accepting a second
used machine as part payment, the company would similarly finance
the second trade-in. As for farmers' notes for either new or used
machines, these were accepted by the company, though the company
normally withheld 3 percent of the face value as reserve against
losses. On such sales, the company required that the dealer take at
least a 30 percent down payment, permitting the balance to be
spread over as many as 40 months on expensive machines. It is thus
clear that as much as five years could conceivably elapse between the
time of original shipment to the dealer and the receipt of final
payment.

This is a tremendous credit commitment for a manufacturing
enterprise. The widespread use of financial subsidiaries, however,
suggests some diminution of the importance of credit extension as
a competitive instrument. The more systematic the individual
companies become in their credit practices, the less likely does it
seem that these would be varied solely to secure a competitive edge
over rival firms, and the more opportunity for ensuring that this
does not happen. The reason the industry has assumed such a
heavy credit burden seems to be twofold. First, the lending policies
of most banks have proved to be not readily adaptable to the particular needs of large-scale farm machinery credit, leaving the
industry little practical alternative to assuming the credit load itself.
Secondly, the operation itself is by no means unprofitable by nature;
given a strong market, in fact, it can be quite rewarding. It is still,
however, questionable whether any credit company, dealing only
in farm equipment loans and holding only farm equipment as
security, could survive the strain of a prolonged agricultural
depression.

The industry's attitude is partly summed up in the following
communication from one large company to the author:

The trend in financing retail sales by the Company has been entirely satisfactory, notwithstanding that we strongly urge and encourage that banking be done on Main Street rather than through the manufacturers.

We have found in so many instances that the local banker is more interested in placing real estate mortgages or personal loans than collateral loans, such as are covered by agricultural or construction equipment. We have gone so far as to openly campaign for this project by sending representatives into the field to interview bankers and solicit their cooperation. The program would seem to take hold for a while and then, as money became tight, the more desirable loans would be picked up, leaving our dealer in a position of looking elsewhere for financing. Stated otherwise, we have been driven to this decision (to set up a credit company) rather than to seek it as a money-making venture.

## PERFORMANCE

Among data having a direct bearing on performance, profit stands out. In farm machinery, profit rates have varied sharply at different times and from one firm to another at the same time. Table 13.7 shows the rate of return on investment after tax, of six leading firms in 1929 and 1943. Both 1929 and 1943 were relatively profitable years. Over a longer period, including the lean years, rates of return have been less. This is illustrated in Table 13.8, for the same six companies and covering the period 1919 (or 1929) to 1946.

Since 1950, profit rates have been generally lower and have continued to show marked variations among firms. Profit rates as computed by Deere and Company for presentation to the Committee on Agriculture and Colonization (see Footnote 29) were based on total assets and contained a comparison with all manufacturing in the United States. These are shown in Table 13.9.

In spite of their extreme variability, profit rates in farm machinery do not appear to have been excessive over the long term. Table 13.9 indicates that in the 1957–1960 period even

TABLE 13.7

AFTER-TAX PROFITS RATES OF LEADING FARM MACHINERY FIRMS, 1929 AND 1943

| Company | 1929 | 1943 |
|---|---|---|
| International Harvester | 15.21 | 6.33 |
| Deere and Co. | 26.27 | 10.44 |
| J. I. Case | 7.93 | 5.26 |
| B. F. Avery | 9.99 | 4.12 |
| Oliver Farm Equipment | 6.44 | 6.52 |
| Minneapolis-Moline | 7.93 | 10.32 |

Source: *Report on Manufacture and Distribution of Farm Implements,* Federal Trade Commission (Washington, 1948), p. 99.

TABLE 13.8

AFTER-TAX RATES OF RETURN ON INVESTMENT 1919 (OR 1929) TO 1946

| Company | Rate of Return | Range |
|---|---|---|
| International Harvester | 6.93 | 15.21 to 2.56* |
| Deere and Co. | 9.70 | 26.27 to 7.08* |
| J. I. Case | 5.03 | 15.04 to 4.92* |
| B. F. Avery | 2.87 | 13.34 to 19.41* |
| Oliver Farm Equipment | 2.15 | 12.29 to 9.54* |
| Minneapolis-Moline | 3.32 | 12.75 to 11.19* |

Source: *Report on Manufacture and Distribution of Farm Implements,* Federal Trade Commission (Washington, 1948), p. 9.
* Loss.

the most profitable of the farm machinery producers (Deere) enjoyed a rate of return less than the average for all manufacturing. J. S. Bain calculated average rates of profits of the dominant firms in 20 leading industries for the periods 1936–1940 and 1947–1951. In each case, the farm machinery industry ranked eleventh.[53] Considering that these were generally high sales years in the industry, the relative profit position of farm machinery does not stand out.

More significant are variations in profit rates within the industry. Of the six firms listed in Table 13.7, the three lowest profit ones have subsequently been merged.[54] The fourth, J. I. Case, suffered low returns in the late fifties and large losses in the early sixties, at which time its continued independent existence was uncertain. On the other hand, Deere and Company has enjoyed the highest return in the industry, consistently exceeding even that of the giant International Harvester.

### Progressiveness of the Industry

The disparity of individual firm fortunes raises the persistent question, Why? Cost differentials, discussed above are a partial explanation. But a full answer, far beyond the scope of this chapter, would have to seek further into policies affecting market penetration and general corporate outlook. Remarkable in the past half-century has been the decline in the industry position of International Harvester. A slow, steady decline in Harvester's market share resulted in its being displaced as the largest domestic seller by Deere and Company, and as largest seller abroad by Massey-Ferguson. To some extent, the company's protracted antitrust experience may have caused it consciously to retrench. Vigorous competition from younger rivals played a large part. But also in

[53] Bain, *op. cit.,* p. 195.
[54] B. F. Avery was acquired by Minneapolis-Moline in 1951.

TABLE 13.9

Net Profits Per Dollar of Total Assets All U.S. Manufacturers and
Major Farm Machinery Manufacturers, 1950, and 1957 to 1960
(cents per dollar)

| Company | 1950 | 1957 | 1958 | 1959 | 1960 | 1957–1960 Average |
|---|---|---|---|---|---|---|
| All Manufacturers, U.S. | 10.2¢ | 7.1¢ | 5.7¢ | 6.9¢ | 6.2¢ | 6.5¢ |
| Allis-Chalmers | 9.2 | 3.8 | 4.2 | 4.3 | 2.1 | 3.6 |
| J. I. Case | 13.5 | 0.7 | 1.9 | 2.8 | —18.2 | —3.2 |
| Deere and Co. | 13.3 | 5.9 | 7.7 | 7.8 | 3.0 | 6.1 |
| International Harvester | 8.9 | 4.5 | 4.2 | 6.7 | 3.7 | 4.8 |
| Motec (Minn.-Moline) | 12.3 | —6.5 | —2.9 | 5.7 | 4.6 | 0.2 |
| Oliver | 7.3 | 0.5 | 1.4 | 3.0 | NA | NA |
| Massey-Ferguson | 12.9 | 1.6 | 3.6 | 4.5 | 2.9 | 3.2 |

Source: Federal Trade Commission; Securities and Exchange Commission; individual company annual reports. (Table prepared by Deere and Company for Standing Committee on Agriculture and Colonization.)

the picture was probably an undue emphasis, perhaps not uncommon, in old, highly successful firms, on corporate prestige, leading to such policies as underlay the ill-timed price decrease of 1947. Until recently at least, Harvester was widely felt to be functioning "less as a money-making organization than as a corporate monument."[55] Recently, it appears, the company has engaged in much critical self-assessment, changing its policy to one of halting any further decline in its share of the market.[56] Moreover, a program of complete modernization of its manufacturing plants and consolidation of its distributive system had been carried out by the early sixties. Harvester may yet demonstrate the viability of the older, monolithic dominant firm.

The record of Deere and Company has been something of a phenomenon. Its rate of growth has far exceeded any in the industry, as has its rate of return on investment. Between 1929 and 1946, investment of Deere increased 110.5 percent, compared to 22.6 percent for International, 1.1 percent for Case, 7.7 percent for Oliver, and declines of 1.6 percent and 45.5 percent for Minneapolis-Moline and Avery, respectively.[57] Deere's advance seems attributable to an exceptional combination of aggressive introduction of new products and effective marketing of existing ones. Long after its major competitors had switched their tractors to 4- and 6-cylinder models, Deere continued to market only the 2-cylinder models developed from the "Waterloo Boy" line which it bought

[55] *Forbes* (Sept. 15, 1962), p. 20.
[56] Whitney, *op. cit.,* p. 236.
[57] *Report on the Manufacture and Distribution of Farm Implements, op. cit.,* p. 93.

in 1918. Even with no change in this basic design, the company took a steadily increasing market share, and exceeded International in total sales in 1959. Only in 1960 did Deere completely redesign its tractor.

It is notable that neither of the two top companies acquired any of the small ones which came up for sale after 1950. Thus the reduction of competition which resulted was less than it might have been. Moreover, their ultimate acquisition by White Motor Company reinforces the close affinity which has existed between this industry and the truck industry since Ford and International fought for tractor supremacy in the twenties. Trucks account for some 45 percent of Harvester's sales; of Harvester's total output, in fact, 80 percent are self-propelled (trucks, tractors, and combines).[58] This close tie with the truck industry has had a marked influence on the manufacturing methods used in farm machinery. Intermittently since 1917, competition from Ford compelled the industry to adopt many of the standards and methods in use in the automobile industry, including progressive assembly techniques. White's entry should intensify the competition and the technological progress. The merger of three full-line firms under White Motor, in fact, had aspects of a shake-out of excess capacity from the industry. Protracted rise in the farm machinery market after World War II stimulated considerable rapid and unwarranted investment in plant facilities for which the strain imposed by a series of low sales years in the fifties was too great. Particularly was this so in the smaller firms which had no diversified production to take up the slack. White either did not purchase, or discarded, many of the assets formerly held by the merged firms. As a result of the mergers, therefore, much of the previous excess capacity has been pruned away and the industry structure is such that, for the first time, all full-line firms are heavily engaged in other production than farm machinery.

Summing up on the production side, therefore, the industry merits mainly plus marks, to the extent at least that public policy measures are not at present urgently indicated. Because of the unusually large product-mix and the clear advantages of large-scale production, Whitney's conclusion has much merit:

> An attempt to break up four or six factories making 80 or 90 percent of a given implement into ten or a dozen establishments, in order to increase competition, might have the effect of increasing unit costs of both manufacturing and distribution.[59]

---

[58] *Forbes* (Nov. 15, 1963), p. 14.
[59] Whitney, *op. cit.*, p. 249.

## Promotion and Distribution

Promotional and advertising expenditures are of limited effect in the farm machinery industry compared with the market strength conferred by a long-established reputation. Expenditures on these, therefore, are generally small, especially among the large firms. The Federal Trade Commission found in the thirties that International Harvester had the industry's lowest ratio of selling expense to sales. Conant points out that "the pattern has continued for many years that the largest firms have the lowest selling expense ratios."[60] Deere and Company stated to the Committee on Agriculture and Colonization that its advertising expenditures as a percentage on net sales had been as follows: 1954, 1.3 percent; 1955, 1.1; 1956, 1.5; 1957, 1.2; 1958, 1.1; 1959, 1.0; and 1960, 1.3.[61]

The questionable effectiveness of large-scale promotional and advertising expenditure may be seen in the experience of the J. I. Case Company in the late fifties. This company appears literally to have attempted to spend its way into a larger market share. Half of its operating profit was put into product development. Lavish "world premieres" were staged for dealers and large-scale advertising was aimed at buyers. As a result, sales increased sharply, but costs increased much more sharply. By 1960, the company carried a rising debt load and swollen inventories. At the beginning of 1962, it was saved from a possibly fatal situation when a nationwide syndicate of commercial banks agreed, by a special arrangement, to renew a $140 million credit line through 1965.[62] The experience seems to emphasize that the farm market does not shift suddenly from one product to another. Any attempt to force such a shift may be more costly than it is worth.

## The Retail Level

The position of the retail dealer in distribution still gives rise to concern in spite of the reduced members and the increased financial status of dealers since the war. As has already been suggested, though the dealer is no longer the manufacturer's agent in a legal sense, there is a real question whether his position is in fact any different from what it was under consignment agreements. Dealer franchises take the form of contracts of sale, with the dealer taking possession at the point of delivery to the carrier. Title to the goods, however, does not normally pass to the dealer until he pays for them in cash, or until he has sold them and settled with the

---

[60] Conant, *op. cit.*, p. 29.
[61] *Standing Committee on Agriculture and Colonization, op. cit.*, p. 811.
[62] *Business Week* (Jan. 6, 1962), p. 100.

company in cash and customers' notes. Consequently, the unusually generous terms which the manufacturers extend to dealers have about them the earmarks of a measure to promote dealer compliance in company-ordained prices, terms and methods of sale— a feature somewhat out of keeping with the spirit of a purchase contract.

There is merit, therefore, in Martin Abrahamsen's observation:

> . . . the strong credit ties between manufacturer and dealer place the latter in what some people describe as a "captive" position. The manufacturer makes the basic decisions, establishes the terms, and maintains sufficient control over dealer operations. Thus, in effect, the dealers are vehicles for effectively integrating manufacurers' activities.[63]

Indeed, it appears that any competitive activity which might be initiated solely at the retail level is effectively checked under this system, and that actual competitive forms are not only agreed to by, but originate with, the manufacturers. The system has evolved over many years; essentially it is a reflection of the peculiar credit needs of agricultural enterprise, rather than of any calculated effort to control competition. Nevertheless, the whole company-dealer relationship might well be subjected to review to determine the extent to which it is in the best interests of the dealers themselves and of customers. The companies have repeatedly protested that they would welcome any relief from the credit load they are carrying, and this might possibly be done under some form of encouragement to banks to assume a larger portion of customer financing. To a partial extent at least, this would loosen the credit tie between manufacturer and dealer and be a step toward dealer freedom in retailing.

Another questionable aspect of distribution has to do with the numbers of dealers still found in many areas. This problem was first attacked officially in the consent decree of 1918 in which International Harvester agreed to maintain only one dealership in any city or town, but since then public policy has steered clear of it. Some marked decreases in numbers have been noted since World War II, but it is still not certain that these have kept pace with improvements in roads and communications. There are indications, in fact, that duplication of dealer facilities has been a continual source of pressure on companies from dealers to sanction excesses of competition in prices or terms. This, of course, tends

---

[63] Martin A. Abrahamsen, "The Changing Structure of Markets for Farm Machinery: Discussion," *Journal of Farm Economics* (1958), p. 1183.

to become more insistent as the financial requirements of dealerships increase.

One alternative which has been considered within the industry
is the separation of service facilities from sales facilities, the former
to be run by manufacturers on the basis of fewer, larger service
centers, and the number of dealerships to be cut in such a way as
to leave dealers wider areas over which to sell. Such a system could
probably provide better service than is available under present
methods and might well result in a new injection of selling competition at the retail level.

# 14

# THE FERTILIZER INDUSTRY[1]

## JESSE W. MARKHAM[2]

FERTILIZERS are an important factor of production for farmers. Throughout the 1950's, the average farmer spent 7 cents out of every dollar of his previous year's gross income on fertilizers for the current year's crops. For farm income derived from crops dependent on fertilizers such as grains, cotton, and tobacco, the proportion is considerably higher. Similarly, the proportion is much higher (about 14 percent) in certain regions such as the South Atlantic states where agriculture is more dependent on fertilizer.[3] Clearly the financial success of many farmers depends on the kinds and quantities of fertilizers they buy and how efficiently they use them.

Farmers buy fertilizers and fertilizer materials for their nitrogen, phosphorus, and potash content—the three principal nutrients plants absorb from the soil. These three plant nutrients (hereafter referred to respectively as N, $P_2O_5$, and $K_2O$) may be purchased in a wide variety of forms and combinations: as straight materials containing various percentages of one of the three nutrients, and as mixtures containing two or all of the nutrients N, $P_2O_5$, and $K_2O$. Fertilizers are labeled according to the percentage, by weight, of available plant nutrients they contain. For example, a short ton of anhydrous ammonia (82 percent) contains 1,460 pounds of N; a short ton of superphosphate (48 percent) contains 960 pounds of $P_2O_5$; a short ton of muriate of potash (60 percent) contains 1,200 pounds of $K_2O$; and a ton of mixed fertilizer of the grade 5-10-5 contains 100 pounds of N, 200 pounds of $P_2O_5$, and 100 pounds of $K_2O$—a total of 400 pounds, or 20 percent by weight, of plant nutrients. Because the materials containing plant nutrients also contain

---

[1] This chapter has drawn heavily from the author's book, *The Fertilizer Industry: Study of the Imperfect Market* (Nashville: Vanderbilt University Press, 1958). Wherever possible, the data have been updated to 1963.

[2] Professor of Economics, Princeton University.

[3] *Farm Costs and Returns, 1955*, Agr. Information Bul. 158, U.S.D.A. (June 1956), p. 42.

other compounds and impurities, it is impossible to manufacture a mixed fertilizer containing 100 percent plant nutrients, although theoretically a ton of 28-16-20 fertilizer can be purchased by mixing one-third of a ton each of 84 percent anhydrous ammonia, 48 percent superphosphate, and 60 percent muriate of potash. In the trade, mixed fertilizers containing over 25 percent plant nutrients are referred to as "high-analysis" fertilizers, those containing less as "low-analysis" fertilizers.

While high-analysis fertilizers sell at a higher price per ton, they are generally the cheapest source of plant nutrients available in the form of mixtures. Many cost items such as bagging, mixing, handling, storage, and transportation costs are the same per ton of total material irrespective of its plant nutrient content, making the cost per ton of plant nutrient a decreasing function of plant nutrient content. Similarly, materials having a high plant nutrient content are generally the most economical source of plant nutrients to the farmer and frequently are a cheaper source than the high-analysis mixed fertilizers, although the latter depends on the costs of the labor and equipment required when the mixing is prepared on the farm.

Since the value of a fertilizer depends almost entirely on the plant nutrients it contains, it would seem elementary that fertilizer manufacturers would try to procure plant nutrients at the lowest possible unit cost and that farmers would buy them at the lowest price at which they were offered. In fact, however, a large proportion of fertilizer sales is made on the basis of price per ton of total material rather than price per unit of plant nutrient. This raises what is probably the most important, and certainly the longest standing, public policy issue concerning the domestic fertilizer market which in its crudest form has been embodied in the age-old question, Why is there so much sand in the farmer's fertilizer? Stated in more sophisticated economic language, Why do not the competitive forces of the marketplace discipline producers and consumers so that plant nutrients are marketed in their most efficient form?

The debate this question has precipitated over the years has been characterized by considerable heat, and in recent years by a substantial amount of light. On the one hand, producers have generally contended that they would produce more economical fertilizers if farmers would buy them; on the other hand, spokesmen for farm organizations have argued that farmers would purchase the more efficient fertilizers in greater quantities if manufacturers would make them available in the market. Whatever the merit of these contentions, and no doubt both have some basis in fact, they serve as persuasive evidence that the market has functioned imperfectly and provide at least a partial explanation for the wide variety of actions by state and federal governments that comprise what might loosely be described as a special public policy toward the fertilizer industry.

As in the case of virtually all manufacturing industries, the fertilizer industry is subject to the constraining forces of our national antitrust policy. These forces, as will be shown later, have been exercised frequently. But, unlike most other manufacturing industries, the fertilizer industry is subject to considerable special regulations and policy measures. Since the 1880's, state governments have required that all fertilizer grades be registered with the appropriate state authority and that the plant nutrient content be clearly indicated on the bag. The federal government has actively engaged in fertilizer research since about 1900 and, in 1933, through the Tennessee Valley Authority, became an important producer and distributor of high-analysis fertilizers. As the pace of government activity quickened in the 1930's, there gradually evolved a national fertilizer policy which first took the form of an express statement when the U.S. Department of Agriculture's Interbureau Coordinating Committee on Fertilizer issued its first report in 1941.[4] Succeeding statements were issued in 1945 and 1952. The nation's fertilizer policy, as broadly defined in these statements, was to encourage increases in fertilizer production to meet future needs as estimated by the Department of Agriculture; to develop research and various action programs leading to more efficient production, distribution, and use of fertilizers; and to place certain responsibilities for attaining those objectives in federal agencies and the land-grant colleges.

While these two policies of public control—antitrust and positive fertilizer policy—presumably have the common purpose of reducing the social costs of market imperfections, each is addressed to imperfections arising from a different source. Antitrust policy has been used to attack monopoly power and trade restraints that, in the language of the welfare economist, prevent the market from being equilibrated at the "ideal" output. Positive policy has been used to foster more rational purchasing and use of fertilizers by farmers. Both policies, although by different means, have sought to promote technological innovations which reduce the costs of plant nutrients to the farmer. The two policies, at least in theory, complement each other. If farmers do not buy their fertilizers on the basis of the lowest cost per unit of plant nutrient, the market does not discipline producers to compete on this basis. In these circumstances, effective competition, or the absence of monopoly power, is

---

[4] *Report of the Interbureau Coordinating Committee on Fertilizer,* U.S.D.A. (Nov. 1, 1941).

not enough to insure efficient resource allocation in the production and use of fertilizers. The equilibrium prices and outputs would have been affected by the element of irrational demand even though supply conditions may have reflected perfect competition. The inefficiencies resulting from such irrational choice are peculiarly amenable to more positive policy measures appropriately administered.

## FERTILIZER AND RELATED INDUSTRIES: ORGANIZATION AND STRUCTURE

The fertilizer industry comprises all producers, processors, and mixers of fertilizer nitrogen, phosphate, and potash—the three principal plant nutrients. Producers and processors of sulphur might also be included on the grounds that one of the most important sources of $P_2O_5$, superphosphate, is produced from approximately equal parts of phosphate rock and sulphuric acid. In the flow of these plant nutrient bearing materials from mine and factory to the farmer, the producers of phosphatic fertilizers occupy a pivotal position. The American farmer buys over 60 percent of his fertilizers as mixtures containing at least two of the three principal plant nutrients. A large portion of the mixing industry is vertically integrated with the production and processing of phosphate rock. Nitrogen and potash producers do not sell significant quantities of their output to farmers; instead, they sell to integrated phosphate producers and unintegrated fertilizer mixers who in turn sell to farmers. Even the nitrogen and potash which farmers buy as straight materials usually reach them through those channels.

### The Phosphate Industry

The phosphate industry, including its critically integrated fertilizer operations, comprises three individual processes: the mining and beneficiation (preparation for smelting) of phosphate rock, the manufacture of phosphate fertilizer materials, and the manufacture of mixed fertilizers. The first consists of extracting phosphate rock from the ground and processing it for further manufacture. The second consists principally of the manufacture of ordinary and concentrated superphosphate. Ordinary superphosphate (about 22 percent available $P_2O_5$) is produced by appropriately blending approximately equal parts by weight of phosphate rock and a standard grade of sulphuric acid. Almost half of the ordinary superphosphate plants in the United States have facilities for producing their own sulphuric acid. These plants are buyers of crude sulphur; the remaining plants are buyers of sulphuric acid. Concentrated superphosphate (about 45 percent available $P_2O_5$) is produced by appropriately blending phosphate rock with phosphoric acid (also produced from phosphate rock) or by the electric furnace method. The $P_2O_5$ in superphosphate is much more readily available to growing plants than that in phosphate rock (estimated at from 3 percent to 10 percent available $P_2O_5$). The third industrial process consists of the manufacture of mixed fertilizers from superphosphate, nitrogen, and potash. In the 1962–63 fertilizer year, 32 percent of the N, 81 percent of the $P_2O_5$, and 86 percent of the $K_2O$ used as fertilizer in the United States were sold to the farmer as mixtures. But whether farmers purchased their plant nutrients in separate materials or in mixtures, they generally purchased them from mixed fertilizer manufacturers, the largest of which also produce phosphate rock and superphosphate.

The level of concentration of control among the three processes declines with each successive stage of fabrication, reflecting in part the declining cost of entry. As of 1950 (the latest available data), the five largest phosphate rock producers accounted for 70 percent of total domestic output (Table 14.1); in 1958, the four largest superphosphate producers accounted for 47 percent of total shipments and the four largest mixed fertilizer producers accounted for 24 percent of total mixed fertilizer shipments. In 1950, the six largest integrated producers accounted for 70 percent of the total output of phosphate rock, 50 percent of the total output of superphosphate, and 30 percent of the total output of mixed fertilizers. In addition to the six largest integrated producers, approximately 32 percent of the plants producing superphosphate were operated by companies that also produced mixed fertilizer, but none of these companies produced phosphate rock in substantial quantities, and only a few

TABLE 14.1

MARKET STRUCTURE OF THE INTEGRATED FERTILIZER INDUSTRY

| | 6 Largest Integrated Producers (1950) | No. Companies 1954 | No. Companies 1958 | Percent Value of Shipments 4 largest 1954 | Percent Value of Shipments 4 largest 1958 | Percent Value of Shipments 8 largest 1954 | Percent Value of Shipments 8 largest 1958 |
|---|---|---|---|---|---|---|---|
| Fertilizers | ... | 126 | 157 | 27 | 24 | 45 | 40 |
| Superphosphate and Other Phosphatic Fertilizer Materials | 50 | ... | ... | 50 | 47 | 70 | 68 |
| Mixed Fertilizers | 30 | 437 | 514 | ... | 24 | ... | 39 |
| Phosphate Rock* | 70 | 30 | ... | 70† | ... | ... | ... |

Source: *Concentration Ratios in Manufacturing, 1958,* Part I, U.S. Department of Commerce (Washington, 1962); and Jesse W. Markham, *The Fertilizer Industry: Study of an Imperfect Market* (Nashville: Vanderbilt University Press, 1958), p. 27.
  * 1950.
  † Five largest.

(principally two large regional cooperatives) produced phosphate rock at all.

## The Related Materials Markets

The integrated phosphate fertilizer manufacturers and their unintegrated competitors consume about one-fifth of the total output of sulphur in the production of superphosphates. Those that operate their own acid plants (approximately one-half the total) buy sulphur in the crude; those without acid plants buy sulphuric acid, in many cases from their integrated competitors. The phosphate fertilizer manufacturers and their unintegrated competitors buy over 90 percent of the total domestic output of potash and about one-half the total output of nitrogen. In the 1962–63 fertilizer year, 87 percent of the $K_2O$ and 35 percent of the N they bought and 78 percent of the $P_2O_5$ they produced went into the production of mixtures; and the rest was sold as separate materials. Probably because the sources of potash, nitrogen, and sulphur prior to World War I were located abroad, producers of these materials generally are not integrated with the manufacture of fertilizers.[5]

The markets in which the integrated phosphate and independent mixed fertilizer producers buy these materials have been characterized by high concentration of control, sometimes outright monopoly. Until World War I, a German cartel supplied nearly all the potash consumed in the United States. In the interwar period, a French-German importing agency and from one to three domestic potash mines were the only source of supply. In the mid-1950's, three large and three small domestic companies supplied 90 percent of total domestic consumption of potash and foreign companies supplied the remaining 10 percent. Before World War I, a Chilean nitrate cartel was the fertilizer industry's principal source of nitrogen. At the outbreak of World War II, Chilean sodium nitrate and the output of two domestic synthetic nitrogen producers accounted for over 90 percent of the N consumed by U.S. fertilizer manufacturers. After World War II, the level of concentration in nitrogen production gradually declined, largely because of the way the government disposed of its wartime-constructed nitrogen plants until, by 1962–63, the four largest companies accounted for only 29.5 percent and the number of independent domestic competitors had increased to fifty-one.[6] Until 1900, the United States imported most

---

[5] The Tennessee Valley Authority, a producer of nitrogen and phosphate fertilizers, and the International Minerals and Chemical Corporation, a large integrated fertilizer producer that also operates a potash mine, are two exceptions.

[6] Richard G. Walsh, "Changing Market Structure of the Fertilizer Industry," paper presented at the Ann. Meet. of the Midwest Econ. Assn., Apr. 27, 1963.

of its sulphur, principally from Italy. From 1903, when imports reached their peak and thereafter declined steadily until the present time, domestic sulphur production has been concentrated in the hands of four producers, the largest two accounting in most years for over 90 percent of total sales. In 1958, the four largest sulphuric acid manufacturers accounted for 58 percent and the eight largest for 76 percent of the total output of sulphuric acid.

The central economic issues posed by the organization and structure of the fertilizer and fertilizer materials markets are those relating to the efficiency with which competition regulates them and, in turn, to antitrust and positive policy. In the primary raw materials markets—phosphate rock, sulphur, potash, and nitrogen—concentration of control has traditionally been high and the sellers of these materials have been involved in numerous antitrust actions. However, these markets do not raise for positive policy the important problems of imperfect knowledge and irrational demand. So far as it can be determined, both integrated and unintegrated mixers generally produce particular grades of mixed fertilizer from the cheapest available sources of plant nutrients. While these are not necessarily the most economical fertilizers that could be made available to the farmer, they are produced from materials in which plant nutrients cost the least per unit. In comparison with farmers, mixers' demand is characterized by less irrational choice.

While sellers of mixed fertilizers and materials buy in highly concentrated markets, or are vertically integrated with them, they sell under conditions which, in terms of market structure, are not inconsistent with effective competition. Even though the four largest sellers in the local market might frequently account for the bulk of fertilizer sales, nearly all farmers have at least four or five large national fertilizer companies, several regional and local companies, and usually at least one farmer-owned cooperative as alternative sources of supply. A 1961 study of 73 Nebraska counties showed that each county on the average had twelve fertilizer dealers, of which three were farmer cooperatives, and that the four largest dealers, including cooperatives, accounted for about two-thirds of total sales.[7] However, the markets in which fertilizer manufacturers sell, and farmers buy, appear to be characterized by a fairly high order of imperfect knowledge and irrational demand which adversely affects the efficient functioning of competition as a market regulator. This is a market imperfection that lies beyond the reach of antitrust and requires remedial measures of a more positive sort.

---

[7] Richard G. Walsh and Robert A. Rathjen, "Nebraska Farmers Spend $50 Million a Year for Fertilizer," *Nebraska Experiment Station Quarterly* (Lincoln, Fall 1962), p. 18.

## PRODUCTION PATTERNS AND PRICING PRACTICES IN FERTILIZER AND FERTILIZER MATERIAL MARKETS

### The Phosphate Rock Industry

Over 90 percent of the domestic phosphate reserves are located in Florida, Tennessee, and the four western states of Idaho, Montana, Utah, and Wyoming. Under recovery methods and demand patterns that have prevailed since the origin of the industry, recovery rates among the three sources have varied considerably from the distribution of reserves: Florida, with an estimated 38 percent of domestic sources, supplied in 1962 over 70 percent of total rock output; Tennessee, with only 2 percent of total estimated reserves, supplied 12.5 percent; and the western states, with 60 percent of the reserves, supplied about 16 percent (Table 14.2). The substantial increase in the share of western rock over the past three decades reflects the gradual shift in the geographical center of fertilizer consumption away from the South toward the Midwest and West.

Approximately thirty active companies account for the rock output of the three producing areas—fifteen in Florida, nine in Tennessee, and eight in the west.[8] Seven of the large Florida producers, including their output in other regions, account for nearly three-fourths of all the phosphate rock output, a market share virtually the same companies have had since 1913. All seven are large manufacturers of superphosphates and six of the seven are large manufacturers of mixed fertilizers.

Rock producers typically sell about 80 percent of their output in the United States and export about 20 percent, almost all of which is exported from the Florida fields. In 1962, about 70 percent of the rock sold domestically went into agricultural uses, of which about 65 percent went into the production of superphosphates (Table 14.3). Because of the vertical integration between rock productions and rock-using industrial activities, somewhere between 35 percent and 50 percent of all the phosphate rock mined is consumed in the fertilizer and chemical operations of the mining companies. One of the more striking changes in use patterns in recent years has been the rapid increase in the percentage of rock used in the production of concentrated superphosphate and the corresponding decrease in the percentage used in the manufacture of the less concentrated ordinary superphosphate. In 1954, concentrated superphosphate accounted for only 12 percent of domestic consumption and ordinary for 47 percent; in 1962, each type

---

[8] Two companies operate in both Florida and Tennessee and are included in the totals for both states.

## TABLE 14.2

### PHOSPHATE ROCK MINED IN THE UNITED STATES 1868–1962, SELECTED YEARS, BY STATES

| Year | United States Total | South Carolina Long tons | South Carolina Percent | Florida Long tons | Florida Percent | Tennessee Long tons | Tennessee Percent | Western States Long tons | Western States Percent |
|---|---|---|---|---|---|---|---|---|---|
| 1868 | 12,262 | 12,262 | 100.00 | ... | ... | ... | ... | ... | ... |
| 1890 | 510,499 | 458,118 | 89.74 | 52,381 | 10.26 | ... | ... | ... | ... |
| 1900 | 1,491,216 | 329,173 | 22.07 | 706,243 | 47.36 | 454,491 | 30.48 | ... | ... |
| 1910 | 2,654,988 | 179,659 | 6.77 | 2,067,507 | 77.87 | 392,588 | 14.79 | ... | ... |
| 1920 | 4,103,982 | 44,141 | 1.08 | 3,369,384 | 82.10 | 621,396 | 15.14 | ... | ... |
| 1930 | 4,036,197 | ... | ... | 3,361,786 | 83.29 | 607,814 | 15.06 | 66,597 | 1.65 |
| 1940 | 4,068,077 | ... | ... | 2,782,950 | 68.41 | 1,120,551 | 27.54 | 164,570 | 4.05 |
| 1950 | 11,114,159 | ... | ... | 8,597,227 | 77.35 | 1,472,017 | 13.24 | 1,044,915 | 9.40 |
| 1960 | 17,516,000 | ... | ... | 12,321,000 | 70.40 | 1,939,000 | 11.00 | 3,256,000 | 18.60 |
| 1962 | 19,382,000 | ... | ... | 13,949,000 | 71.90 | 2,418,000 | 12.50 | 3,015,000 | 15.60 |

Sources: Jesse W. Markham, *The Fertilizer Industry: Study of the Imperfect Market* (Nashville: Vanderbilt University Press, 1958), p. 35; and *1962 Minerals Yearbook, Volume I*, U.S. Department of the Interior (Washington, 1963), p. 964.

# TABLE 14.3
## MAJOR USES OF DOMESTIC PHOSPHATE ROCK, 1954 AND 1962

| | 1954 | | | 1962 | | |
|---|---|---|---|---|---|---|
| | Long tons | Percent of total | Percent of total domestic consumption | Long tons | Percent of total | Percent of total domestic consumption |
| Fertilizers | 7,213,468 | 55 | 67 | 10,259,000 | 54 | 68 |
| Ordinary superphosphate | 5,069,176 | 39 | 47 | 4,963,000 | 26 | 33 |
| Concentrated superphosphate | 1,297,719 | 10 | 12 | 4,810,000 | 25 | 32 |
| Nitrophosphate | 12,851 | ... * | ... * | ... | ... | ... |
| Direct application to the soil | 774,016 | 6 | 7 | 493,000 | 2 | 3 |
| Fertilizer filler | 13,764 | ... * | 1 | ... | ... | ... |
| Other fertilizers | 45,942 | ... * | ... * | 3,000 | ... * | ... * |
| Other Agricultural Stock and Poultry Feed | 144,257 | 1 | 1 | 266,000 | 1 | 2 |
| Industrial | 3,407,527 | 26 | 32 | 4,591,000 | 24 | 30 |
| Elemental phosphorous, ferro-phosphorous and phosphoric acid | 3,403,210 | 26 | 32 | 4,584,000 | 24 | 30 |
| Undistributed | 4,317 | ... * | ... * | 7,000 | ... * | ... * |
| Total Domestic Consumption | 10,765,252 | 100 | 100 | 15,126,000 | 100 | 100 |
| Exports | 2,278,572 | 18 | | 3,934,000 | 21 | |
| Grand Total | 13,043,824 | 100 | | 19,060,000 | 100 | |

Sources: Jesse W. Markham, *The Fertilizer Industry: Study of the Imperfect Market* (Nashville: Vanderbilt University Press, 1958), p. 60; and *1962 Minerals Yearbook, Volume I*, U.S. Department of the Interior (Washington, 1963), p. 967.

* Less than 0.5 percent.

367

accounted for about 32 percent. This shift, as will be shown later, reflects the response of farmers' demand to the more economical high-analysis phosphate materials and fertilizer mixtures and a corresponding reduction in the social costs of the use of uneconomical fertilizers lost in plant nutrient content.

From the mid-1920's until the outbreak of World War II, phosphate rock export prices were greatly affected by international cartel arrangements, to which the Phosphate Export Association and the Florida Hard Rock Phosphate Export Association, two domestic Webb-Pomerene export associations organized by Florida producers, were parties. There is also considerable evidence that their enrollment in international cartel arrangements also affected domestic rock prices by making them higher and less flexible than they otherwise could have been[9]. The cartel activities came to an end with World War II and the two associations either voluntarily dissolved themselves or became inactive in 1945 after the Federal Trade Commission investigated their activities. The cessation of the Associations and the growing competition between Florida and western rock producers apparently have had the effect of injecting greater competition into the determination of phosphate rock prices. After World War II and the elimination of price controls, prices (based on a standard grade Florida pebble rock) rose from $2.00 to $5.00 per ton in response to the postwar phosphate fertilizer shortage. By 1950 prices had declined to $4.00 per ton and thereafter gradually moved upward to $4.80 by January 1960 and to $5.13 by December 1962.

### The Superphosphate Industry

Ordinary superphosphate manufacture requires a simple technology familiar to fertilizer manufacturers in the United States since 1850, and modest capital outlays. A mixture of approximately 1,100 pounds each of ground phosphate rock and sulphuric acid yields a short ton of superphosphate. Depending upon geographical location, these two materials account for from 9 percent to 95 percent of total production costs for the average plant having a capacity of 1,000 tons per day. Ordinary superphosphate plants tend to be located near their markets. The largest four of the nearly one hundred ordinary superphosphate manufacturers account for about one-third of the total ouput; the largest five, and six of the largest eight produce phosphate rock, and all of the largest eight are also large producers of mixed fertilizers.

Concentrated superphosphate, which generally contains over twice as much available $P_2O_5$ as the ordinary variety, can be pro-

---

[9] Markham, *op. cit.*, pp. 117–21.

duced by the wet, electric- or blast-furnace method. In the wet process, phosphate rock is treated with phosphoric acid, which has been primarily made by mixing finely ground phosphate rock with sulphuric acid. A ton of concentrated superphosphate (48 percent $P_2O_5$) produced by the wet process requires 3,105 pounds of high-grade phosphate rock and 595 pounds of sulphur; a ton produced by the electric-furnace method requires 3,210 pounds of rock, 415 pounds of coke, and 690 pounds of silica; and a ton produced by the blast-furnace method requires 3,420 pounds of rock, 2,840 pounds of coke, and 755 pounds of silica. The blast-furnace method is the least economical means of production and has not been used in the United States in recent years. Because of the rock requirements and the significant weight and bulk reductions involved in its manufacture, concentrated superphosphate is generally produced near its source of phosphate rock.

As of 1963, about fourteen companies operating seventeen plants comprised the concentrated superphosphate industry. Most of the producers are integrated phosphate rock and fertilizer manufacturers. Concentration data for recent years are not available for concentrated superphosphate separately, but it can be estimated with reasonable accuracy from data on ordinary superphosphate and ordinary and concentrated combined that the four largest producers accounted for about 75 percent of total output.[10] The technology of concentrated superphosphate is more complex than that for ordinary, the capital requirements much higher, and the economies of scale apparently more significant.[11] These factors account in part for the higher level of concentration of control.

For many years concentrated superphosphate has been the most economical source of $P_2O_5$, either when applied as a straight material or in high-analysis mixtures, for more farmers than have purchased their $P_2O_5$ requirements in this form. Recognizing this lag between rational and actual consumption patterns, federal and state governments have gradually developed over the years a comprehensive phosphate-fertilizer program. As early as 1894, the U.S. Department of Agriculture had pointed out in its *Yearbook* that

---

[10] In 1958, the four largest ordinary superphosphate manufacturers accounted for about one-third of total output of ordinary, and the four largest producers of all phosphates accounted for 47 percent of the output of all phosphate fertilizer. Since concentrated accounted for about one-third the total, it can be estimated from $\dfrac{2(33) + X}{3} = 47$, where $X$ is the concentration ratio for concentrated, that the four largest concentrated producers accounted for 75 percent.

[11] In 1963, seventeen concentrated superphosphate plants produced about the same quantity of $P_2O_5$ as 187 ordinary plants. Between 1960 and 1963, the output of concentrated rose 13 percent while the number of plants declined from twenty-two to seventeen.

the substitution of concentrated for ordinary superphosphate would result in considerable savings to farmers. The Tennessee Valley Authority built its agricultural program largely on concentrated superphosphate which it produced in significant quantities until 1958 and distributed through its test-demonstration program, farmer-owned cooperatives, and commercial producers who would promote the usage of the more economical high-analysis fertilizers. The TVA also conducted a large research program in the production of high-analysis phosphatic fertilizers.

While the gap between actual and optimum consumption of high-analysis phosphate fertilizers, and high-analysis fertilizers generally, has not been closed, it apparently has narrowed in recent years. The rapid rate at which concentrated has been substituted for ordinary superphosphate in direct application and in mixed fertilizer production is evident from the data presented in Table 14.4. As recently as 1950, concentrated accounted for scarcely more than 10 percent of total domestic $P_2O_5$ production. By 1963, it accounted for almost half, and had nearly quadrupled in output while that of ordinary was being reduced by 50 percent. Much of this shift to the more economical high-analysis fertilizers can unquestionably be attributed to the efforts behind the positive policies of federal and state governments.

### The Complementary Input Industries

The fertilizer industry buys, either in the form of crude or acid, about one-fifth of the domestic sulphur mined each year, principally

TABLE 14.4
ESTIMATED ANNUAL CAPACITY FOR PRODUCTION OF SUPERPHOSPHATES IN THE
UNITED STATES 1900–63
(in tons of $P_2O_5$)

| Year | Number of Plants | Ordinary Superphosphate | Number of Plants | Concentrated Superphosphate |
|------|------------------|-------------------------|------------------|------------------------------|
| 1900 | . . . | 335,000 | . . . | 1,000 |
| 1910 | 250 | 950,000 | 1 | 3,000 |
| 1920 | . . . | 1,440,000 | . . . | 7,000 |
| 1930 | . . . | 1,600,000 | 5 | 44,000 |
| 1940 | 145 | 1,511,883 | 8 | 180,000 |
| 1945 | 159 | 2,067,503 | 9 | 223,400 |
| 1947 | 176 | 2,384,433 | 7 | 220,000 |
| 1950 | 201 | 2,594,147 | 9 | 315,611 |
| 1960 | 211 | 1,269,523* | 22 | 985,636* |
| 1963 | 187 | 1,226,696* | 17 | 1,112,817* |

Source: Jesse W. Markham, *The Fertilizer Industry: Study of the Imperfect Market* (Nashville: Vanderbilt University Press, 1958), p. 60; and *Current Industrial Report*, U.S. Department of Commerce, 1961–64.
* Actual production figures.

for the production of superphosphates and ammonium sulfate. It also buys about one-half the domestic output of nitrogen and over 90 percent of the domestic output of potash to produce mixed fertilizer and to provide these plant nutrients as straight materials to farmers. Typically, none of the three complementary industries are integrated with the mainstream of fertilizer manufacturing, and neither nitrogen nor potash producers have maintained distribution channels for the sale of their products to the farmers. Since the mid-1950's, some producers of anhydrous ammonia, confronting a rapidly growing market for their product and an increased use of anhydrous ammonia as a straight material, have developed such channels, but the bulk of all the N and $K_2O$ consumed as fertilizer reaches the farmer through commercial fertilizer manufacturers and farmer cooperatives.

Historically, all these industries have been characterized by a high order of oligopoly and have preserved trade practices that precipitated numerous antitrust actions. Members of all three industries have been parties to international cartel agreements. Since the founding of the domestic sulphur industry, it has been in the hands of four producers, with the two largest accounting for over 90 percent of total output. Crude sulphur and sulphuric acid prices have been among the most inflexible prices in the American economy, usually remaining unchanged for a decade. For the thirty-year period ending in 1951, the least profitable of the four sulphur companies earned an average rate of return after federal income taxes of 13.7 percent on invested capital; the most profitable company averaged 25.3 percent. Over the past decade, profits in the industry have trended downward to about 8 percent to 10 percent and in the tax years 1961 and 1962 were much more uniform among producers. Over the same ten-year period, the wholesale price of crude sulphur declined from $26.50 to $23.50 per ton but the wholesale price of sulphuric acid remained unchanged at $22.35.

The structure of the potash industry has paralleled that of the sulphur industry. From its founding under the impetus of the cessation of imports and skyrocketing prices in World War I, the industry has been in the hands of a few large producers with those firms operating in the Carlsbad, New Mexico, fields accounting for over 90 percent of total domestic output. As new domestic producers entered the field, they adopted the prices quoted by the German-French potash cartel for Gulf and Atlantic ports as basing point prices and, thereby, sold throughout the United States at the cartel's prices and at uniform prices among themselves. This pricing system came to an end in 1940 with a consent decree permanently enjoining the large potash producers from agreeing, combining, or conspiring among themselves or with any other potash producers.[12] Since that date, potash has sold at prices quoted for Carlsbad and Trona, with the latter generally about $0.08 per unit of $K_2O$ higher than the Carlsbad price. In 1963 the price at Carlsbad was $0.40 and at Trona $0.485 per unit of $K_2O$, about the same as those prevailing in 1949, but both prices registered several changes between 1949 and 1963.

As in the case of sulphur producers, potash producers have typically earned high rates of return but profits have declined substantially in recent years. From 1936 to 1951 the three major companies averaged a rate of return on invested capital of 34 percent, 24.2 percent and 9.6 percent. In the three-year period 1960–62, these rates were respectively 8.3 percent, 5.3 percent, and 8.2 percent.

The synthetic nitrogen industry grew out of the need for munitions in World War I; restrictions on Chilean exports of sodium nitrate, the most important source of inorganic nitrogen until 1921; and the drive by such industrial nations as the United States, Great Britain, France, and Germany for national self-sufficiency in nitrogen. In the five-year period 1924–29, manufactured nitrogen for the world increased from 908,100 to 1,996,200 short tons of N while Chilean natural nitrogen output increased from 413,300 to only 556,000 short tons of N. As output increased and prices declined, producers turned to the formation of cartels to control prices. Apparently United States producers of synthetic and by-product nitrogen participated in the cartel arrangements and engaged in various restrictive practices on their own for, in 1939, following a Department of Justice investigation, five federal grand jury indictments were issued against the leading members of the industry and an importer of Chilean nitrate.[13] The defendants entered pleas of *nolo contendere* and, after payment of fines, the five cases were disposed of in three civil complaints resulting in consent decrees covering most of the allegations made by the government in the original indictment.[14]

Throughout the prewar period, the synthetic nitrogen industry was highly controlled, with two large chemical companies accounting for about 86 percent of total ouput. The two large producers,

---

[12] *United States v. American Potash and Chemical Corp.*, C.C.H. Trade Reg. Rep., Vol. III, par. 25461, cited in *Report on the Fertilizer Industry,* Federal Trade Commission (Washington, 1950), p. 102.

[13] *U.S. v. Allied Chem. & Dye Corp.*, Crim. Action No. 106-12; *U.S. v. Synthetic Nitrogen Prod., Inc.*, Crim. Action No. 106-16; *U.S. v. E.I. du Pont de Nemours & Co.*, Crim. Action No. 106-15; and *U.S. v. Chilean Nitrate Sales*, Crim. Action No. 106-14, U.S. District Court, So. Dist. of New York, Sept. 1, 1939.

[14] *U.S. v. Allied Chem. & Dye Corp.*, Civil Action No. 14-230 filed May 29, 1941); *U.S. v. Synthetic Nitrogen Products Corp.*, Civil Action No. 15-635 (filed Sept. 5, 1941); and *U.S. v. Imperial Chemical Industries (N.Y.) Ltd.*, Civil Action No. 17-282 (filed Feb. 17, 1942), U.S. District Court, So. Dist. of New York.

five smaller synthetic nitrogen producers, and about sixty-five producers of by-product nitrogen (principally sulphate of ammonia) comprised the domestic manufactured nitrogen industry in 1940. The great need for N during World War II resulted in a phenomenal increase in synthetic nitrogen capacity, most of which was contracted by the federal government. Between 1940 and 1945, capacity increased from 390,000 to 1,231,100 short tons of N, or by 841,100 short tons. The government constructed 800,300 short tons of the increase and private firms already in the industry constructed the remaining 40,800 short tons.

The government's selective disposal program after the war reduced the level of concentration below prewar levels and increased the number of synthetic nitrogen producers from seven to twelve (Table 14.5). However, the spectacular decline in concentration and the entry of new firms into the industry occurred in the

TABLE 14.5

STRUCTURE OF THE SYNTHETIC NITROGEN INDUSTRY, 1940, 1945, 1951, AND 1963

| | | 1945 | | | |
| | | Before disposal of gov't. plants | After disposal of gov't. plants | | |
| | 1940 | | | 1951 | 1963 |
|---|---|---|---|---|---|
| Largest Two | | | | | |
| Share of market | 86.8% | 30.6% | 44.7% | 39.8% | 18.5% |
| Number of plants | 3 | 3 | 5 | 5 | 6 |
| Largest Four | | | | | |
| Share of market | 95.6% | 33.4% | 72.5% | 62.7% | 29.5% |
| Number of plants | 5 | 5 | 7 | 7 | 11 |
| Largest Eight | | | | | |
| Share of market | 100.0% | 35.0% | 91.3% | 87.5% | 44.1% |
| Number of plants | 9 | 9 | 15 | 12 | 20 |
| Farmer Cooperatives | | | | | |
| Share of market | 0 | 0 | 0 | 2.6% | 12.2% |
| Number of plants | 0 | 0 | 0 | 2 | 8 |
| Government (including TVA) | | | | | |
| Share of market | 0 | 65.0% | 4.1% | 3.0% | 4.2% |
| Number of plants | 0 | 10 | 1 | 1 | 2 |
| Other | | | | | |
| Share of market | 0 | 0 | 4.6% | 6.9% | 39.5% |
| Number of plants | 0 | 0 | 3 | 4 | 41 |
| TOTAL | | | | | |
| Percent | 100 | 100 | 100 | 100 | 100 |
| Number of plants | 9 | 19 | 19 | 19 | 71 |
| Number of firms | 7 | 7 | 12 | 13 | 51 |
| TOTAL Synthetic Nitrogen | | | | | |
| (1000 tons) | 476 | 1,501.3 | 1,501.3 | 2,043 | 6,901 |

Sources: Adapted from Jesse W. Markham, *The Fertilizer Industry: Study of the Imperfect Market* (Nashville: Vanderbilt University Press, 1958), p. 103; and Richard G. Walsh, "Changing Market Structure of the Fertilizer Industry," a paper presented at the Annual Meeting of the Midwest Economic Association, April 27, 1963, p. 3.

1950's. Between 1951 and 1962–63, the market share of the top four firms declined from 62.7 to 29.5 percent, and the number of independent firms increased from thirteen to fifty-one. By most of the standards by which industrial structure is assessed, the structure of the synthetic nitrogen industry has evolved from a highly concentrated oligopoly to one consistent with effective competition in the short span of a decade. Over the same period (1951–62), the average wholesale price of anhydrous ammonia increased from $82 to $92 per ton, while the average price paid by farmers declined from $164 per ton in 1954 to $142 per ton in 1961. The decline in farmer prices is therefore attributable to the substantial shrinkage in the margins received by distributors and dealers, and a recent study of the anhydrous ammonia industry concludes that competition is still not sufficiently effective at the manufacturers level to eliminate monopoly profits and to force producers to operate at optimum scale and output rates.[15]

### The Mixed-Fertilizer Industry

Mixed fertilizers and fertilizer materials, including N and $K_2O$, are distributed to farmers principally through mixed-fertilizer manufacturers and through agents and dealers. A simple technology and low capital requirements have led to numerous mixed-fertilizer producers. In 1958, a total of 671 independent firms (including 514 engaged only in mixing) and 157 integrated firms operated 968 mixed-fertilizer plants. Plants are market oriented, with most plants selling well over half their output within a radius of fifty miles from the plant site. Despite the ease of entry and number of producers, a few large integrated phosphate fertilizer firms acquired a significant share of the nation's mixing capacity through wholesale merger between the late 1890's and 1913, which they still hold today. In 1958, the four largest firms accounted for 24 percent of mixed-fertilizer shipments and the largest eight for 39 percent. At least seven of the largest eight are large integrated phosphate rock and phosphate fertilizer companies.

Except for the monopolistic elements contained in the prices of the N, $P_2O_5$, $K_2O$, and $H_2SO_4$ that go into the manufacture of mixed fertilizers, and except for those periods when mixers are involved in price-fixing arrangements, mixed-fertilizer prices reflect considerable competition. Typically, except in certain periods of scarce wartime shortages, rates of return to mixers are low, margins over costs are low, and farmers have a reasonably wide range of choice among sources of supply and often have a range of choice as to price.[16] In fact, probably the best evidence that strong competi-

---

[15] Walsh, *op. cit.*, pp. 14–15.
[16] Markham, *op. cit.*, pp. 159–64.

tive forces regulate fertilizer prices is the frequent attempts on the part of producers to circumvent them. In 1906, 1926, 1941, and 1964, the Department of Justice brought antitrust actions against a large number of fertilizer firms for conspiring to fix prices and for engaging in other restraints of trade.

But while, absent conspiracy, fertilizer prices tend to reflect effective competition, the industry has, over most of its history, lacked that creative entrepreneurship that constantly seeks to improve the product and techniques of production. In truth, until recently, entrepreneurs engaged in the manufacture of mixed fertilizers not only failed to innovate, they even failed to transmit to the farmer the benefits of innovation in industries that supplied their raw materials. For example, in 1910, mixers relied heavily on such raw materials as cottonseed meal, castor pomace, animal tankage, fish scrap, low-grade potash salts, and 12 percent to 16 percent superphosphate. Almost any balanced combination of such materials yielded a mixed fertilizer containing a maximum of about 15 percent plant nutrients. The average plant nutrient content of mixed fertilizers in 1910 was 14.8 or very close to the maximum. Over the past fifty years, however, the chemical industries have developed fertilizer materials having from four to ten times the plant nutrient content of those used in 1910. Chemical nitrogenous materials containing up to 82 percent plant nutrients have replaced low-analysis organic sources of nitrogen. Kainite and manure salts, once the chief source of potash, have since 1920 been gradually replaced by 60 percent muriate of potash. And over the years the $P_2O_5$ content of superphosphates has increased from 12 percent to nearly 50 percent. But in 1950, the average plant nutrient content was still only 22 percent, and 16 percent of the average bag of mixed fertilizer was nonnutrient-bearing filler. In 1963, the average plant nutrient content had climbed to 34 percent, registering a greater increase in the past thirteen years than had occurred over the previous half century. However, even though the gap between optimum and actual plant nutrient content has been closing in recent years, a gap, as will be shown later on, still exists.

Entrepreneurs in the fertilizer industry have not overlooked the newer and more economical sources of plant nutrients. On the contrary, they have substituted them for the less economical low-analysis materials on a large scale. But they have not transmitted the economic gains from technological progress by successfully introducing and promoting the high-analysis fertilizers they could produce and sell at lower costs per unit of plant nutrient. In part this has been the result of imperfect knowledge and irrational demand; farmers have not always purchased those high-analysis fertilizers in which a given quantity and combination of plant nutrients were obtainable at the lowest cost. Such uneconomical buying practices seem to have had the effect of laying a dead hand on the supply side of the market by depriving producers of the incentive to promote the more economical fertilizers. But it has also resulted from entrepreneurial lethargy in the form of succumbing to imperfect knowledge rather than overcoming it.

## THE SOCIAL COSTS OF MARKET IMPERFECTIONS

An abundance of manufacturing, mixing, and transportation cost data show that, as the plant nutrient content of mixed fertilizers and straight fertilizer materials increases, the cost per unit of plant nutrient delivered to the farm decreases. This is to be expected since many of the costs items such as transportation, bagging, storage, handling, mixing, and other such costs vary with total weight of product irrespective of its plant nutrient content. These costs per unit of plant nutrient are cut in half as the nutrient content per ton is doubled. Prevailing market prices generally reflect, at least in substantial part, these differences in costs. Under rational demand patterns and effective competition in all fertilizer and fertilizer materials markets, one fertilizer grade and analysis should be made at the lowest cost per unit of plant nutrient, and those grades and analyses in which a given quantity and combination of plant nutrients are delivered to the farmer at the lowest cost should drive the more costly grades and analyses in terms of plant nutrient costs out of the market. The latter situation should prevail even when, as already indicated, some materials prices contain elements of monopoly.

A comparison of the actual and optimal fertilizer consumption patterns under given technical and price constraints is fraught with complexities. About one thousand grades and analyses of mixed fertilizers are marketed each year. However, forty grades generally account for 90 percent of all sales. Only a small percentage of all the thousand grades and analyses can be compared on a price and quantity basis. For example, a ton of 10-10-6 fertilizer contains twice the plant nutrients, and in exactly the same combination, as a ton of 5-5-3, and half as much plant nutrients as one ton of 20-20-12. Stated another way, unless two tons of 5-5-3 fertilizer can be laid down at the farm at a price not exceeding that of one ton of 10-10-6, the farmer is purchasing unwisely if he buys the desired plant nutrients in the form of 5-5-3 mixtures.

Direct comparisons can be made of fertilizer grades and analyses accounting for about 18 percent of all the mixed fertilizer sold annually. If it can be assumed that the social costs of irrational choice, i.e., the purchasing of less economical sources of plant nutrients when more economical sources were available on the market, and this 18 percent is a reliable sample of fertilizer purchasing generally, it can be estimated that, in 1949, such costs amounted to $61 million, or 10.5 percent of the nation's total mixed-fertilizer bill.[17] And since the total tonnage of high-analysis fertilizers required to obtain the plant nutrients actually purchased would have amounted to only 63.7 percent of the actual tonnage, reductions in on-the-farm costs of handling and applying fertilizers to the soil would have resulted in additional savings.

Since 1949, as the average plant nutrient content of mixed fertilizer has increased markedly, the social cost of irrational buying apparently has diminished but not disappeared. According to similar calculations made by Professor Zvi Griliches, the "cost of imperfect knowledge" dropped to $20 million in 1954 and rose to $44.6 million in 1958. And as Griliches points out, all of this may not be attributable to irrational choice since a part of these calculated potential savings are attributable to the ever-recurring disequilibria in the market as new fertilizers are introduced and old price-quantity relations and price differentials are altered.

## PUBLIC POLICY AND THE FERTILIZER INDUSTRY

The fertilizer industry offers an interesting and complex opportunity to apply the standards of effective competition and assess the effectiveness of public policy. As in the case of numerous American industries, most of the basic materials entering the fertilizer industry are purchased under a high order of oligopoly. Price and production patterns, cost-price relationships, and profits in these industries generally have reflected this structure. Public policy toward those markets, except where they overlap with defense objectives, has consisted almost entirely of applying the antitrust laws. Virtually all the fertilizer materials industries have been defendants in frequent antitrust suits.

The markets in which fertilizer manufacturers are sellers and farmers are buyers, however, present different public policy issues. In these markets, buyers and sellers are numerous but information and buyer knowledge have been imperfect. Public policy toward these markets has consisted of antitrust policy and a variety of state and federal programs designed to eliminate the social costs of unwise fertilizer-purchasing practices by featuring more economical fertilizer usage.

Neither antitrust nor positive policy has completely attained its feasible objectives. Competition, absent conspiracies, and other agreements among manufacturers in restraint of trade appear to have increased in recent years but still do not appear to discipline

---

[17] For the detailed calculation see Markham, *op. cit.*, p. 194.

all firms to produce at the lowest possible costs and sell at competitive prices. Moreover, throughout much of its history, including the present time, producers allegedly have operated under restrictive agreements. And the social costs of imperfect knowledge and irrational choice, while greatly reduced in recent years, have not entirely disappeared. The challenges to those entrusted with both policies in the past remain the challenges to those entrusted with these policies in the future, although perhaps in both cases they are of smaller magnitude.

# 15

# CROSS-SECTIONAL ANALYSIS
# OF THE AGRICULTURAL
# INDUSTRIES

## JOHN R. MOORE

### AND

## RICHARD G. WALSH

RECENT CHANGES in the structure and behavior of industries specialized in supplying agricultural inputs and marketing agricultural products have raised a number of important questions concerning the future of the agricultural economy.

Does the organization of industries related to agriculture contain the number and size of firms consistent with an efficient and competitive market system? Does an emphasis on the nonprice dimensions of competitive behavior build into the system costs which tend to shield inefficient techniques of rivals, suppliers, or customers? Does quality conform to consumer's interests, and are opportunities for better products realized? Are profits at levels which reward investment, efficiency, and innovation at necessary but not excessive rates? Are the existing services and regulatory programs of the federal government achieving workable market conditions in terms of an equitable distribution of power as well as optimum levels of efficiency?

This chapter is designed to provide insight and to help answer some of the many questions that have been raised. It contains a cross-sectional treatment of 14 agricultural industries drawn primarily from the preceding chapters. Its specific objectives are:

1. To classify the different types of structure, conduct, performance, and remedies found in the markets of agricultural industries, and to estimate the degree of adequacy for each;
2. To explain, however tentatively, why some agricultural industries perform more or less adequately than others.

## NORMATIVE NATURE OF THE ANALYSIS[1]

Research underlying the previous 14 chapters is primarily in the realm of positive economics. In other words, analysis of the nature, causes, and consequences of changes in market structure, conduct, and performance of an industry may deal entirely with questions of what is, rather than what should be. In this chapter, we attempt to evaluate the adequacy of market situations described in the preceding chapters and the suitability of alternative remedies available. These are normative questions, and ask what should be.

Had we presented these industry studies only a few decades ago, the normative questions under discussion here would not likely have appeared. For at that juncture in the development of economic theory and research, the concepts of perfect competition and monopoly would have provided sufficient answers to the normative problem. Economists had derived principles concerning the socially desirable performance of an industry characterized by large numbers of small firms, uniform products, and free entry and exit at one end of the scale, and of single-firm monopoly at the other. Thus, if in the baking industry we had found market concentration high, we would have concluded that "the market is not sufficiently competitive." For this conclusion follows from the ideal of perfect competition, as does the antitrust remedy: break up the large firms into small ones. Or if our research into an agriculture-related market had found a natural monopoly, the obvious remedy would have been governmental commission regulation. This either-or variety of normative appraisal was precise. Moreover, its meaning was clear; the professional economist and the average citizen alike had long considered "competition" socially desirable and "monopoly" socially undesirable.

We have available today the considerable progress in economic theory and research of the past 30 years. Contemporary students of industrial organization have found that concepts of perfect competition and monopoly are not reliable bases for the normative appraisal of capitalistic markets,[2] and have tried to formulate ex-

---

[1] The authors acknowledge the substantial contribution made by Stephen H. Sosnick upon whose summarized dissertation this section builds. The dissertation, "Contemporary Norms for Market Structure and Behavior: A Critical Appraisal," was deposited in the library of the University of California, Berkeley, in 1956. The summary appeared as "A Critique of Concepts of Workable Competition," *The Quarterly Journal of Economics* (Aug. 1958), pp. 380–423.

[2] "These arguments are well known and need not be detailed here. What they amount to is recognition that the perfectly competitive structure and conduct are unattainable in any real market, that closer approximation to them may entail worse performance than more distant. . . . The argument covers a variety of issues—nonoptimum conditions elsewhere, economies of scale, poor management, capital shortage, requisites and effects of exploration and of research and development, external economies and diseconomies, dispersion and individuality in traders and variety in outputs, immobile excess capacity, chronic distress, unfair tactics, depression-spreading, incorrect and inconsistent expectations. . . ." For a reference list, see the Sosnick articles, *op. cit.*, pp. 383–94.

plicit criteria of adequate (or workable) and optimum market situations under various intermediate gradations of oligopoly, monopolistic competition, or imperfect market structure. Thus, to a contemporary student of market structure analysis, "if a reduction (or an increase) in a market's concentration proves desirable, it is better to say so directly, not to suggest that the conclusion follows from an ideal of perfect competition."[3] The traditional "monopoly problem," associated with the evils of high concentration, is not very helpful when investigating actual markets. Substituted in its place is the *whole problem of achieving a socially desirable market situation.* The definition of adequacy now encompasses the satisfactory state of all relevant market conditions. A market is defined as *adequate* if its actual performance is not extremely detrimental to the general material welfare with respect to any single market condition, nor moderately detrimental with respect to several. A market is defined as *optimum* if its actual structure, conduct, and performance are as favorable in all respects as unavoidable circumstances permit.

Obviously, not all market conditions will be relevant. As the approach has developed, more and more economists have considered it useful to classify criteria of adequacy into three categories—market structure, conduct, and performance. The widespread interest in giving more precise meaning to these categories and in establishing criteria by which to test their adequacy in terms of the public interest has greatly increased the need for industrial studies which will both illuminate the concepts and furnish guides for public policy. Recently, writers have brought together and related the more important norms of market structure, conduct, and performance developed over the past 30 years, synthesized the common elements in these theories, and formulated them into a framework useful for empirical inquiry. This body of normative theory was termed "workable competition"[4] in its early development, but more recently has been identified by the narrower and less emotive "workable market criteria"[5] and "market structure analysis."[6] Even in its current transitory state, it presents useful criteria.

---

[3] *Ibid.,* p. 385.

[4] J. M. Clark, "Toward a Concept of Workable Competition," *American Economic Review* (June 1940), pp. 241–56.

[5] "Competition" is a misleading term. The term "workable competition" became an expression for labeling whatever standards a writer puts into the workability criteria. It is better to speak just of "adequate" (or "workable") and "optimum" *market situations.* This avoids the implication that atomism and other approximations to perfect competition are either necessary or sufficient market conditions to enhance the general material welfare. Sosnick, *op. cit.,* p. 413. This is not to imply that the number and size of firms is less significant than performance criteria, but rather that both are potentially significant.

[6] Robert L. Clodius and Willard F. Mueller, "Market Structure Analysis as an Orientation for Research in Agricultural Economics," *Journal of Farm Economics* (Aug. 1961), pp. 513–53.

## CRITERIA OF WORKABLE MARKETS[7]

The criteria of workability or adequacy applied here include the following structural dimensions:

1. A large number of companies or no more nor less than plant scale economies and competition permit.
2. Size of company or market concentration no greater than plant scale economies and competition require.
3. Vertical integration no more nor less than efficiency and competition require.
4. Entry as free as the nature of the industry permits.

The criteria of market conduct applied here are:

1. No unfair, exclusionary, predatory, or coercive tactics.
2. No misleading sales promotion.
3. No tacit or express price collusion.
4. No shielding of inefficient practices.
5. No pricing practices which discourage uniform high quality and uniform seasonal output.

The criteria of market performance applied here are:

1. Operations efficient with respect to procurement, plant utilization, plant scale, and distribution.
2. Reasonable promotion expenses.
3. Product quality conforming to consumer's interests.
4. Attention to opportunities for better products and techniques.
5. Output consistent with the optimum allocation of resources.
6. Profits at levels which reward investment, efficiency, and innovation at necessary but not excessive rates.

What basis is there for the selection of these market criteria in the appraisal of agriculture-related industries? Whatever precedent may have been established by 18 writers reviewed by Sosnick is not very reassuring. Their views have changed through time and the criteria used in their analyses have differed in many ways. In general, their derivation has consisted of *assuming* a connection with one or another of the basic goals of our society: greater per capita production, advantageous composition of output, equitable distribution of economic opportunity, favorable influence on the achievement of noneconomic values, and the like. Perhaps, as widely believed, these kinds of judgments are necessarily tentative, but we are convinced that it is possible to minimize the range of possible speculation and dispute about such matters in agricultural marketing research.

---

[7] See Sosnick, *op. cit.*, pp. 389–91, for these and alternative criteria suggested by 18 contemporary writers in the field.

Most of the criteria selected originate in the existing public regulatory and agricultural marketing research legislation. Generally, the former are concerned with the market power criteria and the latter with cost criteria.

Antitrust legislation provides a relationship between certain market power criteria and the equitable distribution of economic opportunity. The Congress of the United States in 1890 forbade a single firm or a group of firms acting jointly to gain a substantially exclusive domination of an industry or a market area (the Sherman Act). In the Federal Trade Commission Act of 1914, Congress set up an independent regulatory commission to police industries against "all unfair methods of competition."[8] The Clayton Act of the same year singled out four specific practices which tended to lessen competition. Through these and more recent preventive measures, Congress has pointed to market power as a criterion of performance of agricultural (and other) markets, and has prescribed specific remedial action. Moreover, Congress has established a connection between public welfare and the prohibited use of market power.

A basis for selecting certain other market criteria may be found in the enabling legislation under which several studies which underlie the chapters in this book were made. The Congress of the United States in 1946 specified that the primary objective of publicly supported research into the economic problems of marketing agricultural products is to improve the efficiency of marketing methods and facilities, and to reduce distribution costs.[9] Congress declared that "an efficient marketing system to distribute in an economical and orderly manner that which is produced" by agriculture is indispensable to "the welfare, prosperity, and health of the nation."[10] Thus, Congress has set efficiency as a norm or criterion of performance in agriculture-related markets and has established a connection between market efficiency and the public welfare.

While suggestive, the list of workable market criteria developed here is by no means exhaustive. Some important market criteria may have been overlooked. Others, although related to important economic goals in our society, may not yet have legal bases. Surely there are additional norms of behavior that are not economic in nature. But the achievement of noneconomic values is usually not a part of industrial analysis. Market criteria are usually limited to the "economic" unless the research is to cover everything involved to which society assigns value. This is not to imply that non-

[8] Senate Rept. 695, 63rd Cong., 2nd Sess., 1914, p. 1.
[9] U.S.C. 1621 (Public Law 733, 79th Cong., Title II, Sec. 202).
[10] H. Rep. 2458, 79th Cong., 2nd Sess., July 8, 1946.

economic values may not be of primary importance to individuals and groups.

An important implication of this discussion is that changes in market concentration and price policy in agricultural markets can (or must) be appraised in terms of market efficiency or cost criteria. Economic analysts, who have operated within the normative cloak of the existing regulatory remedies only, may have lacked Congressional sanction for a thoroughgoing application of cost norms in market structure analysis. The agricultural marketing act of 1946 may provide agricultural economists with considerable normative advantage over market researchers in nonagricultural areas. This creates a situation in which agricultural marketing research can make important contributions to improving the service and regulatory programs of the federal government.

## CONCENTRATION, INTEGRATION, AND EFFICIENCY IN THE AGRICULTURAL INDUSTRIES

A first question concerns the workability of the organization of the agricultural industries. This question has two aspects related to market power and to costs. The market power issue is whether firms will be required by market conditions to attain optimum scale in order to survive, or whether they will have effective options as to the scale and comparative efficiency they attain and will be able to survive at nonoptimum scales if they find it more profitable or otherwise desirable to do so. This possibility is relevant because practically all of the industries sampled have a sufficient degree of seller concentration to be classified as, in one sense or another, oligopolies. For example, in 12 of the 14 industries, 30 percent or more of total output is supplied by the largest 8 firms in the industry.

The substantiative cost issue is whether firms have attained but not exceeded the minimum degree of concentration required in an industry to attain maximum efficiency insofar as efficiency is influenced by plant size and utilization. The larger the share of the market a plant of minimum optimum scale will supply when fully utilized, the fewer the number of plants needed to efficiently supply the product—thus, the fewer the number of efficient companies the industry can accommodate. If in local market A, one plant of minimum optimum scale supplies 25 percent of market demand, then the market can at most accommodate only four plants (each a firm) of efficient scale, and seller concentration will be quite high if efficiency in plant scale is to be attained. In industry B, on the other hand, it may be that one plant of minimum optimum scale will supply only 2 percent of industry output, in which case as many as 50 firms of efficient scale can coexist in the industry, thus allowing much lower concentration consistent with efficiency. The pursuit of efficiency, or lower unit costs, may thus lead to widely differing degrees of concentration among different agricultural industries and markets.

Public interest is concerned with the possibility of maximizing the number of efficient plants to enlarge economic opportunity and widen the distribution of income in the agricultural industries. It matters little that, in some industries, plants many times the size of the minimum optimum scale may be equally efficient. Moreover, the existence of multi-plant firms is probably unnecessary. Several of the industry chapters contained in this volume cite studies of the economies of multi-plant firms associated with management, distribution, and buying from suppliers which show that they are generally small and, when present, can usually be achieved by smaller single-plant companies through voluntary association and other means.

The importance of plant scale economies in an industry depends on (1) the relation between the size of a minimum optimum sized plant and the size of the market, and (2) the extent of the difference between costs of optimum and smaller plants. Additional research is necessary in the case of most agriculture-related industries to say with reasonable assurance how many plants are excessive, and to make an accurate estimate of the aggregate misallocation of resources involved.[11] But the evidence available seems sufficient to conclude that the number of plants is more or less than adequate.

Table 15.1 compares recent levels of concentration and vertical integration to that required for efficiency and competition in the 14 agriculture-related industries. The recent trend in number and size of companies in these industries is compared to the *minimum* degree of concentration required in each industry to attain maximum efficiency (lowest cost per unit) insofar as efficiency is influenced by plant size and utilization.

Indications are that there is an excessive number of companies processing and marketing most farm inputs and farm products. At the national industry level, there is an excessive number of companies in 13 of the 14 agricultural industries considered, and an adequate number in only one. The trend is not very different in local markets of limited geographic coverage. There is an excessive

---

[11] Under conditions of technological change in these industries, there may be some plants that have become obsolescent, but continue to operate because it is more economic to do so than to junk the old equipment and build a new minimum optimal scale plant. Its unit costs of operation are as low as for the new plant. The evidence available suggests that such plants are infrequently found in these industries. Plants considered excessive are those with costs higher than a minimum optimal scale plant.

TABLE 15.1

ADEQUACY OF THE NUMBER AND SIZE OF COMPANIES AND VERTICAL INTEGRATION IN 14 AGRICULTURE-RELATED INDUSTRIES

| Industry | Large Number of Companies or No More nor Less Than Plant Scale Economies and Competition Permit | | Size of Company and Market Concentration No Greater Than Plant Scale Economies and Competition Require | | Vertical Integration No More nor Less Than Efficiency and Competition Require | |
|---|---|---|---|---|---|---|
| | National industry | Local market | National industry | Local market | Ownership | Contract |
| Grocery Retailing | Excessive number, improving* | Inadequate number, improving | Excessive size, deteriorating† | Excessive size, deteriorating | Excessive amount, deteriorating | Excessive amount, deteriorating |
| Meat Packing Fresh | Excessive number, deteriorating | Excessive number, deteriorating | Excessive size, improving | Inadequate size, improving | Excessive amount, deteriorating | Excessive amount, deteriorating |
| Processed | Excessive number, deteriorating | Excessive number, improving | Excessive size, deteriorating | Inadequate size, improving | Excessive amount, deteriorating | Excessive amount, deteriorating |
| Broiler Chicken | Excessive number, improving | Excessive number, improving | Excessive size | ... | Excessive amount, deteriorating | About adequate |
| Fluid Milk | Excessive number, improving | Excessive number | Excessive size, deteriorating | Inadequate size, improving | Excessive amount, deteriorating | Excessive amount |
| Ice Cream | Excessive number, improving | Excessive number | Excessive size, deteriorating | Inadequate size, improving | Excessive amount, deteriorating | Adequate |
| Vegetable Processing | Excessive number, improving | Excessive number, improving | Excessive size, improving | Inadequate size, improving | Excessive amount, deteriorating | Excessive amount, deteriorating |
| Apple Processing | Adequate | Inadequate number, improving | Adequate | Excessive size, improving | ... | ... |

| Industry | Large Number of Companies or No More nor Less Than Plant Scale Economies and Competition Permit | | Size of Company and Market Concentration No Greater Than Plant Scale Economies and Competition Require | | Vertical Integration No More nor Less Than Efficiency and Competition Require | |
|---|---|---|---|---|---|---|
| | National industry | Local market | National industry | Local market | Ownership | Contract |
| Baking | Excessive number, improving | Excessive number, improving | Excessive size, deteriorating | Inadequate size, improving | Excessive amount, deteriorating | Excessive amount, deteriorating |
| Soybean Processing | Excessive number, improving | Excessive number, improving | Excessive size, deteriorating | Inadequate size, improving | ... | ... |
| Grain Procurement | Excessive number, improving | Excessive number, improving | Excessive size, improving | Inadequate size, improving | Excessive amount | Excessive amount |
| Mixed Feed | Excessive number, improving | Excessive number, deteriorating | Excessive size, deteriorating | Inadequate size, deteriorating | Excessive amount, deteriorating | Excessive amount, deteriorating |
| Cotton | Excessive number, improving | ... | Excessive size, deteriorating | ... | ... | ... |
| Farm Machinery Tractors | Excessive number, improving | Excessive number, improving | Excessive size, deteriorating | Inadequate size, improving | Excessive amount, deteriorating | Adequate |
| Implements | Excessive number, deteriorating | Excessive number, improving | Excessive size, deteriorating | Inadequate size, improving | Excessive amount, deteriorating | Adequate |
| Fertilizer | Excessive number | Inadequate number, improving | Excessive size, improving | Inadequate size, improving | Excessive amount, deteriorating | Excessive amount, deteriorating |

* Recent changes have resulted in improvement of the condition.
† Recent changes have resulted in deterioration of the condition.

387

number of companies in local markets of 10 agriculture-related industries. The number of companies is considered inadequate or fewer than would be consistent with scale economies and competition in the local markets of only three industries. Data were unavailable for an estimate in one industry.

Are market conditions leading toward a more workable number of companies in the agricultural industries? Apparently so. The recent trend toward reduced numbers of companies in 11 of the 13 industries for which we have an estimate is a necessary condition for efficient organization of the agricultural industries. This development allows single-plant companies to more nearly approach optimum plant efficiency consistent with size of market.

Despite an excessive number of companies in agricultural industries, the size of a few large, multi-plant companies in all but one of the industries studied was greater than scale economies and competition would require. Available economies of scale and utilization could be realized by single-plant companies smaller than the largest multi-plant companies in these industries, so that industrial concentration could be reduced at the national level without adverse effects on efficiency.

The size of companies in markets with limited geographic coverage is quite another matter. The situation appears to be the very reverse of that found at the national or industry level. In the local markets of 10 of the 12 industries for which information is sufficient for an estimate, the size of some companies and their market shares were insufficient to realize optimum plant efficiency. In only two industries, grocery retailing (multi-plant) and apple processing (single-plant), was size of company in local market areas considered larger than necessary to achieve optimum plant efficiency.

Are there any historical tendencies apparent which are leading us toward more adequate size of companies in the agricultural industries? The trend is mixed. At the national industry level, there is a trend toward increased size of company and higher levels of concentration in nine of the industries, with decreased concentration in four industries.[12] But in local market areas, a trend toward increased size of company in nine industries reflects the fact

---

[12] Fletcher estimated industry concentration levels for all census-defined agriculture-related industries for 1947 and for 1958. At the eight-firm level, for input industries, the average degree of concentration was 57.8 percent in 1947 and 56.6 percent in 1958. For processing industries, this was 53.6 percent in 1947 and 47.8 percent in 1958. These calculations suggest a slight decline on the input side of agriculture, and a significant decline in concentration on the output or product side of agriculture. Agricultural processing industries are still slightly more concentrated than all U.S. manufacturing industries (45.4 percent), but the decline since 1947 has substantially reduced the difference. Lehman B. Fletcher, "Market Structure and Market Power," *Farmers in the Market Economy* (Ames: Iowa State Univ. Press, 1964).

that single-plant companies are more nearly approaching optimum plant efficiency consistent with size of market.

Insofar as firms are impelled by conditions in an industry or by a desire to minimize their costs, they will tend to undertake cost-saving vertical integration. This will increase the size of firms, though not necessarily their share of the market for end products which they supply. A vegetable processing firm supplying 15 percent of the total market demand for vegetables, for example, might integrate downward by contract or operate enough vegetable production acreage to meet the needs of its processing plants, and thus become a larger firm, but still only supply 15 percent of the vegetables sold in his market. In addition, of course, firms may undertake vertical integration which has neutral effects on costs, if they can derive some other advantage from the integration such as increased market power, for example, to exclude new competitors. Vertical integration to achieve market power is considered contrary to the public interest in expanding economic opportunities in a private enterprise economy.

The extent of vertical integration in the agriculture-related industries is greater than required by considerations of efficiency and competition in at least 10 of the 13 industries for which an estimate was made. Recent increases in vertical integration in all but one of these industries suggest that this market condition is deteriorating. Vertical integration by agriculture-related industries, in virtually every case,[13] has had either a neutral or adverse effect on costs while exerting an adverse effect on competition by increasing the integrators' market power. For example, the vertical integration of grocery chains into bread baking has had an adverse effect on costs in the baking industry and places the industry under a severe handicap in securing outlets for its products on grocery shelves. A notable exception is a type of contractual vertical integration of farm machinery manufacturers and their distributors which appears to increase the efficiency of distribution and repair services without undue restrictions on dealer competition.

## BARRIERS TO ENTRY IN THE AGRICULTURAL INDUSTRIES

Barriers to entry include the obstacles firms must overcome to enter a market or industry. They are a measure of the advantage of already established firms in the industry over potential additional firms. They are important in the agricultural industries because they measure the potential of new competition to improve the conduct and performance of sellers who are already in the industries. If the established companies in an industry have some im-

---

[13] In broiler chickens, vertical integration has had a beneficial effect on costs.

portant advantage over possible entrants, they will be able to set prices above least-cost levels without attracting other producers to enter, because the disadvantage of the possible entrant precludes his making satisfactory profits at such prices.

Chief among the potential entry barriers considered here are product differentiation, access to suppliers and outlets, plant scale economies, and capital requirements. A fifth possible entry barrier is the absolute cost advantages of established firms in the control of superior production techniques by patents or secrecy, in the monopolization of resources, and in the prices paid for factors of production arising, for example, in more favorable access to the money market. The available evidence suggests that absolute cost advantages are low or nonexistent in the 14 agriculture-related industries discussed here, and further attention to entry barriers will be directed to other conditions. Access to suppliers has been regarded as an absolute cost advantage by some authors, but will be considered separately here. Access to outlets for products has been judged an aspect of product differentiation elsewhere, but is considered along with access to supplies here. Product differentiation advantages include the accumulated preferences of buyers for an established brand name and company reputation, and control of superior product design or quality. Capital required includes the investment necessary to establish one plant of minimum optimum scale, inventories, and working capital. Scale advantages of established firms are important if the output at the optimum scale is a significant part of the industry or market. It is hazardous to assign any absolute values to entry barriers, but a rough estimate is as follows: (1) in the "very high" category, established firms might be able to elevate price (and/or costs) 10 percent or more above minimum costs while forestalling entry; (2) in the "high" category, the corresponding percentage may range slightly above or below 7 percent; (3) in the "moderate" category, the percentage would not exceed 5 percent; and (4) in the "low" category, the amount would range down to 1 percent.[14]

Table 15.2 shows that, in one way or another, entry tends to be deterred sufficiently in most agricultural industries so that established firms are able to elevate price somewhat above the least-cost levels without attracting entry. The net entry barrier in eight industries is moderate; in five, high; in one, very high; and in only five, low. Five of the 14 industries are ranked in two categories due to the fact that different geographic areas of operation or different phases of activity in the industries experience different barrier heights.

---

[14] Joe Bain, *Barriers to New Competition* (Cambridge: Harvard Univ. Press, 1956), p. 170.

| Industry | Scale Economy Barrier | Product Differentiation Barrier | Capital Requirement Barrier | Outlets, Suppliers Barrier | Net Entry Barrier |
|---|---|---|---|---|---|
| Grocery Retailing | moderate | low to high | moderate | low | low to high |
| Meat Packing Fresh | moderate | low | moderate to high | low | low |
| Processed | moderate | high | low to moderate | moderate | moderate |
| Broiler Chicken | moderate | low to moderate | moderate | high | high |
| Fluid Milk | moderate | high | moderate | high | moderate to high |
| Ice Cream | moderate | low | moderate | high | moderate |
| Vegetable Processing | moderate | moderate | moderate | high | moderate |
| Apple Processing | low | low | low | low | low to moderate |
| Baking | moderate | moderate | moderate | high | high |
| Soybean Processing | moderate | low | low to moderate | moderate to high | moderate |
| Grain Procurement | low | moderate | low | moderate | low |
| Mixed Feed | moderate | moderate | moderate to high | moderate to high | low (local) high (national) |
| Cotton | ... | low | ... | low | ... |
| Farm Machinery Tractors | very high | high | very high | high | very high |
| Implements | moderate | low to high | moderate | moderate | moderate |
| Fertilizer | high | low | high | moderate | moderate |

Product differentiation in the agricultural industries serves as a high entry barrier in five industries, a low entry barrier in nine industries, and a moderate entry barrier in five industries. These estimates of how much of a barrier product differentiation actually imposes are tentative and subject to further refinement. Available evidence is sufficient to conclude that product differentiation is the primary basis for the strong market position of the dominant firms in most of the agricultural industries. It results mainly from extensive advertising and promotion outlays for branded products, the variation in product being largely in the wrapper. Examples are ice cream, fluid milk, bread, processed vegetables, mixed feed, and meat. In other cases, product differences are more real though not always economically significant. An example is farm machinery.

For most industries in which product differentation is high, private label packing of products for corporate and voluntary grocery chains provides a possible market for potential entrants. This is particularly evident for fruits and vegetables, bread, and milk. However, in these industries, there are two or more classes of products—one enjoying general preference and selling for generally uniform prices at a higher level, and the other classes selling for generally uniform prices at a lower level. Prices for branded products are usually higher than for private label products, thus providing a net profit (or advertising resource) advantage of some established brand sellers over entrants supplying private label products.

Economies of plant scale is a moderate entry barrier in 11 of 14 industries. It is a high entry barrier in one industry and a very high barrier in one other subindustry. It is a low entry barrier in two agricultural industries. The amount of capital required is a moderate entry barrier in 11 industries or subindustries, a low entry barrier in four industries, a high entry barrier in only three industries, and a very high barrier in one. These two entry barriers are particularly noteworthy in the case of tractors and fertilizers. In each, very important scale economies in production and distribution are combined with capital requirements (estimated at from $20 million to $125 million) for optimum size operations. The inclusion of fertilizer production in this category might be subject to doubt reflecting the very rapid entry experienced in the past decade were it not for recent evidence showing for anhydrous ammonia a price-to-least-cost gap upwards of 40 percent,[15] which greatly exceeds the entry forestalling price level.

Few other industries would merit the rating of so high an entry

---

[15] Richard G. Walsh and Robert A. Rathjen, "Structural Implications of the Price-to-minimum-cost Gap in Anhydrous Ammonia Production and Distribution," *Journal of Farm Economics* (Dec. 1963), p. 1382.

barrier on the basis of available information, were it not for the restricted access to basic raw materials or to outlets for their products. Availability of outlets for the industry's products or access to suppliers was a high entry barrier in eight agricultural industries, a moderate entry barrier in six industries, and a low entry barrier in four others. Immediate access to sufficient quantities of raw materials is particularly strategic in the case of meat packing, broiler processing, vegetable processing, soybean processing, and grain marketing. Also, outlets on grocery shelves for the branded products of potential entrants are virtually foreclosed in the case of fruits and vegetables, milk and ice cream, and bread products.

Entry is coming from the creation of new firms, the diversification of established firms into new markets and industries, and from vertical integration. Several factors are related to entry into the agriculture-related industries. Improvements in highways, trucks, and containers permit the expansion of some milk and ice cream dealers and wholesale bakers into new markets. Increased labor and transportation costs connected with terminal livestock marketing enable small meat packers to spring up at interior points in competition with the industry giants which experience declining market shares. Integration by farmer cooperatives enables their patrons to obtain fertilizer and feed at cost though their venture into farm machinery has not proved successful. Integration by farmer cooperatives affects returns to apple processors, grain elevators, and feed mixers. Integration by food retailers through both ownership of facilities and contract processing alters the terms of competition in the marketing of ice cream, bread, fluid milk, and processed vegetables.

## MARKET CONDUCT IN THE AGRICULTURAL INDUSTRIES

Market conduct refers to the way in which firms as individuals and as a group act competitively to maximize their individual and joint returns. Individual firms are motivated to take the competitive offensive. Their offensive is limited, however, because of retaliation from competitors who may neutralize their gains. Thus develops an interdependence of prices and profits with each competitor deviating (usually on a nonprice basis) from competitive neutrality as far as he thinks he can go without serious retaliation.

An individual firm may be involved in two basic types of market conduct: first, those acts that help the industry to maximize its joint profits; and, second, those that strengthen the firm's competitive position in relation to its competitors. Conduct of the first type may include such things as overt price fixing, agreements not to compete in certain areas, tacit price fixing through price leadership, price posting, moral suasion through trade associations, and product standardization. Conduct of the second type may include such things as price discrimination, product innovation and differentiation, hidden and nonprice inducements, advertising and promotion, exclusive dealing, full-line forcing, vertical and horizontal integration, predatory and coercive price cutting, commercial bribery, espionage, and harassing lawsuits. Both types of market conduct may coexist in the market. Which type dominates will be determined in a large measure by the characteristics of the market's structure.

Only a few of the many types of market conduct engaged in by agriculture-related firms can be considered here. Included are (1) unfair exclusionary, predatory, and coercive tactics, (2) tacit or express price collusion, (3) pricing to shield inefficient practices, (4) pricing to induce uniform high quality and uniform seasonal output, and (5) sales promotion that is not misleading. These variables are measured qualitatively on an index of workability: very inadequate, inadequate, largely inadequate, almost adequate, adequate, almost optimum, and optimum.

Table 15.3 shows that the price conduct of the agricultural industries is not always consistent with the conditions of workability in a private enterprise economy. There is evidence of at least occasional acts of unfair, exclusionary, predatory, and coercive tactics in 10 of the 14 industries considered. Tacit and express price collusion, primarily price leadership (tacit), are aspects of price behavior in eight of 13 industries for which an estimate could be made. Indications are that price leadership often shields inefficient practices in nine of 14 industries. However, price leadership usually does not interfere with the realization of uniform high quality and uniform seasonal output in the agricultural industries (adequate or almost adequate in eight of 10 industries).

Only one aspect of nonprice conduct in the agricultural industries is considered here. Available evidence suggests that sales promotion practices are often misleading in five of the 12 industries for which an estimate could be made.

Additional research is needed on price and nonprice conduct in agricultural industries before reliable measures of the relation between them and market structure variables can be made. Results of hand tabulations relating the structure, conduct, and performance variables shown in Tables 15.1 to 15.4 suggest that the product differentiation barrier to entry is associated with price conduct in the sample industries. As barriers to entry rise in the agricultural industries, so does the incidence of price leadership, price fixing agreements, and unfair, exclusionary, predatory, and coercive tactics. The higher the barrier to market outlets and suppliers of raw materials, the less adequate is the operating effi-

TABLE 15.3

SUMMARY OF RELATIVE ADEQUACY OF MARKET CONDUCT CONDITIONS IN 14 AGRICULTURE-RELATED INDUSTRIES

| Industry | No Unfair, Exclusionary, Predatory, Coercive Tactics | Sales Promotion Not Misleading | No Tacit or Express Price Collusion | No Shielding of Inefficient Practices | Pricing Induces Uniform High Quality and Uniform Seasonal Output |
|---|---|---|---|---|---|
| Grocery Retailing | inadequate | inadequate | inadequate | inadequate | inadequate |
| Meat Packing Fresh | almost adequate | almost adequate | almost adequate | almost adequate | inadequate |
| Processed | inadequate | inadequate | inadequate | inadequate | inadequate |
| Broiler Chicken | inadequate | adequate | almost adequate | almost optimum | almost optimum |
| Fluid Milk | inadequate | ... | very inadequate | very inadequate | almost adequate |
| Ice Cream | very inadequate | inadequate | inadequate | inadequate | almost adequate |
| Vegetable Processing | inadequate | adequate | inadequate | almost adequate | adequate |
| Apple Processing | almost adequate | ... | almost adequate | adequate | ... |
| Baking | very inadequate | very inadequate | inadequate | very inadequate | adequate |
| Soybean Processing | almost adequate | adequate | almost adequate | adequate | adequate |
| Grain Procurement | almost adequate | almost adequate | almost adequate | inadequate | almost adequate |
| Mixed Feed | inadequate | inadequate | inadequate | inadequate | inadequate |
| Cotton | ... | ... | ... | ... | ... |
| Farm Machinery Tractors | inadequate | almost adequate | inadequate | inadequate | very inadequate |
| Implements | inadequate | almost adequate | inadequate | inadequate | very inadequate |
| Fertilizer | very inadequate | almost adequate | very inadequate | very inadequate | almost adequate |

## TABLE 15.4

SUMMARY OF THE ADEQUACY OF SPECIFIC MARKET PERFORMANCE CONDITIONS IN 14 AGRICULTURE-RELATED INDUSTRIES

| Industry | Operating Efficiency | | | | Promotion Expenses Not Excessive | Product Quality Conforms to Consumers' Interests |
| | Procurement | Plant | | Distribution | | |
| | | utilization | scale | | | |
|---|---|---|---|---|---|---|
| Grocery Retailing | almost adequate | very inadequate | almost adequate | inadequate | almost adequate | almost adequate |
| Meat Packing | | | | | | |
| Fresh | inadequate | inadequate | almost adequate | almost adequate | almost adequate | adequate |
| Processed | inadequate | inadequate | inadequate | inadequate | inadequate | inadequate |
| Broiler | | | | | | |
| Chicken | largely inadequate | almost adequate | almost adequate | almost adequate | optimum | optimum |
| Fluid Milk | almost adequate | inadequate | largely inadequate | very inadequate | very inadequate | optimum |
| Ice Cream | almost adequate | inadequate | largely inadequate | largely inadequate | largely inadequate | almost adequate |
| Vegetable Processing | adequate | largely inadequate | largely inadequate | adequate | inadequate | adequate |
| Apple Processing | adequate | almost adequate | adequate | adequate | adequate | adequate |

396

**TABLE 15.4** (*continued*)

| Industry | Procurement | Operating Efficiency Plant | | Distribution | Promotion Expenses Not Excessive | Product Quality Conforms to Consumers' Interests |
| --- | --- | --- | --- | --- | --- | --- |
| | | utilization | scale | | | |
| Baking | almost adequate | very inadequate | largely inadequate | largely inadequate | largely inadequate | almost adequate |
| Soybean Processing | almost adequate | inadequate, improving | almost adequate, improving | adequate | adequate | adequate |
| Grain Procurement | largely inadequate | inadequate | largely inadequate | almost adequate | adequate | almost adequate |
| Mixed Feed | adequate | inadequate | largely inadequate | largely inadequate | largely inadequate | largely inadequate |
| Cotton | ... | inadequate | inadequate | ... | ... | almost adequate |
| Farm Machinery Tractors | adequate | inadequate | inadequate | very inadequate | almost adequate | almost adequate |
| Implements | adequate | inadequate | inadequate | very inadequate | largely inadequate | largely inadequate |
| Fertilizer | adequate | almost adequate | almost adequate | largely inadequate | largely inadequate | almost adequate |

| Industry | Attention to Opportunities For Better Products and Techniques | Output Consistent With the Optimum Allocation of Resources | Profits at Levels Which Reward Investment, Efficiency, and Innovation at Necessary but Not Excessive Rates | Market Performance, Net |
|---|---|---|---|---|
| Grocery Retailing | almost adequate | almost adequate | inadequate | largely inadequate |
| Meat Packing Fresh | almost adequate | inadequate | adequate | largely inadequate |
| Processed | largely inadequate | ... | inadequate | ... |
| Broiler Chicken | almost adequate | almost adequate | almost adequate | almost adequate |
| Fluid Milk | almost adequate | inadequate | inadequate | largely inadequate |
| Ice Cream | almost adequate | almost adequate | almost adequate | largely inadequate |
| Vegetable Processing | adequate | inadequate | almost adequate | almost adequate |
| Apple Processing | ... | adequate | almost adequate | adequate |
| Baking | almost adequate | adequate | inadequate | largely inadequate |
| Soybean Processing | adequate, improving | adequate | adequate, improving | almost adequate, improving |
| Grain Procurement | largely inadequate | inadequate | inadequate | largely inadequate |
| Mixed Feed | almost adequate | inadequate | almost adequate | largely inadequate |
| Cotton | almost adequate | inadequate | inadequate | largely inadequate |
| Farm Machinery Tractors Implements | very adequate very adequate | inadequate inadequate | almost adequate almost adequate | inadequate inadequate |
| Fertilizer | almost adequate | inadequate | very inadequate | very inadequate |

ciency of plants. Market conduct considered unfair, exclusionary, predatory, or coercive is associated with excessive costs of distribution and promotion, and with low product quality. Moreover, price leadership which shields inefficient industrial practices is related to excess profits in the agricultural industries. Unnecessary expansion in size of companies is related to the presence of misleading sales promotion practices.

## MARKET PERFORMANCE IN THE AGRICULTURAL INDUSTRIES

Market performance indicates how well the market activity of enterprises in an industry contribute to the general material welfare. This is of vital concern to our analysis of the agriculture-related industries. The workability of market structure and conduct patterns in these industries is determined in part by the performance patterns with which they are associated. The dimensions considered here are necessarily few in number. Much of the unique and often important detail concerning individual industries is necessarily omitted in the discussion. Emphasized is a cross-sectional analysis of certain basic dimensions of performance in 14 industries, seeking to reach a first approximation of what the existing research shows to be valid generalizations.

Some aspects of performance are important in all industries: (1) efficiency of the organization of the industry in terms of scale of plant, utilization of plant, procurement, and distribution; (2) promotion expenses; (3) product quality; (4) improvement of product and technique; (5) output consistent with the optimum allocation of resources; and (6) profits at levels which reward investment, efficiency, and innovation at necessary but not excessive rates. Most of these problems have been closely examined by research economists for the 14 agricultural industries, and the summaries here are largely confined to the result of this sample. The variables are measured qualitatively on an index of workability: very inadequate, inadequate, largely inadequate, almost adequate, adequate, almost optimum, and optimum.

The relative adequacy of performance varies considerably among the industries sampled. Table 15.4 compares the 14 industries with respect to these performance norms. For no agricultural industry was performance wholly adequate in all dimensions, nor wholly inadequate. On balance, the general performance of four industries was adequate or almost adequate. The general performance of 10 industries was inadequate or largely inadequate.

Performance of the agriculture-related industries is most satisfactory with respect to product quality and improvements in products and techniques. In only two of the 14 industries considered is the recent performance largely or wholly inadequate. Indications are that product quality conforms to consumers' interests in 12 of the 14 industries considered. Opportunities for better products and techniques are not neglected in 12 of the 13 industries where estimates were made. Yet for many agriculture-related industries producing standardized, simple, and slowly changing products, these dimensions are a very small aspect of the total pattern of performance.

A major aspect of the performance of any industry is its relative efficiency, measured by how closely the firms in the industry approximate the lowest attainable costs. The studies of 14 agriculture-related industries suggest that there is inefficiency due to insufficient scale of plant in at least nine industries, and inefficiency due to underutilization of plants in these same nine and an additional two industries, reflecting more often than not a chronic condition of excess capacity. Most agricultural industries are efficient, or almost so, in the procurement (purchase and assembly) of raw materials. The extent of inefficiency attributable to distribution varies considerably among the industries sampled, but at least eight industries fell short of optimum or even adequate performance.

Excess profits are not a general phenomenon in the agricultural industries. Rather, they occur in only a small fraction of all possible instances, and with varying intensity in those cases where they do occur. Thus, for recent years, contrast the baking and fluid milk industries having an average excess profit rate of moderate magnitude with the fresh meat packing industry which apparently has little or no excess profit on the average. Or compare the fertilizer industry with instances of very high excess profit rates, the processed meat packing industry with moderate rates, and the soybean industry with very low or negligible excess profits. Similar differences would be noted among the profit rates of different firms in the same industry.

Profits are or have been in recent years excessive in half the industries considered. Profits are at, or only slightly above, levels which reward investment, efficiency, and innovation at necessary but not excessive rates in half of the 14 agriculture-related industries for which data are available. For the sample of industries there is no significant incidence of net losses, meaning returns lower than a basic interest return on equity, on the average. In virtually every industry, there is or has been in the recent past some small average margin of excess profits.

Promotion expenses are defined as "selling costs" incurred by companies to stimulate sales in two general ways: first, by informing potential buyers of the availability, characteristics, and prices of the products; and second, by persuading potential customers to buy. Thus, promotional expenses are both informational and persuasive.

Costs devoted to informational purposes are functionally justified and are essential to the effective working of a market system. It is necessary to inform potential buyers of the availability of goods, their specifications and qualities, and their prices. Promotional activities with a persuasive orientation, however, are not usually justified from the standpoint of public welfare, since they reflect a diversion to sales promotion of productive resources which could otherwise be devoted to producing and distributing a larger volume of useful goods and services at lower costs. Promotion expenses are considered excessive of those necessary to inform buyers of real product characteristics in half of the 14 industries and adequate or almost adequate for information promotion in half of the industries.

In at least 8 of the 14 industries, output is less than consistent with the optimum allocation of resources. This means that supply tends to be artificially restricted and prices held artificially higher than least-cost levels, with the result that the quantity consumed is less and the general welfare is lower than reasonably could be expected in a workable private enterprise economy.

## TOWARD A WORKABLE AGRICULTURAL ECONOMY

Having recognized some of the problems of workability in the market structure, conduct, and performance of the agricultural industries, we are concerned here with the means by which they can be remedied through various policy instruments, both public and private. A first consideration is the existing service and regulatory effort of the federal government designed to achieve more adequate market conditions in the agricultural industries. Chief among these are the antitrust laws, commission regulations, market order and agreement administrations, price support programs, grades and standards, information programs, and research. Each is judged by criteria which involve the success of the program in implementing a policy and solving the problem. Only in terms of original problems and present problems can public policies and programs be realistically evaluated. A second consideration is the workability in the public interest of existing private remedies such as the countervailing influence of grocery chains relative to food processors, integration of cooperatives in the agriculture-related industries, and the organization of futures and terminal markets for certain agricultural commodities. These variables are measured qualitatively on an index of workability: very inadequate, inadequate, largely inadequate, almost adequate, adequate, almost optimum, and optimum.

Tables 15.5 and 15.6 illustrate the fact that the predominant feature of public and private programs to improve the workability

## TABLE 15.5

### Summary of Relative Adequacy of Specific Policy Remedies in 14 Agriculture-Related Industries

| Industry | Antitrust Laws | | Anti-discrimination | Government Grades and Standards | Government Information Programs | Government Research |
|---|---|---|---|---|---|---|
| | Anticollusion | Antimerger | | | | |
| Grocery Retailing | inadequate | inadequate | inadequate | inadequate | inadequate | inadequate |
| Meat Packing | | | | | | |
| Fresh | adequate | ... | inadequate | almost adequate | almost adequate | almost adequate |
| Processed | ... | ... | inadequate | inadequate | inadequate | inadequate |
| Broiler Chicken | inadequate | inadequate | inadequate | almost adequate | almost adequate | almost optimum |
| Fluid Milk | inadequate | inadequate | inadequate | inadequate | inadequate | adequate |
| Ice Cream | inadequate | almost adequate | almost adequate | adequate | very inadequate | ... |
| Vegetable Processing | inadequate | inadequate | inadequate | adequate | inadequate | inadequate |
| Apple Processing | ... | ... | ... | adequate | adequate | ... |
| Baking | inadequate | very inadequate | inadequate | adequate | very inadequate | very inadequate |
| Soybean Processing | ... | ... | ... | adequate | almost adequate | inadequate |
| Grain Procurement Markets | ... | ... | inadequate | inadequate | inadequate | ... |
| Mixed Feed | inadequate | inadequate | inadequate | inadequate | very inadequate | almost adequate |
| Cotton | ... | ... | ... | inadequate | adequate | almost adequate |
| Farm Machinery | | | | | | |
| Tractors | almost adequate | inadequate | inadequate | almost adequate | almost adequate | adequate |
| Implements | almost adequate | inadequate | inadequate | almost adequate | almost adequate | adequate |
| Fertilizer | inadequate | inadequate | inadequate | almost adequate | adequate | inadequate |

Summary of Relative Adequacy of Specific Policy Remedies in 14 Agriculture-Related Industries

| Industry | Cooperatives | Grocery Chain Countervailence | Government Price Support Activities | Market Orders and Agreements | Futures and Terminal Markets |
|---|---|---|---|---|---|
| Grocery Retailing | almost adequate | ... | ... | ... | ... |
| Meat Packing Fresh | inadequate | almost adequate | largely inadequate | none | largely inadequate |
| Processed | inadequate | largely inadequate | largely inadequate | none | almost adequate |
| Broiler Chicken | inadequate | largely inadequate | none | none | none |
| Fluid Milk | almost adequate | largely inadequate | almost adequate | almost adequate | ... |
| Ice Cream | very inadequate | almost adequate | ... | almost adequate | ... |
| Vegetable Processing | largely inadequate | largely inadequate | none | largely inadequate | ... |
| Apple Processing | adequate | ... | none | ... | ... |
| Baking | almost adequate | largely inadequate | almost adequate | none | inadequate |
| Soybean Processing | almost adequate | ... | almost adequate | none | almost adequate |
| Grain Procurement | almost adequate | ... | almost adequate | none | inadequate |
| Mixed Feed | almost adequate | ... | ... | ... | ... |
| Cotton | largely inadequate | ... | inadequate | none | ... |
| Farm Machinery Tractors | very inadequate | ... | ... | ... | ... |
| Implements | very inadequate | ... | ... | ... | ... |
| Fertilizer | almost adequate | ... | ... | ... | ... |

403

of the agricultural industries is their mixed application and results. For example, application of the antitrust laws to the agricultural industries has been so lacking in intensity that no estimate
of their effect could be made in the case of 4 of the 14 industries
considered here, and several of the estimates presented as Table
15.6 are tentative. The enforcement of prohibitions against predatory, exclusionary, and collusive market conduct has been adequate or almost adequate in 3 of 11 agricultural industries for which
an estimate could be made. Antimerger enforcement has increased
greatly in recent years but is considered almost adequate in only
1 of 9 industries. As to enforcement of Section 2 of the Clayton
Act against price discrimination, it has proved almost adequate in
only 1 of 11 industries. Taking the generally unintensive enforcement into account along with prevailing interpretations of indirect
effects, we may conclude: (1) practices of predation, exclusion, and
express collusion have been discouraged although not eliminated;
(2) practices of price leadership or tacit price collusion have been
encouraged which has favored the survival of inefficient firms and
the increase of selling costs; (3) increased seller concentration has
been restrained but not stopped, and seller concentration has not
been reduced through breaking up large companies; (4) the price
discrimination laws have had a considerable impact on the differential pricing and discount policies of the agricultural industries
which has strengthened the competitive position of smaller firms,
but also has weakened price competition and encouraged integration into food processing by grocery chains.

Other government programs are somewhat more effective in
improving the workability of market conditions in these industries.
Market information seems to have played an important role in influencing the competitive situation in 6 of 12 industries; government research programs are adequate or almost adequate in terms
of research results generated. However, these results are not always
made available in a usable form and at the right time to adequately meet the information needs of buyers and sellers. In only 6
of 14 industries are government information programs adequate
or almost adequate to meet the information needs in the agricultural industries. Lack of accurate information on prices, quality
discounts, and how grain will be graded results in a wide variation
in prices received by farmers for grain at local elevators. Competition in the mixed feed industry has been strengthened by increased
feeder confidence in locally mixed open formula feeds recommended by state experiment stations where they are in competition
with more highly touted and usually higher priced closed formula
brands.

In 9 of 15 industries or subindustries, government grades and standards are adequate or almost adequate in solving problems of real product specification and differentiation in the exchange process. U.S. government grades, for example, have negated the branding efforts of meat packers in their merchandising of fresh meats while the lack of uniform grades and consequent product differentiation has enabled meat packers to enjoy considerably wider margins on processed meat.

State and federal marketing order and agreement programs are almost adequate in 2 of 3 agricultural industries where they are present. Government price support activities have proved almost adequate in 4 of 7 agricultural industries where they are important. The possible application of these programs in other industries is unknown.

Private remedies have rather mixed application and results in the agricultural industries. The effect of cooperatives on the workability of the agricultural industries is adequate or almost adequate to solve the problems for which they are intended in 8 of 14 industries. Cooperatives tend to thrive both in markets with excessive numbers of companies and in markets with excessive levels of concentration. They operate most effectively in those industries characterized by excessive vertical integration, both via ownership and contract. There is little or no consistent relationship between the effectiveness of cooperatives and the market conduct and performance of sample industry. With the exception of apple processing, their possible "yardstick" effect is not supported by these studies. There is, for example, no general relationship between operating efficiency of plants in the industries and the adequacy of cooperatives in serving their members' interests.

The effectiveness of grocery chains to countervail the influence of food processors through entry and bargaining contributes to a more workable market situation in only 2 of 7 industries where present. The effectiveness of the private organization of futures and terminal markets to improve the workability of agricultural industries is almost adequate in 2 of 5 industries where it is an element of the product market.

These estimates should be viewed as partial and a first approximation to be verified or rejected by further study. There are no complete or final answers to all the relevant economic and noneconomic questions, nor any solution in the sense of guaranteed long-run workable or optimum performance of the agricultural industries. There is a need to study the effectiveness of other programs than those considered here. The possible contribution to workability realized by several additional programs is unknown: (1) government ownership in the case of the T.V.A. fertilizer program and the U.S.D.A. ownership of grain storage facilities; (2) government commission regulation in the case of the farm petroleum and electrical industries; (3) governmental fiscal and monetary policies; (4) I.R.S. allowances for depreciation, business losses, and other allowable expenses; (5) patent laws, compulsory licensing, etc.; (6) government military contracts; (7) small business administration loans and other services; (8) self-imposed standards of acceptable practices. There is also a need to weigh the costs and benefits of the existing programs against the costs and benefits of alternative measures that might be adopted.

Markets cannot be fully appraised by fixed standards that are confined to a few dimensions. To evaluate the workability of only a few aspects of market structure, conduct, and performance is to implicitly assume that other possible strategic conditions either are unimportant or operate in the same direction and in the same magnitude as the conditions measured. Future agricultural marketing research should encompass all possible relevant market conditions and postpone the decision about which ones warrant consideration in the final analysis until knowledge of their relative significance has been developed.

In this chapter is presented some evaluation of existing public and private policies to promote a more workable agricultural economy. This treatment is brief, and far from complete. It is intended to stimulate the reader's interest in further and more intensive study of contemporary policy issues involving industrial organization and control. This all implies a support on the part of the writers of the past accomplishments and future potential of agriculture-related industries which are in large part regulated through the forces of the market, as opposed to direct governmental ownership and control of private management. Indeed, it is because of our belief that conditions of the market are so very important in a private enterprise economy that we explore and evaluate them in this volume.

# INDEX

A & P, 6, 10, 14, 25, 26, 106n, 108, 128, 135, 138, 213n, 214
Abrahamsen, Martin A., 356
ACF-Wrigley Co., 10, 14, 15
Adams, Walter, 303n
Adamy, Clarence, 90
Adelman, M. A., 213
Advertising, 23, 88, 115–16, 148, 217–19
Alexander, William H., 104n
Allis-Chalmers Co., 325, 327, 332n, 335, 337n, 353
American Baking Co., 193, 209n
American Stores, 10, 14
Andrews, Richard A., 167
Antitrust
Clayton Act, 96, 118, 119, 144, 194, 383, 404
Consent Decree (1920), 55, 61, 63
Federal Trade Commission Act, 96, 119, 144, 383
Packers and Stockyards Act, 55–56, 96
Robinson-Patman Act, 29, 144, 161
Sherman Act, 96, 144, 194, 383
Apple processing, 386, 388, 391, 393, 395, 396, 398, 402, 403
Apple processing industry, xiii, 176–91
Apple production, 176–77
Arden Farm Co., 103
Armore, Sidney, 248n
Armour and Co., 47, 48, 61
Arms, D. C., 140n
Askew, W. R., 285n
Auctions, broiler, 83
Avery, B. F., Co., 351–53

**B**

Backman, Jules, 293n
Bain, Joe S., xiv n, 28n, 30n, 32n, 41n, 95n, 203n, 219n, 233, 288, 310n, 330–31, 352, 390n

Baking industry, xiii, 192–224, 387, 391–95, 397–98, 400, 402–3
Bakken, H. H., 101n
Bardwell, E. T., 76n
Baumer, E. F., 120n, 121
Beal, G. M., 101n
Beatrice Foods, 102–3, 128
Beef breakers, 51
Bell, Hugh P., 204n
Berglund, Roger, 78n
Birch, Eleanor M., 27n, 162n, 172n
Biscuits and crackers, 18
Blakley, Leo V., 297, 306
Bohack, 10, 14
Boners, 51
Bonnen, James T., 306n
Bonnette, Victor, 99n
Borden Company, The, 102–3, 128
Bowen, Earl K., 52n
Bowes, C. C., 85
Branch houses, 45, 51, 61
Brandow, G. E., 40n, 311, 312n
Branson, R. E., 72n, 80–81
Breimyer, Harold F., 40n, 252
Brensike, V. J., 285n
Bressler, R. G., Jr., 119
Bridges, Charles S., 35
Broiler chicken industry, xii, 68–100, 386, 389, 391, 393, 395–96, 398, 402–3
Brown, W. H., 314n
Bureau of the Census, 4
Burk, M. C., 204n
Burns, David J., 162n
Business Guide, Inc., 7n
Butz, W. T., 140n

**C**

Cairns, J. P., 80n
California Canners and Growers, Inc., 168